ICAP

ICAP plc
2 Broadgate
London
EC2M 7UR

Tel: + 44 (0) 20 7000 5000

www.icap.com

D1609991

⊚ Harden's

London Restaurants
2014 | "Gastronomes' bible"
Evening Standard

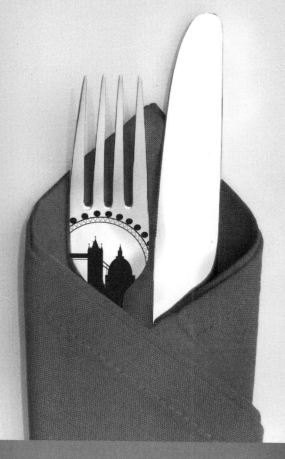

23RD EDITION | Survey driven reviews of over 1,800 restaurants

Put us in your client's pocket!

Branded editions for iPhone, Android and BlackBerry
call to discuss the options on 020 7839 4763.

© **Harden's Limited 2013**

ISBN 978-1-873721-25-4

British Library Cataloguing-in-Publication data:
a catalogue record for this book is available from
the British Library.

Printed in Italy by Legoprint

Research assistants: Helen Teschauer, Gilles Talarek, Sarah Ashpole

Harden's Limited
Golden Cross House, 8 Duncannon Street
London WC2N 4JF

Would restaurateurs (and PRs) please address
communications to 'Editorial' at the above address,
or ideally by email to: editorial@hardens.com

The contents of this book are believed correct at
the time of printing. Nevertheless, the publisher
can accept no responsibility for errors or changes in
or omissions from the details given.

CONTENTS

RATINGS & PRICES

Ratings

Our rating system does not tell you – as most guides do – that expensive restaurants are often better than cheap ones! What we do is compare each restaurant's performance – as judged by the average ratings awarded by reporters in the survey – with other similarly-priced restaurants. This approach has the advantage that it helps you find – whatever your budget for any particular meal – where you will get the best 'bang for your buck'.

The following qualities are assessed:

F — Food
S — Service
A — Ambience

The rating indicates that, *in comparison with other restaurants in the same price-bracket*, performance is...

❶ — Exceptional
❷ — Very good
❸ — Good
④ — Average
⑤ — Poor

Prices

The price shown for each restaurant is the cost for one (1) person of an average three-course dinner with half a bottle of house wine and coffee, any cover charge, service and VAT. Lunch is often cheaper. With BYO restaurants, we have assumed that two people share a £7 bottle of off-licence wine.

Telephone number – all numbers are '020' numbers.

Map reference – shown immediately after the telephone number.

Full postcodes – for non-group restaurants, the first entry in the 'small print' at the end of each listing, so you can set your sat-nav.

Website and Twitter – shown in the small print, where applicable.

Last orders time – listed after the website (if applicable); Sunday may be up to 90 minutes earlier.

Opening hours – unless otherwise stated, restaurants are open for lunch and dinner seven days a week.

Credit and debit cards – unless otherwise stated, Mastercard, Visa, Amex and Maestro are accepted.

Dress – where appropriate, the management's preferences concerning patrons' dress are given.

Special menus – if we know of a particularly good value set menu we note this (e.g. "set weekday L"), together with its formula price (FP), calculated exactly as in 'Prices' above. Details change, so always check ahead.

'Rated on Editors' visit' – indicates ratings have been determined by the Editors personally, based on their visit, rather than derived from the survey.

SRA Rating – the sustainability index, as calculated by the Sustainable Restaurant Association – see page 8 for more information.

HOW THIS GUIDE IS WRITTEN

Survey

This guide is based on our 23rd annual survey of what 'ordinary' diners out think of London's restaurants. In 1998, we extended the survey to cover restaurants across the rest of the UK; it is by far the most detailed annual survey of its type. Out-of-town results are published in our UK guide.

This year, the total number of reporters in our combined London/UK survey, conducted mainly online, exceeded 9,000, and, between them, they contributed some 80,000 individual reports.

How we determine the ratings

In the great majority of cases, ratings are arrived at statistically. This essentially involves 'ranking' the average survey rating each restaurant achieves in the survey – for each of food, service and ambience – against the average ratings of the other establishments which fall in the same price-bracket. (This is essentially like football leagues, with the most expensive restaurants going in the top league and the cheaper ones in lower leagues. The restaurant's ranking *within its own particular league* determines its ratings.)

How we write the reviews

The tenor of each review and the ratings are very largely determined by the ranking of the establishment concerned, which we derive as described above. At the margin, we may also pay some regard to the proportion of positive nominations (such as for 'favourite restaurant') compared to negative nominations (such as for 'most overpriced').

To explain why a restaurant has been rated as it has, we extract snippets from survey comments ("enclosed in double quotes"). On larger restaurants, we receive several hundred reports, and a short summary cannot possibly do individual justice to all of them.

What we seek to do – *without any regard to our own personal opinions* – is to illustrate the key themes which have emerged in our analysis of the collective view. The only exception to this is the newest restaurants, where survey views are either few or non-existent, and where we may be obliged to rely on our own opinion. Unless the review carries the small print note "Rated on Editors' visit", however, the ratings awarded are still our best analysis of the survey view, not our own impression.

Richard Harden   **Peter Harden**

SUSTAINABLE RESTAURANT ASSOCIATION

If issues such as climate change, animal welfare and treating people fairly matter to you, look out for the SRA Sustainability Ratings next to restaurant listings.

The Sustainable Restaurant Association (SRA) is a not for profit body helping restaurants achieve greater sustainability. To help diners, it has developed Sustainability Ratings to assess restaurants in 14 key areas across three main sustainability categories of Sourcing, Environment and Society.

In a 2013 consumer survey for the SRA, more than 80% of diners said they knew little or nothing about the sustainable things restaurants are doing despite the same number wanting restaurants to communicate that information. Harden's has partnered with the SRA to include its Sustainability Ratings, giving diners the information to identify those restaurants doing great things. For example, we know diners want to know restaurants are sourcing from local producers, using high welfare meat and dairy and served sustainable fish. Improving waste energy and water efficiency are more ways for restaurants to be sustainable. The most sustainable restaurants engage with their communities.

By choosing a sustainable restaurant, you can be sure that your meal isn't costing the earth.

Chefs, restaurateurs and diners can make the difference by embracing sustainable values and in doing so create a better food chain. We hope diners will consider these ideals when choosing to dine out.

Raymond Blanc OBE, President of the SRA

We're proud to support the SRA, and hope that by including SRA Sustainability Ratings to the restaurants we include, we can help set diners' expectations as to which of their choices will ensure the trade thrives for many years to come.

Harden's

More than 50% = Good Sustainability
More than 60% = Excellent Sustainability
More than 70% = Exceptional Sustainability

SURVEY FAQs

Q. How do you find your reporters?
A. Anyone can take part. Simply register at
www.hardens.com. Actually, we find that many people
who complete our survey each year have taken part
before. So it's really more a question of a very large and
ever-evolving panel, or jury, than a random 'poll'.

Q. Wouldn't a random sample be better?
A. That's really a theoretical question, as there is no
obvious way, still less a cost-efficient one, by which one
could identify a random sample of the guests at each of,
say, 5000 establishments across the UK, and get them to
take part in any sort of survey. And anyway, which is
likely to be more useful: a sample of the views of
everyone who's been to a particular place, or the views
of people who are interested enough in eating-out to
have volunteered their feedback?

Q. What sort of people take part?
A. A roughly 60/40 male/female split, from all adult age-
groups. As you might expect – as eating out is not the
cheapest activity – reporters tend to have white collar
jobs (some at very senior levels). By no means, however,
is that always the case.

Q. Do people ever try to stuff the ballot?
A. Of course they do! A rising number of efforts are
weeded out every year. But stuffing the ballot is not as
trivial a task as some people seem to think: the survey
results throw up clear natural voting patterns against
which 'campaigns' tend to stand out.

Q. Aren't inspections the best way to run a guide?
A. It is often assumed – even by commentators who
ought to know better – that inspections are some sort
of 'gold standard'. There is no doubt that the inspection
model clearly has potential strengths, but one of its
prime weaknesses is that it is incredibly expensive.
Take the most famous practitioner of the 'inspection
model', Michelin. It doesn't claim to visit each and every
entry listed in its guide annually. Even once! And who
are the inspectors? Often they are catering
professionals, whose likes and dislikes may be very
different from the establishment's natural customer
base. On any restaurant of note, however, Harden's
typically has somewhere between dozens and hundreds
of reports each and every year from exactly the type of
people the restaurant relies upon to stay in business.
We believe that such feedback, carefully analysed, is far
more revealing and accurate than an occasional
'professional' inspection.

SURVEY MOST MENTIONED

These are the restaurants which were most frequently mentioned by reporters. (Last year's position is given in brackets.) An asterisk* indicates the first appearance in the list of a recently opened restaurant.

1   J Sheekey (1)
2   Le Gavroche (4)
3   Scott's (2)
4   Clos Maggiore (6)
5   Brasserie Zédel*
6   Chez Bruce (3)
7   Dinner (5)
8   The Ledbury (7)
9   The Wolseley (9)
10   Pollen Street Social (8)

11   The Delaunay (16)
12   The Square (15)
13= La Trompette (14)
13= Medlar (26)
15   Marcus Wareing (10)
16   Bleeding Heart (13)
17   The Cinnamon Club (20)
18   Galvin Bistrot de Luxe (11)
19   The River Café (18)
20= Galvin La Chapelle (17)

20= Le Caprice (22)
22   La Poule au Pot (24)
23= Benares (34)
23= Bocca Di Lupo (26)
25   Amaya (34)
26   The Ivy (21)
27   Dabbous*
28   Trinity (-)
29   MEATLiquor (32)
30   Gordon Ramsay (31)

31   Balthazar*
32   Bar Boulud (23)
33   Terroirs (19)
34   Zuma (26)
35   Tayyabs (-)
36   Colbert*
37   Andrew Edmunds (32)
38   Gauthier Soho (-)
39   Hunan (-)
40   Pied à Terre (-)

SURVEY NOMINATIONS

Top gastronomic experience

1. Le Gavroche (3)
2. The Ledbury (2)
3. Dinner (1)
4. Chez Bruce (5)
5. Pollen Street Social (6)
6. Marcus Wareing (4)
7. Dabbous*
8. The Square (7)
9. Medlar*
10. Pied à Terre (8)

Favourite

1. Chez Bruce (1)
2. Le Gavroche (5)
3. The Wolseley (6)
4. Le Caprice (7)
5. J Sheekey (3)
6. The Delaunay (-)
7. Trinity (9)
8. The Ledbury (-)
9. Pollen Street Social (4)
10. The River Café (10)

Best for business

1. The Wolseley (1)
2. The Square (2)
3. The Delaunay (7)
4. Galvin La Chapelle (5)
5. The Don (3)
6. Bleeding Heart (4)
7. L'Anima (8)
8. Scott's (9)
9. 1 Lombard Street (-)
10. Savoy Grill (-)

Best for romance

1. Clos Maggiore (1)
2. La Poule au Pot (2)
3. Andrew Edmunds (3)
4. Bleeding Heart (4)
5. Le Gavroche (7)
6. Galvin at Windows (5)
7. Chez Bruce (6)
8. The Ritz Restaurant (-)
9. Le Caprice (8)
10. Café du Marché (-)

Best breakfast/brunch

1   The Wolseley (1)
2   The Delaunay (-)
3= Roast (2)
3= Cecconi's (4)
5   Riding House Café (-)
6   Granger & Co (-)
7   The Modern Pantry (-)
8   Duck & Waffle*
9   Smiths (Ground Floor) (3)
10 Dean Street Townhouse (-)

Best bar/pub food

1   The Anchor & Hope (1)
2   The Bull & Last (3)
3   The Harwood Arms (2)
4   The Thomas Cubitt (8)
5   The Anglesea Arms (7)
6   The Grazing Goat*
7   The Canton Arms (4)
8   The Gun (6)
9   The Orange (5)
10 The Ladbroke Arms (-)

Most disappointing cooking

1   Oxo Tower (Rest') (1)
2   Balthazar*
3   Gordon Ramsay (5)
4   Brasserie Zédel*
5   Colbert*
6   Dinner (-)
7   The Wolseley (7)
8   The Ivy (3)
9   Alain Ducasse (-)
10 Ametsa with Arzak Instruction*

Most overpriced restaurant

1   Oxo Tower (Rest') (1)
2   Gordon Ramsay (3)
3   The River Café (5)
4   Dinner (-)
5   Alain Ducasse (7)
6   Cut (-)
7   Marcus Wareing (4)
8   Le Gavroche (8)
9   The Ivy (-)
10 Pollen Street Social (-)

SURVEY HIGHEST RATINGS

FOOD	SERVICE

£85+

FOOD	SERVICE
1 The Ledbury	1 Le Gavroche
2 Le Gavroche	2 The Ledbury
3 One-O-One	3 Pied à Terre
4 Pied à Terre	4 Pétrus
5 Viajante	5 The Square

£65-£84

FOOD	SERVICE
1 Chez Bruce	1 The Goring Hotel
2 Story	2 Chez Bruce
3 Assaggi	3 Story
4 Zuma	4 Trinity
5 Hunan	5 Alyn Williams

£50-£64

FOOD	SERVICE
1 Sushi Tetsu	1 Sushi Tetsu
2 Dinings	2 About Thyme
3 Gauthier Soho	3 Oslo Court
4 St John Bread & Wine	4 Outlaw's
5 Dabbous	5 Caraffini

£40-£49

FOOD	SERVICE
1 Jin Kichi	1 Il Bordello
2 Babur	2 Lamberts
3 Il Bordello	3 Quality Chop House
4 Corner Room	4 The Crooked Well
5 Zucca	5 Indian Zilla

£39 or less

FOOD	SERVICE
1 Ganapati	1 Paradise Hampstead
2 Santa Maria	2 Taiwan Village
3 José	3 Carob Tree
4 Taiwan Village	4 José
5 Paradise Hampstead	5 Ganapati

SURVEY HIGHEST RATINGS

AMBIENCE

OVERALL

AMBIENCE	OVERALL
1 The Ritz Restaurant	1 Le Gavroche
2 Galvin at Windows	2 The Ledbury
3 Le Gavroche	3 Pied à Terre
4 Hélène Darroze	4 Pétrus
5 Sketch (Lecture Rm)	5 The Greenhouse

1 The Bingham	1 Chez Bruce
2 Rules	2 The Bingham
3 The Goring Hotel	3 Story
4 Bibendum	4 The Goring Hotel
5 Galvin La Chapelle	5 J Sheekey

1 La Poule au Pot	1 Sushi Tetsu
2 Clos Maggiore	2 Clos Maggiore
3 Randall & Aubin	3 J Sheekey Oyster Bar
4 Bob Bob Ricard	4 Gauthier Soho
5 Grazing Goat	5 L'Aventure

1 Andrew Edmunds	1 Il Bordello
2 The Atlas	2 The Atlas
3 The Swan	3 Babur
4 Pizarro	4 Lamberts
5 Spuntino	5 The Swan

1 Gordon's Wine Bar	1 José
2 José	2 Paradise Hampstead
3 Brasserie Zédel	3 Ganapati
4 Barrica	4 Barrica
5 Chicken Shop	5 Taiwan Village

SURVEY BEST BY CUISINE

These are the restaurants which received the best average food ratings (excluding establishments with a small or notably local following).

Where the most common types of cuisine are concerned, we present the results in two price-brackets. For less common cuisines, we list the top three, regardless of price.

For further information about restaurants which are particularly notable for their food, see the cuisine lists starting on page 246. These indicate, using an asterisk*, restaurants which offer exceptional or very good food.

British, Modern

£50 and over
1. The Ledbury
2. Chez Bruce
3. Story
4. Trinity
5. Kitchen W8

Under £50
1. Lamberts
2. The Clove Club
3. Abbeville Kitchen
4. 10 Greek Street
5. The Ladbroke Arms

French

£50 and over
1. Le Gavroche
2. Gauthier Soho
3. Pied à Terre
4. Pétrus
5. The Square

Under £50
1. Charlotte's Bistro
2. Brawn
3. Charlotte's Place
4. Green Man & Fr Horn
5. Mill Lane Bistro

Italian/Mediterranean

£50 and over
1. Assaggi
2. Al Boccon di'vino
3. Murano
4. The River Café
5. Quirinale

Under £50
1. Il Bordello
2. Zucca
3. Dehesa
4. Pentolina
5. Portobello Ristorante

Indian & Pakistani

£50 and over
1. Amaya
2. Rasoi
3. The Cinnamon Club
4. Tamarind
5. Benares

Under £50
1. Ganapati
2. Babur
3. Paradise Hampstead
4. Potli
5. Tayyabs

Chinese

£50 and over
1. HKK
2. Hunan
3. Yauatcha
4. Min Jiang
5. Princess Garden

Under £50
1. Taiwan Village
2. Mandarin Kitchen
3. Dragon Castle
4. Pearl Liang
5. Singapore Garden

Japanese

£50 and over
1. Sushi Tetsu
2. Dinings
3. Zuma
4. Umu
5. Sumosan

Under £50
1. Sushi-Say
2. Jin Kichi
3. Pham Sushi
4. Koya
5. Shoryu Ramen

British, Traditional
1. St John Bread & Wine
2. Scott's
3. Dinner

Vegetarian
1. Ganapati
2. Ragam
3. Vanilla Black

Burgers, etc
1. Patty and Bun
2. Tommi's Burger Joint
3. MEATLiquor

Pizza
1. Santa Maria
2. Il Bordello
3. Franco Manca

Fish & Chips
1. Toff's
2. Brady's
3. Golden Hind

Thai
1. Sukho Fine Thai Cuisine
2. Churchill Arms
3. Blue Elephant

Steaks & Grills
1. Goodman
2. Hawksmoor
3. Relais de Venise

Fish & Seafood
1. One-O-One
2. J Sheekey
3. Outlaw's

Fusion
1. Viajante
2. Champor-Champor
3. E&O

Spanish
1. José
2. Moro
3. Barrica

Turkish
1. Mangal 1
2. Ishtar
3. Best Mangal

Lebanese
1. Chez Marcelle
2. Levant
3. Al-Waha

TOP SPECIAL DEALS

The following menus allow you to eat in the restaurants concerned at a significant discount when compared to their evening à la carte prices.

The prices used are calculated in accordance with our usual formula (i.e. three courses with house wine, coffee and tip).

Special menus are by their nature susceptible to change – please check that they are still available.

Weekday lunch

£80+ Gordon Ramsay

£70+ Hélène Darroze

£65+ Alain Ducasse
Apsleys
Cut
Dinner
Pied à Terre
Wiltons

£60+ L'Atelier de Joel Robuchon
Benares
Hibiscus
The Ledbury
Marcus Wareing
Oxo Tower (Rest')

£55+ Le Gavroche
Murano
Pollen Street Social
Seven Park Place
Theo Randall
Thirty Six
Tom Aikens
Viajante

£50+ Babbo
Bibendum
Bo London
Corrigan's Mayfair
Cotidie
HKK
Lutyens
One-O-One
Oxo Tower (Brass')
Pétrus
Le Pont de la Tour
Sumosan

£45+ Alyn Williams
L'Autre Pied
The Cinnamon Club
Club Gascon
Criterion
Dabbous
Galvin at Windows
Galvin La Chapelle
Gauthier Soho
Koffmann's
Launceston Place
Mari Vanna
maze
maze Grill
Orrery
The Providores
Spice Market

Trinity

£40+ Angelus
L'Anima
Babylon
Bar Boulud
Belvedere
Bonds
Cambio de Tercio
Chor Bizarre
Le Colombier
Hix
Kitchen W8
Lucio
Morgan M
Novikov (Italian restaurant)
La Poule au Pot
Quirinale
Sale e Pepe
Tamarind
Zaika

£35+ Albannach
The Almeida
aqua kyoto
L'Aventure
Benihana
Bradley's
Butlers Wharf Chop House
Caffè Caldesi
La Collina
Les Deux Salons
Dorchester Grill
The Enterprise
Essenza
L'Etranger
Franco's
Frederick's
Galvin Bistrot de Luxe
High Timber
Magdalen
The Malt House
Mint Leaf
Momo
Moti Mahal
Odette's
Pellicano
Quo Vadis
Racine
Red Fort
Les Trois Garçons
Villa Bianca

£30+ Archipelago
Bistrotheque
Bluebird
La Bouchée

Boudin Blanc
Chez Patrick
Cinnamon Kitchen
Cinnamon Soho
El I even Park Walk
Formosa Dining Room
Franklins
The Frontline Club
The Gun
The Hoxton Grill
Lamberts
Latium
The Lockhart
Market
Mazi
Mediterraneo
Mon Plaisir
Osteria dell'Arancio
Pissarro
Sam's Brasserie
Sonny's Kitchen
Sophie's Steakhouse
Verru
The Victoria

£25+ Alquimia
Chabrot Bistrot des Halles
Chapters
China Tang
Daquise
Le Deuxième
Grumbles
Indian Zing
Ishtar
Polish Club
The Orange Tree
The Palmerston
Tierra Peru

£20+ Cellar Gascon
Empress of Sichuan
Joe Allen
Le Sacré-Coeur
Sichuan Folk
Yum Yum

£15+ Chelsea Bun Diner

£10+ Sree Krishna

Pre/post theatre (and early evening)

£80+ Marcus Wareing

£60+ L'Atelier de Joel
Robuchon
Thirty Six

£55+ Theo Randall
Wiltons

£50+ Bentley's
The Ivy
Koffmann's
Oxo Tower (Brass')

£45+ Axis
Brasserie Max
Le Caprice
The Cinnamon Club
Criterion
Galvin La Chapelle
Homage
Indigo
maze
maze Grill
Tamarind

£40+ Bar Boulud
L'Etranger
Hix
Kitchen W8
Morgan M

Quirinale

£35+ Albannach
The Almeida
The Avenue
The Balcon
Bradley's
Christopher's
Dean Street Townhouse
L'Escargot
Frederick's
Galvin Bistrot de Luxe
Odette's
Orso
Quo Vadis
Red Fort
Trishna

£30+ Bistrotheque
La Bouchée
Cinnamon Soho
Harrison's
Latium
Mele e Pere

£25+ Le Deuxième
Grumbles
Mon Plaisir

£20+ Joe Allen

£15+ Carom at Meza

Sunday lunch

£45+ Bradley's
Le Colombier
Galvin Bistrot de Luxe
Koffmann's

£40+ The Almeida
Garnier
MASH Steakhouse

£35+ Maggie Jones's
Sonny's Kitchen
The Wells

£30+ Les Associés

£25+ Grumbles
Malabar
Polish Club

THE RESTAURANT SCENE

No change... but all change

This year we record 125 openings, a little down on last year (134), but comfortably within the range – 120 to 142 – which history suggests is normal in the current century. Closings, at 56, are well down on the previous year (74), and very low by historical standards – the lowest, in fact, since 2000. (See lists of openings and closings on pages 22 and 23.)

In fact, so low is the number of closings this year that the number of *net* openings (openings minus closings), 69, is not far short of the all-time record net openings figure of 75, which was in our 2006 guide.

This same impression of robustness is conveyed by a bellwether ratio we track each year: the ratio of openings to closings, which tends to follow a clear cycle. This year's ratio (2.2:1) emphatically continues the rebound which was apparent last year (1.8) from the low point of the cycle (1.5) recorded the year before that.

These numbers suggest that the market is in an up phase, which impression is confirmed if we look at our annual best-of-crop selection. Every year, we choose what seem to us to be the ten most significant openings of the year, and our selection for this year is as follows:

Balthazar	The Clove Club
Five Fields	Grain Store
HKK	Kitchen Table
Shiori	Story
Tartufo	White Rabbit

The initial impression is of continuity: last year was a very strong year, and this is too. The impression of steady-as-she-goes is, however, misleading. Of our selection last year, no fewer than seven of the ten were in the key West End postcode, W1. And this year... just one!

Next stop: the doughnut

Historically, London restaurants have had a homeland. Pre War, it was those ill-matched W1 twins, Soho and Mayfair. In the '60s, then-bohemian Chelsea began to take over. In 1992, when we published our first guide, the heartland was still the SWs. Many readers under 30 will be surprised to know that it was only in the late-'90s that a restaurant scene of any note re-emerged in W1 itself!

And now? Well, the interesting thing about our top ten of the year is that not only are they largely non-central, but they come from all points of the compass – a sort of doughnut, if you like, of which the West End is the hole.

As the new skyscrapers and tower cranes looming over many non-central areas of London suggest, London is well on the way to becoming a city with many nodes of economic and cultural activity, rather in the style of a Tokyo or

Shanghai. (And less and less like the Parisian model, where more or less everything still — more than two centuries on from the Revolution — radiates from the Place de la Concorde.) London's restaurant scene — or rather, now, scenes — cannot help reflecting this, and ever more so over coming years.

New York, of course, has already been through all this — Greewich Village, to Midtown, to Downtown, over the bridge to Brooklyn… and now people even talk of Queens as the next frontier!

Perhaps the fact that NYC has 'been through it all before' to some extent explains the ongoing popularity of American, and especially NYC, concepts and influences in London at the moment. These include:

• the opening of new operations by US-based operators (*Balthazar, Chop Shop, Five Guys, Hoi Polloi* and *Shake Shack*)

• explicitly US-inspired culinary concepts, such as *Jackson & White, The Lockhart* and *Soho Diner*

• meat-based cooking generally, and particularly the ongoing obsession with steaks and burgers

• a general desire to imitate New York (and especially Brooklyn) styling, even in non-US restaurants.

It would not be unfair to note that much of the American inspiration has had much more to do with style than content! Reporters' (and press critics') poor reception of the long-awaited *Balthazar* is a case in point.

We observed this American trend last year, and many of the other macro-trends currently apparent are also by and large a continuation of what has gone before. Small plates presentation, for example, is now almost the new normal. South American and Hispanic influences continue to be important. The idea that London has 'no good Japanese restaurants' recedes ever further into history.

One new significant trend: very small restaurants, such as *Marianne* and *Kitchen Table at Bubbledogs*. Such ventures, which might once have been dismissed as bizarre, are signs that London's restaurant goers should be ready for pretty much anything. Alongside the huge expansion of the geographical area of restaurant-going London, we are seeing, and will see in the future, more and more different and exciting concepts from all parts of the globe. And — who knows? — perhaps even some generated here in London!

Prices

The average price of dinner for one at establishments listed in the guide is £47.68 (compared to £46.55 last year). Prices have risen by 3.5% in the past 12 months — exactly the same as last year's increase and, once again, a whisker ahead of the rise in consumer prices more generally.

OPENINGS AND CLOSURES

Openings (125)

A Wong
Albion, SE1
Alquimia
Ametsa with
  Arzak Instruction
Amica Bio, WC1
Assiette Anglaise
Beard to Tail
The Berners Tavern
Big Easy WC2
Bird in Hand
Bird of Smithfield
Bo London
Bone Daddies
Bonnie Gull
Bouchon Fourchette
Boulestin
Brasserie Chavot
Bubbledogs, Kitchen Table
Bumpkin SW3
Burger & Lobster
  SW1 & EC4
Bush Dining Hall
Caffe Vegnano WC1
Il Calcio W1 & SW5
Carom @ Meza
Casse-Croute
Chabrot Bistrot des Halles
Chop Shop
Chotto Matte
The Clove Club
Le Coq
Coya
The Dairy
Dirty Burger
Dishoom E2
Duke's Brew & Que
Eat Tokyo W6
The Fish & Chip Shop
The Five Fields
Five Guys
Flat Iron
Flesh & Buns
Foxlow
Garufin
Gin Joint
Grain Store
Greenberry Café
Grillshack

Gymkhana
Haché EC1
Hoi Polloi
Honest Burgers
  W11 & NW1
Honey & Co
Hummus Bros EC1
Hutong
Jackson & Whyte
The Jam Tree SW4
John Salt
Jubo
K10 Appold Street
Kaspar's Seafood & Grill
The Keeper's House
Kerbisher & Malt W5
Kirazu
Koya-Ko
Little Social
The Lockhart
Made in Italy, James Street
The Magazine Restaurant
The Malt House
Marianne
Maxela
Meat Mission
MEATmarket
Michael Nadra NW1
Moxon's Fish Bar
Natural Kitchen EC3
Newman Street Tavern
Notes N7
Notting Hill Kitchen
No 11 Pimlico Road
The Oak W12
Obika, W1, SW3, E14
Oblix
Olivocarne
One Canada Square
Ostuni
Patty & Bun
Picture
Pig & Butcher
Pizza Pilgrims
Plum + Spilt Milk
Prawn on the Lawn
Il Ristorante, Bulgari Hotel
Rossopomodoro
  N1, NW1, SW18

Openings (cont'd)

Sager & Wilde
Season Kitchen
Shake Shack
The Shed
The Shiori
Shoryu Ramen SW1 & W1
The Sign of the Don
Smiths Brasserie
The Smokehouse Islington
Social Eating House
Soho Diner
Sticks & Sushi
Story
Sweet Thursday
Tartufo
Toasted

Tom's Kitchen E14
Tommi's Burger Joint
Tozi
Tramontana Brindisa
28-50 W1
White Rabbit
Whyte & Brown
Wright Brothers E1
Yashin SW7
Zoilo

Closures (56)

The Ark
Aurelia
Back to Basics
Bar Trattoria Semplice
Bincho Yaktori, EC1
Butcher & Grill, SW19
Cantinetta
Casa Batavia
Le Cassoulet
The Chelsea Brasserie
Chez Liline
Chrysan
Cicada
Daphne
Delfina
La Delizia SW18
The Ebury
Fig
Fish Place
The Forge
Frankies Italian
Gordon Ramsay at Claridges
Great Eastern Dining Room
Green's, EC3
Hix Belgravia
Langan's Bistro
The Luxe
Mar I Tera, W1
The Markham Inn
Mennula
Moolis

Nahm
North Road
Notting Hill Brasserie
Odin's
L'Oranger
Prism
Ransome's Dock
Ristorante Semplice
Roganic
Le Saint Julien
Sardo Canale
Savoy, River Restaurant
Searcy's Brasserie
Serafino
Le Suquet
Sushi of Shiori
Tapasia
Tempo
Tom Ilic
Trojka
Uli
Verta
Wabi
Waterloo Brasserie

EATING IN LONDON FAQs

'How should I use this guide?

You will often wish to use this guide in a practical way. At heart, the issue will usually be geographical – where can we eat near…? To answer such questions, the Maps (from page 300) and Area Overviews (from page 262) are the place to start. The latter tell you all the key facts about the restaurants – perhaps dozens of 'em – in a particular area in the space of a couple of pages. These Area Overviews are unique, so please do spend a second to have a look!

This section, though, is about seeking out restaurants for the joy of it – a few thoughts to lead you to London's best restaurants for particular types of events, or to lead you down byways you might not otherwise have considered.

What makes London special?

Cosmopolitanism has always been part of London's make-up, but in recent years this diversity has more and more been allied with quality. A 'virtuous' circle has set in, with London becoming an acknowledged destination for chefs and restaurateurs from all over the word, which has further reinforced the capital's name as the 'place to be', which has then sucked in further talent. This process has now gone on for long enough that London is often identified (and not just by Londoners) as one of the world's great restaurant cities.

This process has been accompanied and in part sustained by another virtuous circle – a greater interest in dining out by the capital's under-35s than was traditionally the case. This has encouraged a greater provision of dining out opportunities suited to that demographic. Younger people being, generally speaking, more novelty-seeking than silver haired types, the whole restaurant scene has become much buzzier.

The result is that there is no restaurant scene in the world today which is more exciting – and deservedly so – than the one we enjoy in London.

Which is London's best restaurant?

In a restaurant scene as diverse and interesting as London's, 'best' – more and more – means different things to different people, so it gets ever harder to give a single answer. If the question is translated to mean 'which is the best grand French restaurant in town', the answer is pretty clearly – still! – Le Gavroche. London's original grand restaurant of recent times has been performing particularly strongly of late. If you're looking for a more modern – and informal – take on the grand dining experience, The Ledbury is probably the place to go. For other truly tip-top suggestions, please use the lists on pages 14-15.

What about something a little more reasonably priced?

There is a reason that *Chez Bruce* has just been voted London's favourite restaurant for an amazing 9th consecutive year – if you're looking for a top quality all-round experience at a level which, if not inexpensive, is less than ruinous, it is a destination it's hard to beat. The only downside is that you have to make the schlep to Wandsworth to enjoy it.

A step down in the price-and-grandeur stakes, how about the excellent *Lambert's*… but that's even further out, in Balham. Just too far? A formula rather similar to Chez Bruce (if not yet quite as good) can be enjoyed, somewhat more conveniently for many people, at Chelsea's rising *Medlar*. Or, for an all-round foodie treat of a much trendier type, head to Shoreditch's former Town Hall, now home to *The Clove Club*.

What about some really good suggestions in the heart of the West End?

It is becoming less the case than once it was that you need to head out of the West End for a really good meal without breaking the bank. Witness such possibilities as *Little Social*, cutely hidden away in Mayfair, and *Gauthier Soho*. You have to ring for entry to the latter's townhouse premises, adding to the sense of occasion.

What about a big night out?

Sometimes, of course, the food is just part of the package, and you're looking for theatre and people-watching as much as a meal. The obvious choice for such a trip, especially if you are entertaining visitors from out-of-town, is *The Wolseley* – the food may not be that remarkable, but the 'package' – which includes a remarkable Edwardian interior and a location right next to the Ritz – is very hard to beat. The food may not be earth-shattering, but no one seems to mind.

Other West End establishments offering a grand all-round formula, of which the food is just one part of the whole, albeit an important one, include such stand-outs as *Scott's* (Mayfair), *Le Caprice* (St James's), *The Delaunay* (Covent Garden) and *J Sheekey* – the long-established fish restaurant, hidden-away in Theatreland, which was once again this year the survey's most commented-on restaurant.

Small is beautiful

Much of the gastronomic excitement of recent years has come from 'tapas' specialists, inspired not just by Spain but by SW France and beyond. Such concepts have brought sophisticated yet affordable formats to the heart of the West End. *Barrafina* represents the classic tapas ideal, with outfits such as *Bocca di Lupo*, *Ceviche*, *Copita*, *Dehesa*, *Lima* and *Salt Yard* all offering their own variations on the theme.

What about British cooking?

Until recently, the idea of British restaurants (other than simple grill or roast houses) was pretty much unknown, as most restaurants were French or Italian, or, in more recent times, Indian or Chinese.

It was the Smithfield restaurant *St John*, established in 1994, whose dedication to old-fashioned (and usually offal-heavy) British cooking captured the zeitgeist and re-awakened an interest in traditional food culture. Other notable British restaurants often trace their roots back to St John, including *Magdalen* (South Bank), *Great Queen Street* (Covent Garden), *Hereford Road* (Bayswater) and, of course – currently best of all – *St John Bread & Wine* (Shoreditch).

A couple of years ago, the trend reached a zenith, at least in a media-friendly sense, with the opening of Heston Blumenthal's good-but-pricey *Dinner* (Knightsbridge). But a lot of the 'British' cooking is taking place in gastropubs…

What are gastropubs?

Essentially, bistros in pub premises. They come in many styles. What many people think of as the original gastropub (*The Eagle*, 1991) still looks very much like a pub with a food counter. Few of the best gastropubs are particularly central. The handy location of the *Anchor & Hope*, on the South Bank, is part of the reason for its great popularity. Other stars include the *Bull & Last* (Kentish Town), the *Canton Arms* (Stockwell) and the *Harwood Arms* (Fulham).

Isn't London supposed to be a top place for curry?

Many visitors come to London wanting to 'try Indian'. The choice of 'Indians' – a term including Pakistani and Bangladeshi restaurants in this context – is so great, however, that you then need to decide what sort of Indian you want to try.

You want value? Two top names in the East End (and hence relatively accessible from central London) are almost legendary 'experiences' – the *Lahore Kebab House* and *Tayyabs*. The predominantly veggie *Rasa* group also includes some very good value options. Or, for an immersive experience, go down to Tooting, and check out a fixture like *Sree Krishna*.

At the other end of the scale (and, for the most part, right in the heart of town) are the 'nouvelle Indians', where spicy dishes are presented with a heavy European influence. *Amaya, Benares, The Cinnamon Club, The Painted Heron, Quilon, Rasoi, Trishna, Veeraswamy* and *Zaika* are all examples of plush restaurants just as suited to business (and in many cases romance) as their European price-equivalents.

In fact, wherever you are in London, you should be in reach of an Indian restaurant of more-than-average note – search out the asterisked restaurants in the Indian and Pakistani lists commencing on pages 257 and 259 respectively.

Any money-saving tips?

● If you have the luxury of being in charge of your own timetable, there are some extraordinary bargains to be had simply by lunching rather than dining, and the more reasonably priced menus often available at the lunch service give you the opportunity to check out establishments which might otherwise be simply unattainable. See the spread on pages 18 and 19.

● Think ethnic – for a food 'experience' at modest cost, you're likely to be better off going Indian, Thai, Chinese or Vietnamese (to choose four of the most obvious cuisines) than English, French or Italian. The days when there was any sort of assumption that ethnic restaurants were – in terms of comfort, service and décor – in any way inferior to European ones is long gone, but they are still often somewhat cheaper.

● Don't assume the West End is the obvious destination. It is becoming less and less true anyway that the best and most interesting London restaurants are necessarily to be found within the confines of the Circle Line, so don't be reluctant to explore! Use the maps at the back of this book to identify restaurants near tube stations on a line that's handy for you.

● If you must dine in the West End, try to find either pre-theatre (generally before 7 pm) or post-theatre (generally after 10 pm) menus. You will generally save at least the cost of a cinema ticket, compared to dining à la carte. Many of the more upmarket restaurants in Theatreland do such deals. For some of our top suggestions, see page 19.

● Use this book! Don't take pot luck, when you can benefit from the pre-digested views of thousands of other diners-out. Choose a place with a ❶ or ❷ for food, and you're very likely to eat much better than if you walk in somewhere 'on spec' – this is good advice anywhere, but is most particularly so in the West End.

● Once you have decided that you want to eat within a particular area, use the Area Overviews (starting on p262) to identify the restaurants that are offering top value. We have gone to a lot of trouble to boil down a huge amount of data into the results which are handily summarised in such lists. Please use them! You are unlikely to regret it.

● Visit our website, www.hardens.com for the latest reviews, news and offers, and to sign up for our annual spring survey.

DIRECTORY

Comments in "double quotation-marks" were made by reporters.

Establishments which we judge to be particularly notable have their NAME IN CAPITALS.

A Cena TW1 £50 ❸❷❸
418 Richmond Rd   8288 0108   1–4A
For "the best Italian food around Richmond", many locals would seek out this "always convivial" St Margaret's spot – the cooking "maintains high standards", and "you can always find something different on the wine list". / TW1 2EB; www.acena.co.uk; @acenarestaurant; 10 pm; closed Mon L & Sun D; booking: max 6, Fri & Sat.

A Wong SW1 NEW £33 ❸❸❸
70-71 Wilton Rd   7828 8931   2–4B
"Not your standard Chinese menu!" – this "noisy" café-style newcomer has made quite a splash in under-provided Pimlico (though it's rather less of a hit with reporters than it has been with the critics); "particularly good" dim sum is a highlight. / SW1 1DE; www.awong.co.uk/; 10.15 pm; closed Mon L & Sun.

The Abbeville SW4 £44 ❹❸❷
67-69 Abbeville Rd   8675 2201   10–2D
"Just as good for a pint and a packet of crisps as a three-course meal", this "busy" Clapham back street boozer is invariably hailed as an "enjoyable" destination. / SW4 9JW; www.renaissancepubs.co.uk; @renaissancepubs; 10.30 pm, Sun 9 pm; SRA-56%.

Abbeville Kitchen SW4 £46 ❷❷❸
47 Abbeville Rd   8772 1110   10–2D
"An exceptional neighbourhood restaurant" – with its "genuinely interesting" British fare, "fantastic" staff and "very convivial" setting, this Clapham yearling is a real all-round crowd-pleaser. / SW4 9JX; www.abbevillekitchen.com; @abbevillek; 10.30 pm, Sun 9.30 pm; closed Mon L, Tue L & Wed L.

Abeno £40 ❸❸❸
47 Museum St, WC1   7405 3211   2–1C
17-18 Great Newport St, WC2   7379 1160   4–3B
"Unique" and "fun", these West End 'okonomi-yaki' (Japanese omelette) parlours – where the cooking takes place at your table – make entertaining venues for a light bite. / www.abeno.co.uk; 10 pm-11 pm; WC2 no booking.

The Abingdon W8 £55 ❸❸❷
54 Abingdon Rd   7937 3339   5–2A
"The best local ever" – this "buzzy" backstreet Kensington fixture may be on the "expensive" side, but it's "always popular", thanks to its "solid" standards and "welcoming" style; the cute booths at the back suit "small groups or romance". / W8 6AP; www.theabingdon.co.uk; 10.30 pm, Fri & Sat 11 pm, Sun 10 pm; set Sun L £39 (FP).

Abokado £17 ❹❹❹
16 Newman St, W1   7636 9218   2–1B
160 Drury Ln, WC2   7242 5600   4–2D
The Lexington, 40-56 City Rd, EC1   7608 2620   12–1A
63 Cowcross St, EC1   7490 4303   9–1A
33 Fleet St, EC4   7353 8284   9–2A
"Fresh choices for a light lunch, and a quick turnaround", especially "a nice range of cheap sushi" – most reports on this small (mainly) take-away chain are complimentary. / www.abokado.com; 7.30 pm Mon-Fri, NW1 9 pm, 5 pm Sat & Sun; no Amex; no booking.

About Thyme SW1 £55 ❷❶❸
82 Wilton Rd 7821 7504 2–4B
"By far the best restaurant round Victoria", say fans – this "charming and welcoming" Pimlico stalwart is "not cheap", but its "hearty" Iberian-influenced food is "consistently good and interesting". / SW1V 1DL; www.aboutthyme.co.uk; 10.30 pm; closed Sun.

L'Absinthe NW1 £45 ④❷❸
40 Chalcot Rd 7483 4848 8–3B
"Très francais!"; the owners "delight in their Gallic roots", and offer a "warm welcome" to this "closely-packed" Primrose Hill corner bistro, which serves a "limited" menu of "well-presented" classic dishes. / NW1 8LS; www.labsinthe.co.uk; @absinthe07jc; 10.30 pm, Sun 9.30 pm; closed Mon.

Abu Zaad W12 £23 ❸❸④
29 Uxbridge Rd 8749 5107 7–1C
"A delightful Syrian landmark, in buzzing Shepherd's Bush" – a café/takeaway near the market, where "the prices are excellent, and the food's even better!" / W12 8LH; www.abuzaad.co.uk; 11 pm; no Amex.

Adams Café W12 £30 ❸❶❷
77 Askew Rd 8743 0572 7–1B
A (very good) Shepherd's Bush greasy spoon by day which, as it "turns Tunisian" by night, develops a "warm family atmosphere"; the owners are "delightful", and offer "generous" portions of North African grills, couscous and tagines, plus some "well-priced" wines (or BYO). / W12 9AH; www.adamscafe.co.uk; 10 pm; closed Sun.

Addie's Thai Café SW5 £31 ❷❸❸
121 Earl's Court Rd 7259 2620 5–2A
"Top-value Bangkok street cooking, with genuine flavours" – this "Earl's Court staple" continues to please all who comment on it… "when you can get a table", that is. / SW5 9RL; www.addiesthai.co.uk; 11 pm, Sun 10.30 pm; no Amex.

Admiral Codrington SW3 £53 ❸④④
17 Mossop St 7581 0005 5–2C
"Tucked away" in a back street, a "fun" (and noisy) Chelsea stalwart that's "always packed"; menu highlight? – the burgers are "unexpectedly brilliant". / SW3 2LY; www.theadmiralcodrington.co.uk; @TheAdCod; 10 pm, Thu-Sat 11 pm, Sun 9.30 pm.

Afghan Kitchen N1 £26 ❷④④
35 Islington Grn 7359 8019 8–3D
A tiny café, in the heart of Islington – "the menu only has a few items, but they're "all delicious, fresh and incredibly tasty". / N1 8DU; 11 pm; closed Mon & Sun; no credit cards.

Aglio e Olio SW10 £41 ❸❸④
194 Fulham Rd 7351 0070 5–3B
"Crazy-cramped" and "amazingly noisy", this "efficient" little café, by the Chelsea & Westminster Hospital, offers "large portions of hearty and fresh Italian staples" at "very reasonable prices". / SW10 9PN; 11.30 pm.

Akari N1 £38 ❷❸❸
196 Essex Rd 7226 9943 8–3D
"You don't expect amazing sushi to be served in a converted pub", but this family-run Japanese in Islington does just that – "everything is delicious". / N1 8LZ; 11 pm; closed Mon, Tue-Fri D only, Sat & Sun open L & D; no Amex.

Al Duca SW1 £45 ④④⑤
4-5 Duke of York St 7839 3090 3–3D
*Fans say it offers "good modern cooking at reasonable prices",
but this St James's Italian has quite a few critics too – they find the
style "nondescript" and service "cold". / SW1Y 6LA;
www.alduca-restaurant.co.uk; 11 pm; closed Sun.*

Al Forno £37 ④❸❷
349 Upper Richmond Rd, SW15 8878 7522 10–2A
2a King's Rd, SW19 8540 5710 10–2B
*These "buzzing" Italians are classic examples of the "old school",
complete with "friendly", if sometimes "chaotic", service; they don't
delight everyone though – doubters say they're "like a step back into
the '80s". / SW15 11 pm; SW19 11.30 pm, Sun & Mon 10.30 pm.*

Al Hamra W1 £53 ④④④
31-33 Shepherd Mkt 7493 1954 3–4B
*A "pricey" Lebanese stalwart, once regarded as quite an 'institution',
but which is mainly of note nowadays for its charming al fresco tables
in Mayfair's Shepherd Market. / W1J 7PT; www.alhamrarestaurant.co.uk;
11.30 pm.*

Al Sultan W1 £45 ❸❷④
51-52 Hertford St 7408 1155 3–4B
*This rather nondescript Lebanese, just off Mayfair's Shepherd Market,
inspires only modest survey commentary; most reporters, though,
would say the food is at least "good". / W1J 7ST; www.alsultan.co.uk;
11 pm.*

Al-Waha W2 £46 ❷④④
75 Westbourne Grove 7229 0806 6–1B
*"Everyone we take loves its high quality!" – a low-key Bayswater
fixture, serving "authentic" Lebanese cuisine. / W2 4UL;
www.alwaharestaurant.com; 11 pm; no Amex.*

Alain Ducasse
Dorchester W1 £121 ④❸④
53 Park Ln 7629 8866 3–3A
*"The three Michelin stars are for the Ducasse name, not anything
achieved here!" – this "bland" Mayfair super-chef outpost is a "lazy"
sort of operation; it's not that "exquisite" dishes are unknown,
but they are not sufficiently prevalent to justify the "extortionate"
prices. / W1K 1QA; www.alainducasse-dorchester.com; 9.30 pm; closed Mon,
Sat L & Sun; jacket; set weekday L £68 (FP).*

Alba EC1 £46 ❸❷④
107 Whitecross St 7588 1798 12–2A
*"Hearty and rustic" Piedmontese cooking is the speciality at this
veteran restaurant, in a side street near the Barbican – a "high-
quality" establishment that's "great for a business lunch"; "lovely"
staff add life to the rather "airport lounge" interior. / EC1Y 8JH;
www.albarestaurant.com; 10.45 pm; closed Sun.*

Albannach WC2 £58 ④④❸
66 Trafalgar Sq 7930 0066 2–3C
*Bang on "Tourist Central", a large Scottish-themed bar/restaurant;
it's a "noisy", quite "fun" venue, but the food is "missing something".
/ WC2N 5DS; www.albannach.co.uk; 10.45 pm, Sun 6 pm; closed Sun D;
set weekday L & pre-theatre £37 (FP).*

Albertine W12 £33 ④❷❷
1 Wood Ln 8743 9593 7–1C
"Boldly resisting the rise of Westfield over the road", this wine bar "oasis" is a "reliable" old-timer, where "a wonderful wine list", "competitively priced", accompanies the "simple but tasty fare". / W12 7DP; 10.30 pm; closed Sat L & Sun; no Amex.

The Albion N1 £45 ❸❸❶
10 Thornhill Rd 7607 7450 8–3D
"It'll redeem your faith in gastropubs!"; fans adore the "lovely", "cosy" style (and beautiful garden) of this "quintessential North London boozer", where the "wonderful Sunday roasts" are a particular highlight. / N1 1HW; www.the-albion.co.uk; @thealbionpub; 10 pm, Sun 9 pm; SRA-63%.

Albion £44 ④④❸
NEO Bankside, Holland St, SE1 7827 4343 9–3B **NEW**
2-4 Boundary St, E2 7729 1051 12–1B
Especially for breakfast, Sir Terence Conran's "airy" and "buzzy", "'50s-style" café, in an "über-cool" part of Shoreditch, can make a "fabulous" destination; service, though, is "not that effective", and other meals can seem decidedly "unremarkable"; now also on the South Bank. / 11 pm.

Ali Baba NW1 £23 ❸❷④
32 Ivor Pl 7723 5805 2–1A
"Authentic Egyptian food in an authentic Egyptian restaurant" – this living-room-style Marylebone café (behind a takeaway) is "not very atmospheric" (unless you like the TV blaring much of the time), but it makes an interesting budget destination; BYO. / NW1 6DA; midnight; no credit cards.

All Star Lanes £46 ④❸❸
Victoria Hs, Bloomsbury Pl, WC1 7025 2676 2–1D
Whiteley's, 6 Porchester Gdns, W2 7313 8363 6–1C
Old Truman Brewery, 95 Brick Ln, E1 7426 9200 12–2C
Westfield Stratford City, E20 3167 2434 1–1D
"Like being in Happy Days!" – these American diners attached to bowling alleys may not be places of culinary pilgrimage, but they're undoubtedly "fun", and they dish up "reasonable" burgers and other staples. / www.allstarlanes.co.uk; WC1 10.30 pm, Fri & Sat midnight, Sun 9 pm; E1 10 pm; W2 10.30 pm, Fri-Sun 11 pm; E2 9.30 pm; WC1 & W2 closed L Mon-Thu.

Alloro W1 £59 ❸❸④
19-20 Dover St 7495 4768 3–3C
"A discreet location for a snappy business lunch" – this Mayfair Italian is almost invariably touted as an "utterly reliable" destination, where the food is "good, if a touch forgettable". / W1S 4LU; www.alloro-restaurant.co.uk; 10.30 pm; closed Sat L & Sun.

The Almeida N1 £58 ❸④④
30 Almeida St 7354 4777 8–2D
Fans of this D&D group operation near Islington's eponymous theatre tout it as a "straightforwardly good" option with "a little more style than the local norm"; critics though still see it as "uninspired" – "it could be so much better". / N1 1AD; www.almeida-restaurant.co.uk; 10.30 pm; closed Mon L & Sun D; set weekday L & pre-theatre £37 (FP); SRA-65%.

Alounak £29 ❸④❸
10 Russell Gdns, W14   7603 1130   7–1D
44 Westbourne Grove, W2   7229 0416   6–1B
"Tasty kebabs and the best meze" inspire high loyalty to these "authentic", "easy-going" and "incredibly cheap" Persian cafés in Bayswater and Olympia; BYO is another bonus. / 11.30 pm; no Amex.

Alquimia SW15 NEW £54 ❷❷❷
Putney Wharf   8785 0508   10–2B
"A new local favourite that deserves to do well" – a tapas bar in Putney Wharf, which impresses early-days visitors with its "quality" cooking and its "charming" service; the setting is "attractive" too (though only the window/al fresco tables have views). / SW15 2JX; www.alquimiarestaurant.co.uk; 11.30, Sun 10.30 pm; set weekday L £28 (FP).

Alyn Williams
Westbury Hotel W1 £73 ❷❶④
Bond St   7078 9579   3–2C
Alyn Williams creates some "sophisticated" and "stunningly executed" dishes at this "well-spaced" chamber, hidden away inside a Bond Street hotel; while "stylish", its decor lacks va va voom, but the "fantastically unstuffy" service offers much compensation; "unbeatable" set lunch. / W1S 2YF; www.westburymayfair.com; 10.30 pm; closed Sat L & Sun; jacket; set weekday L £45 (FP).

Amaranth SW18 £30 ❷❸❷
346 Garratt Ln   8874 9036   10–2B
"Amazing food at incredible-value prices, and BYO too!" – that's the deal at this "cramped" but "very friendly" Earlsfield Thai. / SW18 4ES; 10.30 pm; D only, closed Sun; no Amex.

Amaranto
Four Seasons Hotel W1 £83 ④④⑤
Hamilton Pl   7319 5206   3–4A
A shadow of its one-time gastronomic self; this Mayfair hotel boasts a "spacious" dining room in "James-Bond-goes-Arabic" style – it inspires few reports, too many of the "absolutely awful" variety. / W1J 7DR; www.fourseasons.com; @amarantolondon; 10.30 pm; jacket.

Amaya SW1 £73 ❶❸❷
Halkin Arc, 19 Motcomb St   7823 1166   5–1D
"Chef Karunesh Khanna is a magician!"; his "very clever" tapas-style dishes – cooked on an open grill, and offering "clean and aromatic flavours across the board" – make this sleek and "tucked away" Belgravian arguably "the best of London's aspirational Indians". / SW1X 8JT; www.realindianfood.com; 11.30 pm, Sun 10.30 pm.

Ametsa with Arzak Instruction
Halkin Hotel SW1 NEW £85 ⑤④⑤
5 Halkin St   7333 1234   2–3A
"A pig's ear!"; for fans, the "invigorating" cuisine at Juan Mari Arzak's Basque import to Belgravia may offer a "superlative" culinary fantasy, but many critics just report a "dismal" experience, and at "mad" prices too; the room that was Nahm (RIP) remains as "cold and clinical" as ever. / SW1X 7DJ; www.comohotels.com/thehalkin/dining/ametsa; @COMOHotels; 10 pm.

Amico Bio £37 ❸❹❸
43 New Oxford St, WC1   7836 7509   4–1C **NEW**
43-44 Cloth Fair, EC1   7600 7778   9–2B
*"Nourishing" veggie Italian fare is "an excellent concept", say fans,
and it's one that's realised well at the Smithfield original of these
"inviting" low-key spots; good early reports on the new Holborn
branch too. / EC1 10.30pm; EC1 closed Sat L & Sun.*

Anarkali W6 £33 ❸❸④
303-305 King St   8748 1760   7–2B
*"The chef really looks after you", at this age-old Hammersmith
Indian; it certainly appears "basic", but fans insist the food is "great".
/ W6 9NH; midnight, Sun 11.30 pm; no Amex.*

The Anchor & Hope SE1 £45 ❶❸❸
36 The Cut   7928 9898   9–4A
*"The crème de la crème of gastropubs!"; this "always jam-packed"
institution, near the Old Vic, is again voted London's No. 1, thanks
to its "hearty" British fare at "unbeatable" prices; "just a shame you
can't book" – "arrive early". / SE1 8LP; 10.30 pm; closed Mon L & Sun D;
no Amex; no booking.*

Andrew Edmunds W1 £46 ❸❷❶
46 Lexington St   7437 5708   3–2D
*"The quintessence of shabby chic" – this "quirky", "candlelit" Soho
phenomenon is "the kind of place you find in Paris not London",
and "incredibly romantic"; its "simple", "refreshingly honest" cooking
is "good (but not knock-out)", but the "eclectic, encyclopaedic
list of wines is truly wonderful"; "sit upstairs if you can". / W1F 0LW;
10.45pm, Sun 10.30 pm; no Amex; booking: max 6.*

The Angel & Crown WC2 £44 ❸④④
58 St Martin's Ln   7748 5244   4–3B
*"Unpretentiously good" cooking makes this year-old Covent Garden
pub a handy destination, especially for "good-value" pre-theatre
sustenance; by the standards of the Martin brothers' gastropub
empire, though, it's only made a modest splash. / WC2N 4EA.*

Angels & Gypsies
Church Street Hotel SE5 £41 ❷❸❷
29-33 Camberwell Church St   7703 5984   1–3C
*"Very cool", "hip" and "buzzing", a Camberwell bar which offers
"a welcome taste of Spain" with its "cleverly worked" tapas –
"not the standard stuff" at all. / SE5 8TR; www.angelsandgypsies.com;
@angelsngypsies; 10.30 pm, Fri & Sat 11 pm.*

Angelus W2 £74 ❸❷❸
4 Bathurst St   7402 0083   6–2D
*"Thierry Tomassin is a star", whose "wine choice can be totally relied
upon" – so say fans of the ex-Gavroche sommelier's conversion of a
former Bayswater boozer, which is nowadays a "traditional" Gallic
restaurant, where the fare is "artery-clogging but delicious". / W2 2SD;
www.angelusrestaurant.co.uk; 11 pm, Sun 10 pm; set weekday L £44 (FP).*

Angler
South Place Hotel EC2 £69 ❸❷❷
3 South Pl   3503 0000   12–2A
*A "stunning, lovely and bright top floor room" (over a trendy City
hotel, and with an exceptional terrace) is the venue for this D&D
group yearling, often praised for "really lovely" fish-centric cuisine.
/ EC2M 2AF; www.southplacehotel.com.*

The Anglesea Arms SW7 £47 ④④❷
15 Selwood Ter 7373 7960 5–2B
"A proper pub", in a leafy South Kensington location, whose attractions include *"fine beer"*, and a *"great terrace"*; the food is *"competent"*, but *"it isn't cheap, and you can wait a long time to be served"*. / SW7 3QG; www.angleseaarms.com; @angleseaarms; 10 pm, Sun 9.30 pm.

The Anglesea Arms W6 £50 ❷❸❷
35 Wingate Rd 8749 1291 7–1B
"Best in the West!" – thanks to its *"simple but superbly executed"* British dishes, and its *"successful balance between gastro and pub"*, this Ravenscourt Park fixture is *"always rammed"*; the food rating, though, no longer hits the dizzying heights it once did. / W6 0UR; www.anglesea-arms.co.uk; Mon 10 pm, Tue-Sat 10.30 pm, Sun 9.30 pm; no Amex; no booking.

Anglo Asian Tandoori N16 £35 ❸❷❸
60-62 Stoke Newington Church St 7254 3633 1–1C
Stoke Newington's *"stalwart curry house"* par excellence – an impressive all-rounder that's still *"always dependable"*. / N16 0NB; 11 pm; no Amex.

L'Anima EC2 £77 ❷❷❸
1 Snowden St 7422 7000 12–2B
"Thoroughly professional" and *"sharp"*, in a rather *"NYC"* sort of way – this major *"City lunch favourite"* serves *"understated but superior"* Italian dishes, alongside a *"creative wine list"* in a *"spacious"* setting; not everyone loves the *"goldfish bowl"* of an interior, though. / EC2A 2DQ; www.lanima.co.uk; 11 pm, Sat 11.30 pm; closed Sat L & Sun; set weekday L £44 (FP).

Annie's £45 ④❷❷
162 Thames Rd, W4 8994 9080 1–3A
36-38 White Hart Ln, SW13 8878 2020 10–1A
Really *"fun"* and *"cosy"*, these Barnes and Strand on the Green local restaurants are handy all-rounders – *"very welcoming with kids, but also good for a romantic dinner"*, they offer food which is decent and *"reasonably priced"*. / www.anniesrestaurant.co.uk; 10 pm, Sat 10.30 pm, Sun 9.30 pm.

Antelope SW17 £40 ❸❷❷
76 Mitcham Rd 8672 3888 10–2C
"A rare non-Indian gem in Tooting"; this *"eclectic"* and *"really engaging"* gastropub wins plaudits all round, not least for its *"hearty"* scoff; *"no wonder the Antic chain are taking over south London"*! / SW17 9NG; www.theantelopepub.com; @theantelopesw17; 10.30 pm; closed Mon-Fri L & Sun D; no Amex.

Antepliler £34 ❸④❸
139 Upper St, N1 7226 5441 1–1C
46 Grand Pde, N4 8802 5588 1–1C
A particular *"gem"* amidst the overpriced restaurants of Islington's Upper Street, this *"above-average"* Turkish operation impresses with its sheer consistency; the Newington Green outlet is just the same. / www.anteplilerrestaurant.com; 11 pm.

The Anthologist EC2   £41   ❸❸❷
58 Gresham St   465 0101   9–2C
A "casual", "large" and "busy" hang-out, near Guildhall, serving
a "wide-ranging" menu – "it looks like it should be a case of style-
over-substance, but they actually manage to pull off doing a lot
of things at once". / EC2V 7BB; www.theanthologistbar.co.uk; 10 pm; closed
Sat & Sun; SRA-73%.

Antico SE1   £47   ❸❸④
214 Bermondsey St   7407 4682   9–4D
A "reliable", if occasionally "frantic", Bermondsey yearling offering
"well thought-out" Italian dishes. / SE1 3TQ; www.antico-london.co.uk;
10.30 pm; closed Mon.

Antidote W1   £50   ❸④❸
12a Newburgh St   7287 8488   3–2C
Just off Carnaby Street, a cramped Gallic operation offering "tasty"
bistro staples; star of the show, however, is the "fantastic selection
of wines". / W1F 7RR; www.antidotewinebar.com; @AntidoteWineBar;
11 pm; closed Sun D.

Antipasto & Pasta SW11   £40   ❸❷④
511 Battersea Park Rd   7223 9765   10–1C
A "safe local favourite" par excellence; as all Battersea folk know,
"you can't beat the half-price nights" at this long-established Italian.
/ SW11 3BW; 11.30 pm, Sun 11 pm; need 4+ to book.

Apollo Banana Leaf SW17   £20   ❶❷⑤
190 Tooting High St   8696 1423   10–2C
"The interior isn't great, the service is competent... but the food,
for the price, is simply brilliant" – all reports confirm the "sublime"
quality of the cuisine at this inauspicious-looking Tooting BYO.
/ SW17 0SF; 10.30 pm; no Amex.

Apostrophe   £18   ❸❸❸
Branches throughout London
"Decadent hot chocolate, sparky coffee and real chai" are all
highlights of these "cheerful" and "efficient" Gallic cafés, which sell
some "very good sandwiches" too. / www.apostropheuk.com;
most branches 6 pm, Sat 5.30 pm; no booking.

Applebee's Cafe SE1   £42   ❸❸④
5 Stoney St   7407 5777   9–4C
The "great selection of fresh fish" – "simply grilled or fried" –
can come as a "nice surprise" to first-time visitors to this "noisy"
outfit, in the heart of Borough Market. / SE1 9AA;
www.applebeesfish.com; @applebeesfish; 10 pm, Fri 10.30 pm; closed Sun;
no Amex.

Apsleys
Lanesborough Hotel SW1   £109   ④④❸
1 Lanesborough Pl   7333 7254   5–1D
Shame that this lavish and "calming" Belgravia outpost of a top
Roman chef undermines its appeal with such "terrifying" prices –
the food is often "fabulous"; change may be afoot in 2014 as a
major refurb is planned. / SW1X 7TA; www.apsleys.co.uk; 10.30 pm; jacket;
booking: max 12; set weekday L £65 (FP).

aqua kyoto W1 £71 ④④❸
240 Regent St (entrance 30 Argyll St) 7478 0540 3–2C
"Lovely" terraces apart, this nightclubby fusion-restaurant, six floors
above Regent Street, inspires notably mixed reports – all the way
from "outstanding", via "not a patch on the HK original", to "what a
disaster"! / W1B 3BR; www.aqua-london.com; @aqualondon; 10.45 pm,
Thu-Sat 11.15 pm; closed Sun D; set weekday L £39 (FP).

aqua nueva W1 £66 ⑤⑤④
240 Regent St (entrance 30 Argyll St) 7478 0540 3–2C
The design of this nightclubby sixth-floor Spanish operation, up above
Regent Street, may be "amazing", but it again drew flak this year for
"tiny" portions and "inflated" prices; it's the service, though, which
attracts particular ire. / W1B 3BR; www.aqua-london.com; @aqualondon;
11 pm.

Arbutus W1 £49 ❸❸④
63-64 Frith St 7734 4545 4–2A
"Interesting food with an edge" (plus an "excellent choice of wines
by the glass and 250ml carafe") has won renown for this "slightly
bland and cramped" bistro; "it's not the bargain it once was",
however, and the Soho market has got a lot more competitive
of late… / W1D 3JW; www.arbutusrestaurant.co.uk; 10.45 pm, Fri & Sat
11.15 pm, Sun 10.30 pm.

Archduke Wine Bar SE1 £52 ⑤⑤④
Concert Hall Approach, South Bank 7928 9370 2–3D
Incredibly convenient for the Royal Festival Hall, this outpost of steak
'n' burger chain Black & Blue occupies a series of characterful railway
arches; it rarely excels, but it's still "better than some of the places
on the South Bank". / SE1 8XU; www.blackandbluerestaurants.com;
10.30 pm, Sun 10 pm.

Archipelago W1 £54 ④④❸
110 Whitfield St 7383 3346 2–1B
OTT decor helps lend a romantic ambience to this tiny spot, near the
Telecom Tower; the cooking from the bizarrely exotic menu
(wildebeest, ostrich…) only intermittently lives up. / W1T 5ED;
www.archipelago-restaurant.co.uk; 10.15 pm; closed Sat L & Sun;
set weekday L £30 (FP).

Ark Fish E18 £41 ❶❷④
142 Hermon Hill 8989 5345 1–1D
"The freshest fish you can hope for" – the raison d'être of this
popular (expect to queue later in the week), if "rather noisy", South
Woodford spot; friendly and efficient service too. / E18 1QH;
www.arkfishrestaurant.co.uk; 9.45 pm, Fri & Sat 10.15 pm, Sun 8.45 pm;
closed Mon; no Amex.

L'Art du Fromage SW10 £49 ❷❸❸
1a Langton St 7352 2759 5–3B
In World's End, this "small and cosy paradise for cheese-lovers" has
acquired a modest reporter following; its rather "away-from-it-all"
charms, however, seduce all who comment on it. / SW10 0JL;
www.artdufromage.co.uk; 10.30 pm; closed Mon L, Tue L, Wed L & Sun.

Artigiano NW3 £45 ❸④❸
12a Belsize Ter 7794 4288 8–2A
"Simply-prepared food, in a smart but relaxed atmosphere" –
the enduring formula for this "very agreeable" Belsize Park Italian.
/ NW3 4AX; www.etruscarestaurants.com; 10 pm; closed Mon L.

L'Artista NW11 £34 ④❸❸
917 Finchley Rd 8731 7501 1–1B
"Under the arches by Golders Green Station since forever!" –
this *"enthusiastic"* Italian institution thrives on its *"lively"* (*"impossibly noisy"*) style, and its *"ridiculously large"* lashings of pizza and other fare. / NW11 7PE; www.lartistapizzeria.com; 11.30 pm.

L'Artiste Musclé W1 £43 ④④❸
1 Shepherd Mkt 7493 6150 3–4B
"An affordable gem in the heart of Mayfair"; this *"old-fashioned"* Gallic bistro certainly has *"no gastronomic pretensions"*, but fans claim it as a *"a perfect piece of Paris"*, transported to Shepherd Market. / W1J 7PA; 10 pm, Fri-Sun 10.30 pm.

Asadal WC1 £39 ❸④④
227 High Holborn 7430 9006 2–1D
A *"solid"* subterranean operation, implausibly located below Holborn tube; *"it makes no bones about being high end, but for Korean food with bite at a good price, you can't go too far wrong"*. / WC1V 7DA; www.asadal.co.uk; 10.30 pm; closed Sun L.

Asakusa NW1 £35 ❶④④
265 Eversholt St 7388 8533 8–3C
"Fantastic sushi at amazingly cheap prices" ensures that this *"unassuming"* operation, in the shadow of Euston station, is often *"incredibly busy"*, largely with Japanese people; *"try it once – I guarantee you'll be back!"* / NW1 1BA; 11.30 pm, Sat 11 pm; D only, closed Sun.

Asia de Cuba
St Martin's Lane Hotel WC2 £89 ④⑤④
45 St Martin's Ln 7300 5588 4–4C
"Fusion that hits the spot" can still wins fans for this *"atmospheric"* but often *"noisy"* Theatreland veteran (one of the very first upmarket 'trendy' restaurants to open in the West End); service, though, is patchy and prices *"stratospheric"*, especially when *"not all of the eclectic combinations work out"*. / WC2N 4HX; www.morganshotelgroup.com; @asiadecuba; midnight, Sun 10 pm.

Ask £40 ④④④
Branches throughout London
"Passable", *"wholesome"*, *"nothing wrong with it"*… – it may rarely excite, but this pizza/pasta chain is generally hailed as a pretty decent stand-by. / www.askcentral.co.uk; most branches 11 pm, Fri & Sat 11.30 pm; some booking restrictions apply.

Assaggi W2 £72 ❶❶❸
39 Chepstow Pl 7792 5501 6–1B
"The best Italian food anywhere… and that includes Italy!" – this *"simply furnished"* (and *"noisy"*) room, above a former Bayswater boozer, has rightly won fame for its *"incredibly fresh"* cooking, supplied by *"entertaining"* staff. / W2 4TS; 11 pm; closed Sun; no Amex.

Assiette Anglaise N7 NEW £45 ❷❸❸
489 Liverpool St 7609 0300 8–2D
"Slightly incongruous at the less salubrious end of Islington", this *"wonderful"* Gallic neighbourhood newcomer has taken up where Morgan M (re-located to Clerkenwell) left off, but in a simpler vein and at *"amazing value"* prices; *"the word got out very quickly and it can be hard to get a table"*. / N7 8NS; www.assietteanglaise.co.uk; @AAnglaise; 10 pm, Sat 10.30 pm; closed Mon, Tue L, Wed L, Thu L, Fri L & Sun D.

Les Associés N8 £45 ❸②④
172 Park Rd 8348 8944 1–1C
"Run by a Frenchman, who is the real McCoy!" – this perennially popular Crouch End bistro is a local favourite, where "reasonable prices" compensate for decor that's on the shabby side of chic. / N8 8JT; www.lesassocies.co.uk; @lesassociesn8; 10 pm; closed Mon, Tue L, Sat L & Sun D; 24 hr notice for L bookings; set Sun L £32 (FP).

Atari-Ya £31 ❶④⑤
20 James St, W1 7491 1178 3–1A
7 Station Pde, W3 8896 1552 1–2A
1 Station Pde, W5 8896 3175 1–3A
595 High Rd, N12 8446 6669 8–1B
31 Vivian Ave, NW4 8202 2789 1–1B
75 Fairfax Road, London, NW6 7328 5338 8–2A
Some of "the best and most authentic Japanese food in London" – these no-frills cafés offer "sparklingly fresh" sushi that's "the real deal"; the menu, though, is "not especially easy to follow" ("and some of the staff don't seem that keen to clarify"). / www.atariya.co.uk; W1 8 pm, NW4 & NW6 9.30 pm, W9 9 pm; NW4, NW6 closed Mon.

L'Atelier de Joel Robuchon WC2 £84 ❷❷❷
13-15 West St 7010 8600 4–2B
OK, prices are "sky high", but the "divine little morsels" on offer at the Parisian über-chef's "very sleek" and "seductive" Theatreland outpost are a total "wow" for most reporters (especially at lunch, which is "tremendous value"); "sit at the bar, so you can see what's going on in the open kitchen". / WC2H 9NE; www.joelrobuchon.co.uk; @latelierlondon; midnight, Sun 10 pm; no trainers; set weekday L & pre-theatre £62 (FP).

Athenaeum
Athenaeum Hotel W1 £78 ❷①❸
116 Piccadilly 7499 3464 3–4B
Looking for an "excellent-value set lunch" or a "wonderful afternoon tea"? – this "lovely" low-key hotel delivers "five-star" service, and attracts much more consistent feedback than many of its flashier Mayfair peers. / W1J 7BJ; www.athenaeumhotel.com; 10.30 pm.

The Atlas SW6 £45 ❷❷❷
16 Seagrave Rd 7385 9129 5–3A
A "very chilled" backstreet stalwart, near Earl's Court 2, that's "just how a pub should be"; it offers "Mediterranean-inspired food far superior to the average", and has a "nice garden" too. / SW6 1RX; www.theatlaspub.co.uk; @theatlasfulham; 10 pm.

Aubaine £57 ⑤⑤④
4 Heddon St, W1 7440 2510 3–2C
260-262 Brompton Rd, SW3 7052 0100 5–2C
37-45 Kensington High St, W8 7368 0950 5–1A
Perhaps "more refined" than many rivals, but these Gallic café/bistros are increasingly seen as a "wasted opportunity" – for the "indifferent" overall experience, critics find prices "absurd". / www.aubaine.co.uk; @balanslondon; SW3, SW19 10 pm, Sun 9.30 pm; Heddon St 11 pm, Oxford St 9 pm, Sun 6 pm, W8 10 pm, Sun 6 pm, Dover St 10 pm, Sun 9.30 pm; W8 no booking.

Aurora W1 £47 ❸❷❶
49 Lexington St   7494 0514   3–2D
"Perfect for informal intimacy", this Soho stalwart is "the epitome of cosiness", and it has a secret weapon – "a wonderful little courtyard for al fresco dining"; the food (from "a small menu") is "good too". / W1F 9AP; www.aurorasoho.co.uk; 10 pm, Wed-Sat 10.30 pm, Sun 9 pm.

Automat W1 £61 ④④④
33 Dover St   7499 3033   3–3C
"A classic American diner in the heart of Mayfair", where the "top breakfast (and lots of it)" and "excellent" burgers are highlights of the menu of "high-quality US comfort food"; prices, though, fully reflect the location. / W1S 4NF; www.automat-london.com; 11.45 pm, Sat 10.45 pm, Sun 9.45 pm.

L'Autre Pied W1 £78 ❷❷④
5-7 Blandford St   7486 9696   2–1A
"Each plate is like performance art", say fans of Pied à Terre's Marylebone sibling, where the tasting menu in particular is "imaginative and sublime"; the room, though, can feel rather "bland". / W1U 3DB; www.lautrepied.co.uk; 10 pm; closed Sun D; set weekday L £47 (FP).

Avalon SW12 £41 ④④❸
16 Balham Hill   8675 8613   10–2C
On the way to Balham, a "huge" and "hectic" gastropub which is "great for families or large groups"; food and service, though, can be "hit -and-miss". / SW12 9EB; www.theavalonlondon.com; 10.30 pm, Sun 9 pm; SRA-56%.

L'Aventure NW8 £58 ❷❶❶
3 Blenheim Ter   7624 6232   8–3A
With its "charmingly arrogant service", "fashionably outdated decor", and "absolutely gorgeous" Gallic cooking, this "delightful" St John's Wood classic offers a perfect combination "for a memorable night", and it is "as romantic as its name suggests" too. / NW8 0EH; 11 pm; closed Sat L & Sun; set weekday L £38 (FP).

The Avenue SW1 £55 ❸❸❸
7-9 St James's St   7321 2111   3–4D
A "very good value" lunch menu is the stand-out attraction at this "slick" and "airy" (but sometimes "noisy") D&D group venue; its "roomy" (and slightly "cavernous") modern interior is well suited to its primary role as a St James's business rendezvous. / SW1A 1EE; www.avenue-restaurant.co.uk; 10.30 pm; closed Sat L & Sun; set weekday L £28 (FP), set pre-theatre £37 (FP); SRA-62%.

Axis
One Aldwych Hotel WC2 £63 ④④④
1 Aldwych   7300 0300   2–2D
"Relaxed" and "classy", or "cold" and "impersonal"? – as ever, views on the decor of this large Covent Garden basement are mixed; it's undeniably a "handy" location, however, and a "good value" one pre-theatre. / WC2B 4RH; www.onealdwych.com; 10.30 pm; closed Mon, Sat L & Sun; set pre theatre £46 (FP).

Azou W6 £41 ❸❷❷
375 King St   8563 7266   7–2B
"Compared favourably to our actual trip to Morocco!" – this sweet little café is a Hammersmith "favourite", thanks to its friendly service and tasty fare. / W6 9NJ; www.azou.co.uk; @azourestaurant; 11 pm.

Ba Shan W1 £48 ❷④④
24 Romilly St 7287 3266 4–3A
"Sensational" Hunanese cooking that's "much hotter than the
Chinatown norm" helps make this "unpretentious" Soho café –
a sibling to Bar Shu, just over the road – a "great-value" destination.
/ W1D 5AH; 11 pm, Fri & Sat 11.30 pm.

Babbo W1 £76 ⑤④④
39 Albermarle St 3205 1099 3–3C
Despite its handy location and "nice premises", near the Ritz,
this Mayfair Italian attracts relatively few reports – it can't help that
the food is pricey and "not that distinguished". / W1S 4JQ;
www.babborestaurant.co.uk; @BabboRestaurant; 11 pm, Sun 10.30 pm; closed
Sun L; set weekday L £50 (FP).

Babur SE23 £50 ❶❶❷
119 Brockley Rise 8291 2400 1–4D
A "gastronomic jewel"; this "unfailingly impressive" Honor Oak Park
Indian attracts a huge amount of feedback, almost all of which tends
to confirm it as "the best restaurant in SE London". / SE23 1JP;
www.babur.info; @BaburRestaurant; 11.30 pm.

Babylon
Kensington Roof Gardens W8 £72 ④④❷
99 Kensington High St 7368 3993 5–1A
"What girl doesn't like a flamingo?" – they're sometimes to be
spotted in the extraordinary 8th-floor roof garden overlooked by this
Kensington eyrie; "the menu is workmanlike and perhaps a little
uninspiring, but with views like this who cares?" / W8 5SA;
www.virgin.com/roofgardens; 10.30 pm; closed Sun D; set weekday L £44
(FP); SRA-75%.

Il Bacio £42 ❸❸❸
61 Stoke Newington Church St, N16 7249 3833 1–1C
178-184 Blackstock Rd, N5 7226 3339 8–1D
"Yummy, thin-crust, wood-fired pizza" is served "with gusto" at these
"cosy" Sardinian spots, in Stoke Newington and Highbury.
/ www.ilbaciohighbury.co.uk; 10 pm-11 pm; Mon-Fri L; no Amex.

Baker & Spice £40 ④④④
54-56 Elizabeth St, SW1 7730 5524 2–4A
47 Denyer St, SW3 7225 3417 5–2D
20 Clifton Rd, W9 7289 2499 8–4A
Good but "absurdly expensive" – same verdict as ever on this chichi
pâtisserie/deli chain, which continues to disenchant some reporters
with service that's "slow" or "off-hand". / www.bakerandspice.uk.com;
7 pm, Sun 6 pm; closed D; no Amex; no booking.

Balans £47 ⑤④④
34 Old Compton St, W1 7439 3309 4–3A
60-62 Old Compton St, W1 7439 2183 4–3A
239 Old Brompton Rd, SW5 7244 8838 5–3A
Westfield, Ariel Way, W12 8600 3320 7–1C
214 Chiswick High Rd, W4 8742 1435 7–2A
187 Kensington High St, W8 7376 0115 5–1A
Westfield Stratford, Westfield Startford, E20 8555 5478 1–1D
"Watch the hive of activity that is Soho" from the most central
branch of this "buzzing" diner chain, which is especially popular for
brunch; critics, though, feel the food has "gone from adequate
to mediocre". / www.balans.co.uk; midnight-2 am; 34 Old Compton St 24 hrs,
E20 11pm; some booking restrictions apply.

The Balcon
Sofitel St James SW1 £60 ❸❸❸
8 Pall Mall 7968 2900 2–3C
"Large", "airy" and "relaxed", and just by Trafalgar Square too –
this "reliable" brasserie certainly makes a handy West End
rendezvous; the pre-theatre menu, in particular, is "hard to beat".
/ SW1Y 5NG; www.thebalconlondon.com; 10.45 pm, Sun 9.45 pm; set pre
theatre £36 (FP).

Bald Faced Stag N2 £47 ❸❹❸
69 High Rd 8442 1201 1–1B
"One of the few East Finchley places worth visiting" – it offers
"all that you expect from a good gastropub", including "well-
executed" fare. / N2 8AB; www.thebaldfacedstagn2.co.uk;
@thebaldfacestagn2; 10.30 pm, Sun 9.30 pm.

The Balham Bowls Club SW12 £40 ❸❸❷
7-9 Ramsden Rd 8673 4700 10–2C
The dining room at this spacious haunt (which has nothing to do with
bowls) serves "decent home-made food", and fans say this
is "the best pub in Balham". / SW12 8QX; www.balhambowlsclub.com;
11 pm, Fri & Sat midnight; closed weekday L; no Amex.

Balthazar WC2 £64 ⑤❹❸
4-6 Russell St 3301 1155 4–3D
"Oh dear!"; Keith McNally's "very disappointing" Manhattan-comes-
to-Covent-Garden import wows reporters as little as it did the press;
the room may be "beautiful, buzzy, fun, and very NYC", but it's
"greedily packed-in", and the food is "like a glorified Café Rouge".
/ WC2E 7BN; www.balthazarlondon.com.

Baltic SE1 £50 ❸❸❷
74 Blackfriars Rd 7928 1111 9–4A
A "claustrophobic" front bar gives little hint of the attractions of this
"spacious" bar/restaurant lying behind a small Borough frontage –
a "slick", "crowded" and "fun" operation, where the "Polish-fusion"
fare rarely disappoints. / SE1 8HA; www.balticrestaurant.co.uk; 11.15 pm,
Sun 10.15 pm; closed Mon L.

Bam-Bou W1 £54 ❸❸❷
1 Percy St 7323 9130 2–1C
"They've mastered the art of casual dining", at the Caprice group's
"lovely" French colonial-style Fitzrovia townhouse – a "fun" venue,
offering "high-quality" pan-Asian food and "amusing" cocktails.
/ W1T 1DB; www.bam-bou.co.uk; midnight; closed Sun; booking: max 6.

The Banana Tree Canteen £34 ❹❹❸
103 Wardour St, W1 7437 1351 3–2D
21-23 Westbourne Grove, W2 7221 4085 6–1C
166 Randolph Ave, W9 7286 3869 8–3A
237-239 West End Ln, NW6 7431 7808 1–1B
75-79 Battersea Rise, SW11 7228 2828 10–2C
412-416 St John St, EC1 7278 7565 8–3D
"Always popular and busy" – these pan-Asian canteens have
a "pleasing upbeat" style, and offer food that's "decent for a chain";
"a recent revamp has improved the SW11 branch".
/ @bananatree247; 11 pm, Sun 10.30 pm; booking: min 6.

Bangalore Express   £38   ④④❸
103-105 Waterloo Rd, SE1   7021 0886   9–4A
1 Corbet Ct, EC3   7220 9195   9–3C
"Indian food with a western twist" (and "a hint of wit" too) wins
majority approval for these contemporary-style establishments, in the
City and Waterloo (the latter with funky, double-decker seating);
for sceptics, though, the supposed wackiness is all a bit "stereotyped".
/ www.bangaloreuk.com; 10.30 pm.

Bangkok SW7   £39   ❷❷❸
9 Bute St   7584 8529   5–2B
"Forty years on, and still the same delicious food, friendly owner,
chef…and clientele!" – London's original Thai restaurant, near South
Kensington tube, soldiers on magnificently. / SW7 3EY; 10.45 pm;
no Amex.

Bank Westminster
St James Court Hotel SW1   £61   ④④④
45 Buckingham Gate   7630 6644   2–4B
Handy for Buckingham Palace, a bar/restaurant with the surprise
attraction of a "large glass gazebo"; its "well-spaced" tables make
it particularly useful as a business lunch venue. / SW1E 6BS;
www.bankrestaurants.com; @bank_westmin; 11 pm; closed Sat L & Sun.

Banners N8   £45   ❸❸❶
21 Park Rd   8348 2930   1–1C
It may look a bit "like a US burger joint", but this Crouch End
"perennial" in fact offers an "eclectic" (Caribbean-tinged) menu that's
especially "great for breakfast or brunch" (particularly en famille);
"it can be hard to get a table". / N8 8TE; www.bannersrestaurant.com;
11.30 pm, Fri & Sat midnight, Sun 11 pm; no Amex.

Baozi Inn WC2   £18   ❸④④
25 Newport Ct   7287 6877   4–3B
"Don't plan on making an evening of it", but this "respectable"
Chinatown Sichuanese is a handy spot for "cheap and tasty steamed
buns", plus a "limited" range of soups, noodles and so on.
/ WC2H 7JS; 10 pm, Fri-Sat 10.30 pm; no credit cards; no booking.

Bar Boulud
Mandarin Oriental SW1   £60   ❸❷❸
66 Knightsbridge   7201 3899   5–1D
"A perfect combination of posh and casual!" – this "buzzy"
Knightsbridge basement outpost of a top NYC chef offers "'stylish"
Gallic bistro fare (plus some "out-of-this-world" burgers); no denying
a growing feeling, though, that standards here are now "good, rather
than exceptional". / SW1X 7LA; www.barboulud.com; 10.45 pm,
Sun 9.45 pm; set weekday L & pre-theatre £44 (FP).

Bar Italia W1   £28   ④❷❶
22 Frith St   7437 4520   4–2A
"The only place in Britain where the espresso tastes like a proper
Italian one!" – this 24/7 Soho landmark retains its cult status;
"you don't lack entertainment" either, especially from the "interesting
clientele" in the early hours. / W1D 4RT; www.baritaliasoho.co.uk;
@TheBaristas; open 24 hours, Sun 4 am; no Amex; no booking.

Barbecoa EC4 £67 ④④④
20 New Change Pas 3005 8555 9–2B
"Make sure you get a view of St Paul's", if you visit Jamie's
"cavernous" and *"loud"* City BBQ; for business, it can provide
an *"impressive"* destination – given the *"crazy"* prices, though, those
paying their own way may find standards *"uninspiring"*. / EC4M 9AG;
www.barbecoa.com; @barbecoa; 10.45 pm.

La Barca SE1 £56 ④❷❷
80-81 Lower Marsh 7928 2226 9–4A
"The last of the old-school Italians"? – this *"friendly and cosy"*
Waterloo veteran has more claim than most, and it retains *"a huge
regular clientele"* with its *"well-executed"* (if *"expensive"*) menu.
/ SE1 7AB; www.labarca-ristorante.com; 11.15 pm; closed Sat L & Sun.

Il Baretto W1 £63
43 Blandford St 7486 7340 2–1A
"Completely Italian" in style, this *"good but expensive"* Marylebone
basement has many fans; it also inspires an impressive array
of niggles, though, including *"hit-and-miss"* cuisine, *"patchy"*
or *"arrogant"* service, and, of course, the *"din"*; it relaunches in late-
2013 after a major refurbishment. / W1U 7HF; www.ilbaretto.co.uk;
10.30 pm, Sun 10 pm.

Barrafina £41 ❶❶❷
54 Frith St, W1 7813 8016 4–2A
10 Adelaide St, WC2 awaiting tel 4–2D
*"The best tapas bar in London"… "possibly the world!"; "it's worth
the hour's wait"* to nab a perch at this tiny (23-seat) and *"too busy"*
Soho phenomenon, where there's an *"intimacy"* to having *"incredible"*
dishes *"entertainingly prepared"* before your very eyes; a WC2
branch opens in early-2014. / www.barrafina.co.uk; 11 pm, Sun 10 pm;
no booking.

Barrica W1 £39 ❷❷❶
62 Goodge St 7436 9448 2–1B
"You could almost be in Madrid!" – such is the *"hustle and bustle"*
at this *"fun and friendly"* Fitzrovia haunt, where the *"gorgeous"* tapas
are *"the real deal"*. / W1T 4NE; www.barrica.co.uk; 10.30 pm; closed Sun.

Bar Shu W1 £51 ❷⑤④
28 Frith St 7287 6688 4–3A
If you like it *"really hot"*, this Soho café – with its *"fiery"* and
"fragrant" Sichuanese cuisine – is, say fans, *"a revelation"*; service,
though, *"needs getting used to"*, and the odd sceptic feels the place
is *"overrated"*. / W1D 5LF; www.bar-shu.co.uk; 11 pm, Fri-Sat 11.30 pm.

Basilico £35 ❸❷④
690 Fulham Rd, SW6 0800 028 3531 10–1B
26 Penton St, N1 0800 093 4224 8–3D
51 Park Rd, N8 8616 0290 1–1C
515 Finchley Rd, NW3 0800 316 2656 1–1B
175 Lavender Hill, SW11 0800 389 9770 10–2C
178 Upper Richmond Rd, SW14 0800 096 8202 10–2B
"Simply the best pizza delivery!" – *"tasty thin-crusts with imaginative
toppings"*, plus *"prompt"* service, please all who comment on this
small chain. / www.basilico.co.uk; @basilicopizzas; 11 pm; no booking.

Bayee Village SW19   £45   ❸④④
24 High St   8947 3533   10–2B
*"As good as any Soho Chinese", say fans, this Wimbledon Village
fixture is a "dependable" sort of destination, where the fare
is "more authentic than you might expect". / SW19 5DX;
www.bayee.co.uk; 10.45 pm.*

Beach Blanket Babylon   £61   ⑤④❸
45 Ledbury Rd, W11   7229 2907   6–1B
19-23 Bethnal Green Rd, E1   7749 3540   12–1C
*"Great for cocktails and hen nights!"; the decor at these Gaudi-esque
Notting Hill and Shoreditch hang-outs is wonderful, but the notably
"average" and "highly-priced" food is not. / www.beachblanket.co.uk;
10.30 pm; W11 booking advisable Fri-Sat.*

Beard to Tail EC2   £49   ④❸④
77 Curtain Rd   7739 4781   12–1B
*Still few and uneven reports on this "manly" ('nose-to-tail') and rather
barely furnished Shoreditch yearling; some reporters "have never
been disappointed", but our own experience chimed with those who
find it "average all-round"; "good selection of beers and whiskies",
though. / EC2A 3BS; www.beardtotail.co.uk.*

Bedford & Strand WC2   £47   ④④❸
1a Bedford St   7836 3033   4–4D
*Handily located just off the Strand, a sometimes "noisy" basement
offering "good food, for what's basically a wine bar"; "nice staff" too.
/ WC2E 9HH; www.bedford-strand.com; 10.30 pm; closed Sat L & Sun.*

Bedlington Café W4   £30   ❷❸④
24 Fauconberg Rd   8994 1965   7–2A
*This Chiswick fixture has had a bit of a "spruce up" of late; however,
the main attraction – the "rustic, spicy and authentic" Thai dishes –
remains much the same as ever; BYO. / W4 3JY; 10 pm; closed Sun L;
no credit cards.*

The Begging Bowl SE15   £38   ❶❷❸
168 Bellenden Rd   7635 2627   1–4D
*"Phenomenal" Thai cooking – that's "really the whole story" on this
Peckham yearling, which occupies a light and airy corner site.
/ SE15 4BW; www.thebeggingbowl.co.uk.*

Beirut Express   £42   ❷④④
65 Old Brompton Rd, SW7   7591 0123   5–2B
112-114 Edgware Rd, W2   7724 2700   6–1D
*"Amazing fresh juices" and "authentic" meze and wraps win praise
for this Lebanese duo, in Bayswater and South Kensington.
/ www.maroush.com; W2 2 am; SW7 midnight.*

Beiteddine SW1   £51   ❸❷④
8 Harriet St   7235 3969   5–1D
*A "first-rate" Lebanese whose "nice, quiet and leisurely" ambience,
in the old style, seems ever more at odds with its location, just off
Euro-glittery Sloane Street. / SW1X 9JW; www.beiteddinerestaurant.com;
midnight.*

Belgo £42 ④④④
50 Earlham St, WC2   7813 2233   4–2C
67 Kingsway, WC2   7242 7469   2–2D
72 Chalk Farm Rd, NW1   7267 0718   8–2B
44-48 Clapham High Rd, SW4   7720 1118   10–2D
The appeal may have "diluted" over the years, but these "monastic" Belgian brasseries – majoring in moules-frites and Continental lagers – are still "lively" ("noisy") and "reasonably priced", and notably good with kids too. / www.belgo-restaurants.co.uk; most branches 10.30 pm-11.30 pm; SW4 midnight, Thu 1 am, Fri & Sat 2 am, Sun 12.30 am.

Bellamy's W1 £65 ❸❷❷
18-18a Bruton Pl   7491 2727   3–2B
Run by the ex-MD of nearby Annabel's nightclub, this Mayfair mews operation is a "discreet" and "well-spaced" rendezvous, where "the quality of the cooking is disguised by its simplicity". / W1J 6LY; www.bellamysrestaurant.co.uk; 10.30 pm; closed Sat L & Sun.

Bellevue Rendez-Vous SW17 £47 ❸❷❷
218 Trinity Rd   8767 5810   10–2C
"A haven of romantic calm away from the not-so-beautiful Trinity Road" – this "absolute gem" offers a "short menu bursting with well-cooked traditional dishes"; top tip – "the cheese board is second only to Chez Bruce" (round the corner). / SW17 7HP; www.bellevuerendezvous.com; 10.30 pm; closed Mon L; no Amex.

Belvedere W8 £69 ④④❷
Holland Pk, off Abbotsbury Rd   7602 1238   7–1D
"Want to feel special, with someone who is special?" – this "chic, spacious and classy" veteran not only has "a beautiful park location", but is "one of the best dining rooms in London" too; notwithstanding a "top-value Sunday lunch", however, the food is "ordinary". / W8 6LU; www.belvedererestaurant.co.uk; 10.30 pm; closed Sun D; set weekday L £40 (FP).

Ben's Canteen SW11 £48 ④④④
140 St John's Hill   7228 3260   10–2C
"Comfort food, well-cooked" has made this Wandsworth spot a popular local destination; "brunch is the meal", though – at other times, prices for what's on offer can seem "very full". / SW11 1SL; www.benscanteen.com; @benscanteen; 10 pm.

Benares W1 £82 ❷❷❸
12a Berkeley Square Hs, Berkeley Sq   7629 8886   3–3B
Atul Kochhar's "impressive" cuisine ("exciting tasting menu" a highlight) maintains this Mayfair operation as one of London's foremost 'nouvelle Indians'; the windowless first-floor space is "impersonal" to some, but fans insist it's "spacious" and "stylish". / W1J 6BS; www.benaresrestaurant.co.uk; 10.30 pm; closed Sun; no trainers; set weekday L £60 (FP); SRA-68%.

Bengal Clipper SE1 £40 ❸❸❷
Shad Thames   7357 9001   9–4D
This grand and long-established Indian is certainly a "good neighbourhood standby" for those who live near Tower Bridge; indeed, the worst anyone can find to say about it is that it's "always reliable"! / SE1 2YR; www.bengalclipper.co.uk; 11.30 pm, Sun 11 pm.

Benihana £65 ④④④
37 Sackville St, W1   7494 2525   3–3D
77 King's Rd, SW3   7376 7799   5–3D
Children (of all ages) "love the show" (which involves much knife-wielding) at these long-established, and not inexpensive, teppanyaki parlours, which can make quite a "treat" as a party destination; lunchtime menus include less drama, but can be surprisingly "good value". / www.benihana.co.uk; @Benihanauk; 10.30 pm, Sun 10 pm; set weekday L £37 (FP).

Benito's Hat £26 ❸❸④
12 Great Castle St, W1   7636 6560   3–1C
56 Goodge St, W1   7637 3732   2–1B
19 New Row, WC2   7240 5815   4–3C
King's Cross Station, N1   7812 1304   8–3C
These self-service Mexicans are especially worth visiting for a great-value Happy Hour cocktail; while you're there, pick up a "great" and "filling" burrito – one of the range of "tasty" bites. / www.benitos-hat.com; 10 pm, Thu-Sun 11 pm; Great Castle St closed Sun.

Bentley's W1 £74 ❷❸❷
11-15 Swallow St   7734 4756   3–3D
"Always first-class", this "beautifully elegant" Mayfair fish "institution" wins high acclaim for its "super, no-nonsense seafood" – the "down-to-earth" ground floor champagne and oyster bar (with nice al fresco tables) is often preferred to the "quieter" upstairs. / W1B 4DG; www.bentleys.org; @bentleys_london; 10.30 pm; no jeans; booking: max 8; set pre theatre £53 (FP).

Bento Cafe NW1 £36 ❷❷④
9 Parkway   7482 3990   8–3B
"A real find"; all reports attest to the standards of this Camden Town spot, where "both the Chinese and Japanese menus are very good"; "excellent" sashimi is a highlight, and the Bento boxes offer "terrific value" too. / NW1 7PG; bentocafe.co.uk; 10.15 pm, Fri-Sat 10.45 pm.

Benugo £35 ④④❷
14 Curzon St, W1   7629 6246   3–4B
23-25 Gt Portland St, W1   7631 5052   3–1C
V&A Museum, Cromwell Rd, SW7   7581 2159   5–2C
Natural History Museum, Cromwell Rd, SW7   7942 5011   5–2B
Westfield, Unit 1070 Ariel Way, W12   8746 9490   7–1C
St Pancras International, , NW1   7833 0201   8–3C
BFI Southbank, Belvedere Rd, SE1   7401 9000   2–3D
Museum Of Childhood, Cambridge Heath Rd, E2   8983 5215   1–2D
116 St John St, EC1   7253 3499   9–1A
82 City Rd, EC1   7253 1295   12–1A
Generally improving standards of late at this "friendly" fast-food chain, which inhabits some "stunning" sites; it's a mixed bag, though – the V&A outlet is quite a "hidden gem", but the prominent BFI Southbank branch has "gone downhill" in recent times. / www.benugo.com; 4 pm-10 pm; W1 & EC1 branches closed Sat & Sun; W1 & EC1 branches, no credit cards.

The Berners Tavern
London EDITION W1 NEW £65
10 Berners St   7908 7979   3–1D
Local hero Jason Atherton has teamed up with seminal boutique hotelier Ian Schrager to launch this spectacular all-day dining room, near Oxford Circus; early-days press reports suggest it looks set to become quite a 'scene'. / W1T 3NP.

Best Mangal £35 ❷❸❸
619 Fulham Rd, SW6 7610 0009 5–4A
104 North End Rd, W14 7610 1050 7–2D
66 North End Rd, W14 7602 0212 7–2D
*"I go back again and again for the great, and cheap, food" –
especially "if it's protein you need", these west London Turkish BBQs
are "the business". / www.bestmangal.com; midnight, Sat 1 am; no Amex.*

Bevis Marks E1 £65 ④④④
3 Middlesex St 7247 5474 9–2D
*It may still be "the best kosher restaurant in the City", but since this
business-friendly venue shifted from the synagogue to this new site,
its ratings have dived; fans feel it's still "superb", but critics say:
"if this is gourmet kosher, I'd rather eat at home!" / E1A 7AA;
www.bevismarkstherestaurant.com; 9 pm; closed Fri D, Sat & Sun.*

Beyoglu NW3 £39 ❸❸④
72 Belsize Ln 7435 7733 8–2A
*"A great small Turkish restaurant", in Belsize Park; the decor can
seem a bit "tired", but it does offer "better-than-average food
at cheaper-than-average prices". / NW3 4XR; www.beyoglu.co.uk; 11 pm;
no Amex.*

Bianco43 SE10 £42 ❸❸④
43 Greenwich Church St 8858 2668 1–3D
*Still rather mixed commentary on this two-year-old Greenwich Italian
– pizzas often come "recommended", but the same can't be said
about the "hot" and "crowded" setting, or the "intrusive funky
music". / SE10 9BL; www.bianco43.com; @bianco_43; 11.30 pm; no Amex.*

Bibendum SW3 £79 ❸❷❶
81 Fulham Rd 7581 5817 5–2C
*"Full of elegance and light" – the "peaceful" first floor of this
Brompton Cross landmark is, for fans, "still London's most beautiful
restaurant", and "always a safe bet" for "superior" cuisine matched
by a "biblical" wine list; sceptics, however, find prices excessive.
/ SW3 6RD; www.bibendum.co.uk; 11 pm, Sun 10.30 pm; booking: max 12
at L, 10 at D; set weekday L £50 (FP).*

Bibendum Oyster Bar SW3 £58 ❷❸❸
81 Fulham Rd 7589 1480 5–2C
*"For a crab, or a dozen oysters and a bottle of vino", this swish
seafood bar, off the entrance to the Chelsea Conran Shop, is just the
job – now that nearby Le Suquet has closed, where else would you
go for "top fruits de mer"? (as we go to press, the bar is set to re-
open after a major refurb). / SW3 6RD; www.bibendum.co.uk; 10 pm;
no booking.*

Bibimbap Soho W1 £29 ❸❸④
11 Greek St 7287 3434 4–2A
*A Korean pit stop in Soho, named after its speciality – "a DIY stir-fry
in a hot stone bowl, with or without fried egg on top"; "does what
it says on the tin, and does it well". / W1D 4DJ; www.bibimbapsoho.com;
@bibimbapsoho; 11 pm; closed Sun; no Amex.*

Big Apple Hot Dogs EC1 £12 ❷❷–
239 Old St 387441 12–1B
*"No brains, no bones and no butts!" – the inspiring promise of the
quality of meat sold at this "passionate" little cart, near Old Street
Tube, which sells "amazing franks", with "light and fluffy buns" and
"inspiring" sauces. / EC1V 9EY; www.bigapplehotdogs.com.*

Big Easy £50 ❸❸❷

12 Maiden Ln, WC2 awaiting tel 4–3D NEW
332-334 King's Rd, SW3 7352 4071 5–3C
"New Orleans was never closer!"; in the face of all the upstart
competition, this ever-"lively" Chelsea surf 'n' turf shack still offers
"excellent ribs and burgers, and other stuff that isn't too healthy
either", plus the "best-value" lobster in town. / www.bigeasy.co.uk;
@bigeasytweet; Mon-Thu 11 pm, Fri-Sat 11.30, Sun 10.30 pm.

Bill's £38 ❸❸❷

Branches throughout London
The "buzzy" branches of this fast-expanding chain – "decked out like
an old-fashioned produce store" – make great standbys for "easy-
going" occasions; "fantastic" breakfast and brunches are a highlight.
/ most branches 11 pm.

Bincho Yakitori W1 £37 ❸❸❸

16 Old Compton St 7287 9111 4–2A
"A winner for a quick eat"; now bereft of its former sibling,
this "buzzing" Soho venue serves "very tasty small bites". / W1D 4TL;
www.bincho.co.uk; 11.30 pm, Sun 10.30 pm; closed Mon L.

The Bingham TW10 £70 ❷❷❶

61-63 Petersham Rd 8940 0902 1–4A
"Stunning Thames views plus wonderful food served with style" –
that's the formula that wins huge acclaim for this "sophisticated"
Richmond hotel dining room; indeed, since the removal of the
dreaded Michelin star, reporters are clearer than ever that it's
"always a delight!" / TW10 6UT; www.thebingham.co.uk; 10 pm; closed
Sun D; no trainers; SRA-58%.

Bird in Hand W14 NEW £42 ❸❸❸

Brook Green 7371 2721 7–1C
"Transformed from a second-rate pub to a first-rate Italian
restaurant" – a family-friendly Brook Green newcomer offering
"a generous range of freshly-prepared pizzas, and an interesting wine
list". / W14 0LR; www.thebirdinhandlondon.com; @TBIHLondon; 10 pm.

Bird of Smithfield EC1 NEW £51 ❹❹❸

26 Smithfield St 7559 5100 9–2B
A very mixed survey reception for this ex-Ivy chef's "brasserie-style"
Smithfield newcomer; fans say it's a "wonderful" place with
an "excellent and simple" menu, while others cite "teething
problems" – let's hope they can sort them out. / EC1A 9LB;
www.birdofsmithfield.com; @BirdoSmithfield; 10.15 pm; closed Sun D;
SRA-57%.

Bistro 1 £23 ❹❷❸

27 Frith St, W1 7734 6204 4–3A
75 Beak St, W1 7287 1840 3–2D
33 Southampton St, WC2 7379 7585 4–3D
"A good choice when you're in a hurry"; these "basic" –
but "efficient" and "friendly" – bistros have handy West End
locations, and offer a "good selection" of dishes at "reasonable"
prices. / www.bistro1.co.uk; @bistro1_london; midnight.

Bistro Aix N8 £53 ❷❶❷

54 Topsfield Pde, Tottenham Ln 8340 6346 8–1C
A "little piece of Paris", in Crouch End – "a wonderful neighbourhood
restaurant" where the cuisine is "authentic", the service
"very helpful", and the setting "incredibly romantic". / N8 8PT;
www.bistroaix.co.uk; 10 pm, Fri & Sat 11 pm; no Amex.

Bistro Union SW4 £44 ❷❷❸
40 Abbeville Rd 7042 6400 10–2D
Adam Byatt's Clapham bistro yearling is "less formal than its big sister
Trinity", and is a "fun" and "casual" venue for food that's "hearty"
and "satisfying"… if not quite as exciting as the pedigree might
suggest. / SW4 9NG; www.bistrounion.co.uk; 10 pm; closed Sun D.

Bistrot Bruno Loubet
The Zetter EC1 £53 ❸❸❸
St John's Square 86-88 Clerkenwell Rd 7324 4455 9–1A
Fans of Bruno Loubet's "airy" Clerkenwell three-year-old still laud his
creative "take on classic bistro cuisine", all "at a non-astronomical
price"; quite a few reports of late, however, suggest "the spirit has
gone out of the place" – the strain of opening Grain Store, perhaps?
/ EC1M 5RJ; www.bistrotbrunoloubet.com; 10.30 pm, Sun 10 pm; SRA-73%.

Bistrotheque E2 £52 ❸❸❷
23-27 Wadeson St 8983 7900 1–2D
"The absence of a sign" is all part of the "intrigue" that's made this
"great East End local", in a former warehouse, a major boho hit –
a "buzzy" and "bright" space, sometimes with a pianist, where the
food has "definitely improved in recent times". / E2 9DR;
www.bistrotheque.com; @BISTROTHEQUE; 10.30 pm, Fri & Sat 11 pm; closed
weekday L; set weekday L & pre-theatre £33 (FP).

Black & Blue £52 ❸❸④
37 Berners St, W1 7436 0451 2–1B
90-92 Wigmore St, W1 7486 1912 3–1A
215-217 Kensington Church St, W8 7727 0004 6–2B
1-2 Rochester Walk, SE1 7357 9922 9–4C
"Can't be beaten for quality, price and consistency"; these "no-frills"
steakhouses generally make a virtue of being "predictable", although
the odd "average all-round" experience is not unknown.
/ www.blackandbluerestaurant.com; @BlackBlueGroup; most branches 11 pm,
Fri & Sat 11.30 pm; W1 closed Sun; no booking.

BLEEDING HEART EC1 £62 ❸❷❶
Bleeding Heart Yd, Greville St 7242 8238 9–2A
"Tucked-away on the edge of the City", this hugely popular and
immensely characterful warren – combining bistro, tavern and
restaurant – is, "curiously, as suited to romance as it is to power
dining"; its "stereotypically Gallic" staff offer "a gem of a wine list"
to complement the "classic" bourgeois fare. / EC1N 8SJ;
www.bleedingheart.co.uk; 10.30 pm; closed Sun.

Blue Elephant SW6 £49 ❸❸❷
The Boulevard 7751 3111 10–1B
Fans do vaunt the "lovely location overlooking Chelsea Harbour",
but it's difficult to avoid the conclusion that this grand Thai institution
has "lost its mojo" since it moved to the fringes of Fulham;
the Sunday buffet, in particular, "just doesn't taste the same".
/ SW6 2UB; www.blueelephant.com; @BlueElephantLon; 11.30 pm,
Sun 10.30 pm.

Blue Legume £40 ④❷❷
101 Stoke Newington Church St, N16 7923 1303 1–1C
177 Upper St, N1 7226 5858 8–2D
130 Crouch Hill, N8 8442 9282 8–1C
"Find a space amongst the buggies", if you visit these "bright" and
"welcoming" north London diners – "super places for brunch", where
"growth doesn't seemed to have compromised quality".
/ www.thebluelegume.co.uk; 10.30 pm; N8 closed L, N16 closed Sun D.

Bluebird SW3 £64 ⑤④④
350 King's Rd 7559 1000 5–3C
*The D&D group's Chelsea landmark has the occasional fan,
but, given its size and prominence, inspires remarkably limited survey
feedback – "it has such potential", bemoans one reporter, "but only
the location makes it popular". / SW3 5UU; www.bluebird-restaurant.co.uk;
10.30 pm, Sun 9.30 pm; set weekday L £32 (FP); SRA-64%.*

Bluebird Café SW3 £42 ⑤⑤④
350 King's Rd 7559 1000 5–3C
*"Oh dear, even the chips were appalling" – like its parent restaurant,
this prominently-sited café seems to rely very heavily on the charms
of its fashionable King's Road location; at least it's "great for people-
watching". / SW3 5UU; www.bluebird-restaurant.co.uk; @bluebirdchelsea;
10 pm, Sun 9.30 pm; no reservations.*

**Blueprint Café
Design Museum SE1** £47 ④④❶
28 Shad Thames, Butler's Wharf 7378 7031 9–4D
*You'll be "bowled over by the views" of Tower Bridge ("they put
binoculars on every table"), at this South Bank D&D group
restaurant; it's striking how little survey feedback it has inspired since
its longtime former chef departed – this averages out somewhere
round "OK". / SE1 2YD; www.blueprintcafe.co.uk; 10.30 pm; closed Sun D;
SRA-61%.*

Bo London W1 NEW £80 ❸❷④
4 Mill St 7493 3886 3–2C
*Alvin Leung's new Mayfair restaurant, on the former site
of Patterson's (RIP), specialises in "incredible" ("don't-try-this-at-
home") Chinese dishes at "second mortgage" prices;
fans (the majority) say you "you must try it once", but the doubters
just "can't see the point". / W1S 2AX; www.bolondonrestaurant.com;
@Bo_London; 11 pm; closed Sat L & Sun; set weekday L £52 (FP).*

Bob Bob Ricard W1 £63 ❸❷❶
1 Upper James St 3145 1000 3–2D
*"Frankly ridiculous decor" – complete with boothed seating, and a
champagne call-button on every table – sets the decadent tone
of this "quirky" but "glamorous" Soho venue, where "high-end
comfort food" is twinned with "wonderful bargains on top-end wine".
/ W1F 9DF; www.bobbobricard.com; 10.30 pm; closed Sat L & Sun; jacket.*

Bocca Di Lupo W1 £59 ❶❷❷
12 Archer St 7734 2223 3–2D
*"Inspired", "regional" Italian tapas – "matched by no other Italian
restaurant in London", and served by "passionate" and
"unpretentious" staff – win adulation for this "bustling" venture,
tucked away near Piccadilly Circus; "get a counter seat to watch the
brigade in action". / W1D 7BB; www.boccadilupo.com; 11 pm, Sun 9.15 pm;
booking: max 10.*

Al Boccon di'vino TW9 £64 ❶❷❷
14 Red Lion St 8940 9060 1–4A
*"You eat what the owner bought in the market" ("you have no option
but to go with the flow") at this slightly "wacky", old-fashioned Italian,
in Richmond town centre; pratically all reporters are "bowled over"
by it – an "always fun, interesting, and filling" experience with
"wonderful" food. / TW9 1RW; www.nonsolovinoltd.co.uk; 8 pm; closed Mon,
Tue L & Wed L.*

Bodean's £44 ❸④❸
10 Poland St, W1   7287 7575   3–1D
4 Broadway Chambers, SW6   7610 0440   5–4A
169 Clapham High St, SW4   7622 4248   10–2D
16 Byward St, EC3   7488 3883   9–3D
"It certainly feels like you're in the US of A", if you visit these
"OTT sports-bar-style" BBQ joints; "ribs, wings, fries and slaw",
and "delicious beers" too – "ain't nothing fancy, but boy do you get
fed!" / www.bodeansbbq.com; 11 pm, Sun 10.30 pm; 8 or more.

La Bodega Negra W1 £47 ④❸❷
13-17 Moor St   7758 4100   4–2B
This "busy" and "dimly-lit" Soho basement Mexican can be "a fun
night out"; it's "quite pricey for what it is", though, and critics dismiss
it as "all gimmicks". / W1D 5NH; www.labodeganegra.com; 1 am,
Sun 11.30 pm.

Boisdale SW1 £55 ❸❸❷
13-15 Eccleston St   7730 6922   2–4B
"A superb cigar terrace" is amongst the manly attractions of this
Belgravia "bastion" of Scottish Baronial sensibility; it is also known for
its "perfect" steak, "excellent" wine, and "splendid" whiskies, all at
prices some find "a bit OTT". / SW1W 9LX; www.boisdale.co.uk;
11.30 pm; closed Sat L & Sun.

Boisdale of Canary Wharf E14 £60 ④④❸
Cabot Pl   7715 5818   11–1C
"Panoramic views of Cabot Square" underpin the "power-lunch"
(or "power dinner with jazz") appeal of this Caledonian-themed
restaurant, where "great steaks and burgers" are the stock-in-trade;
no huge surprise, though, that it can seem a bit "investment banker-
pricey". / E14 4QT; www.boisdale.co.uk; 10.30 pm; closed Sun.

The Bolingbroke SW11 £43 ④❸❸
174 Northcote Rd   7228 4040   10–2C
"Lots of kids create a happy atmosphere" for the "great breakfasts",
and lunches too, at this reliable Battersea boozer; it is, however,
"not the place for a quiet supper". / SW11 6RE;
www.renaissancepubs.co.uk; 10.30 pm, Sun 9 pm; SRA-56%.

Bombay Brasserie SW7 £56 ❸④④
Courtfield Close, Gloucester Rd   7370 4040   5–2B
This "cavernous" South Kensington subcontinental is a "top tip" for
some reporters, who particularly praise the "excellent weekend
buffet"; it also has plenty of critics, though, who find it "overpriced,
pretentious, and living on past glories". / SW7 4QH;
www.bombaybrasserielondon.com; 11.30 pm, Sun 10.30 pm.

Bombay Palace W2 £55 ❶❶❸
50 Connaught St   7723 8855   6–1D
"By far the best, putting all other Indians to shame!" – this "warm"
and "friendly" Bayswater "hidden gem", recently refurbished, dazzles
all reporters with its "classic" dishes, realised "to a standard rarely
found". / W2 2AA; www.bombay-palace.co.uk; 11.30 pm.

Bonds
Threadneedles Hotel EC2 £67 ④④❸
5 Threadneedle St 7657 8088 9–2C
This "refined" dining room, in a former banking hall, inspires surprisingly little comment, given its heart-of-the-City location; with its "good-value lunch menu" and "well spaced tables", though, some reporters find it a handy business rendezvous. / EC2R 8AY; www.bonds-restaurant.co.uk; 10 pm; closed Sat & Sun; set weekday L £44 (FP).

Bone Daddies W1 NEW £22 ❷④❸
30-31 Peter St 7287 8581 3–2D
"Delicious and innovative ramen, with rock 'n' roll as the soundtrack" – the unlikely formula that's made this "well-priced" Soho noodle-soup newcomer an instant hit; needless to say, it's "not the place for a relaxing dinner". / W1F 0AR; www.bonedaddiesramen.com; @bonedaddiesRbar; 10 pm, Tue-Wed 11 pm, Thu-Sat midnight, Sun 9 pm.

Bonnie Gull W1 NEW £48 ❷❸❷
21a, Foley St 7436 0921 2–1B
"Small but perfectly formed" – this "hip" but "friendly" Fitzrovia fish specialist (on the site of Back to Basics, RIP) has made itself an instant hit. / W1W 6DS; www.bonniegull.com; @BonnieGull; 9.45 pm.

Boqueria SW2 £33 ❷❷❷
192 Acre Ln 7733 4408 10–2D
"A hidden gem between Clapham and Brixton", this "fantastic" funky yearling serves "really excellent" tapas alongside a "small but decent" selection of wines and sherries; even fans note, though, it can get "very loud". / SW2 5UL; www.boqueriatapas.com; @BoqueriaTapas; 11 pm, Fri-Sat 12 am, Sun 10 pm; closed weekday L.

Il Bordello E1 £48 ❷0❷
81 Wapping High St 7481 9950 11–1A
"On a quiet Wapping street", a "chaotic" and "very friendly" pizza and pasta stop that's "always heaving", thanks to its "outstanding" all-round value (and "huge" portions). / E1W 2YN; www.ilbordello.com; 11 pm, Sun 10.30 pm; closed Sat L.

La Bota N8 £32 ❸④④
31 Broadway Pde 8340 3082 1–1C
"Well-prepared classic dishes, no fuss, decent portions and low prices" – this Crouch End favourite is "just what a neighbourhood tapas restaurant should be". / N8 9DB; www.labota.co.uk; 11 pm, Fri-Sun 11.30 pm; closed Mon L; no Amex.

The Botanist SW1 £61 ⑤⑤⑤
7 Sloane Sq 7730 0077 5–2D
Thanks perhaps to its first-rate "people-watching" possibilities, this "heaving" Sloane Square bar/restaurant has become a self-perpetuating local hub – it seems to have little to do with the actual quality of the food or service! / SW1W 8EE; www.thebotanistonsloanesquare.com; 10.45 pm.

La Bottega £17 ❸❸❷
20 Ryder St, SW1 7839 5789 3–4C
25 Eccleston St, SW1 7730 2730 2–4B
65 Lower Sloane St, SW1 7730 8844 5–2D
97 Old Brompton Rd, SW7 7581 6622 5–2B
"Perfect cappuccinos", "inexpensive lunchtime snacks", "good wine" and "friendly" service – what's not to like about these smart Italian café/delis? / www.labottega65.com; Lower Sloane St 8 pm, Sat 6 pm, Sun 5 pm; Eccleston St 7 pm; Old Brompton Rd 8 pm; Ryder St closed Sat & Sun; no booking.

La Bouchée SW7 £47 ④④❸
56 Old Brompton Rd 7589 1929 5–2B
*With its "petit coin de Paris" charm, this "dark, cosy and romantic"
(and "cramped") South Kensington cellar remains a "safe bet" for
a "tasty" meal. / SW7 3DY; 11 pm, Sun 10.30 pm; set weekday L &
pre-theatre £31 (FP).*

Bouchon Fourchette E8 NEW £36 ❷❷❸
171 Mare St 8986 2702 1–2D
*"You could be in Paris", at this "totally French" newcomer... "which
feels a bit odd, in Hackney!"; its "tiny kitchen" produces
a "very simple menu" of "good-value" classics. / E8 3RH; @BFourchette;
10 pm, Fri & Sat 11 pm; closed Mon L.*

Boudin Blanc W1 £60 ④④❷
5 Trebeck St 7499 3292 3–4B
*"Busy, cramped, and with bags of atmosphere", this "very French"
bistro remains a "reliable" old-favourite for most reporters (and it has
some great al fresco tables in Shepherd Market); critics, however,
find the cuisine "undemanding", and complain of "Parisian attitude"
on the service front. / W1J 7LT; www.boudinblanc.co.uk; 11 pm;
set weekday L £30 (FP).*

Boulestin SW1 NEW £66 ❸❷❸
5 St James's St 7930 2030 3–4D
*On the former St James's site of L'Oranger (RIP), an elegant new
French restaurant offering a straight-down-the-line comfort formula
de luxe, of a type rarely found nowadays; it was already well into its
swing on our early-days visit. / SW1A 1EF; www.boulestin.co.uk.*

Boulevard WC2 £44 ④④❸
40 Wellington St 7240 2992 4–3D
*This stereotypical but "attractive" Theatreland brasserie divides
opinion; to cynics, it's "the worst sort of tourist trap", but it also has
its fans who say it offers "no-nonsense" fare at reasonable prices.
/ WC2E 7BD; www.boulevardbrasserie.co.uk; 11 pm, Fri & Sat 11.30 pm,
Sun 10.30 pm.*

The Boundary E2 £62 ❷❷❷
2-4 Boundary St 7729 1051 12–1B
*Sir Terence Conran's "luxurious" basement restaurant, in trendy
Shoreditch, offers Gallic dining in a surprisingly "classic"
(and "pricey") style – "ideal for power dining", with "attentive"
service and an "excellent wine selection"; "in summer, have a drink
at the rooftop bar first". / E2 7DD; www.theboundary.co.uk; 10.30 pm;
D only, ex Sun L only.*

The Bountiful Cow WC1 £53 ④④④
51 Eagle St 7404 0200 2–1D
*"Big, bloody and juicy" – the burgers at this Bloomsbury basement
are "amazing", say fans; overall, though, there's less survey
commentary than we'd like, not all of it especially complimentary.
/ WC1R 4AP; www.thebountifulcow.co.uk; 10.30 pm; closed Sun.*

Bradley's NW3 £57 ④❸④
25 Winchester Rd 7722 3457 8–2A
*"Tucked away in a Swiss Cottage backstreet", this ambitious local is,
say fans, "a real gem"; while all reporters agree the pre-
(Hampstead)-theatre deals are great, however, sceptics find standards
"erratic". / NW3 3NR; www.bradleysnw3.co.uk; 10 pm; closed Sun D;
set weekday L & pre-theatre £35 (FP).*

Brady's SW18 £33 ❷❷❷
513 Old York Rd 8877 9599 10–2B
The burghers of Battersea are very excited about their favourite chippy, which has been "very much improved" by its move to new riverside premises, where the fish 'n' chips are "superb"; "there are still queues, but now there's a smart bar to wait in!". / SW18 1TF; www.bradysfish.co.uk; @Bradyfish; 10 pm, Sun 8.30 pm; closed Mon, Tue L, Wed L & Thu L; no Amex; no booking.

La Brasserie SW3 £56 ❸❹❷
272 Brompton Rd 7581 3089 5–2C
"Yes, the prices are high, but the food is terrific", says one of the fans of this "perennial favourite" Gallic brasserie, on a prominent Chelsea corner; it's "always buzzy" – most famously for breakfast. / SW3 2AW; www.labrasserielondon.co.uk; 11.30 pm; no booking, Sat L & Sun L.

Brasserie Blanc £52 ❹❸❹
8 Charlotte St, W1 7636 4975 2–1C
119 Chancery Ln, WC2 7405 0290 2–2D
35 The Mkt, WC2 7379 0666 4–3D
9 Belvedere Rd, SE1 7202 8470 2–3D
60 Threadneedle St, EC2 7710 9440 9–2C
14 Trinity Sq, EC3 7480 5500 9–3D
1 Watling St, EC4 7213 0540 9–2B
With its "simple" Gallic staples and "helpful" service, Raymond Blanc's brasserie chain makes a "reliable" fall-back; last year, it absorbed the old Chez Gérard outlets, including the WC2 branch, which – with many al fresco tables on the first floor of Covent Garden Market – has one of London's best locations. / www.brasserieblanc.com; most branches close between 10 pm & 11 pm; SE1 closed Sun D, most City branches closed Sat & Sun; SRA-64%.

Brasserie Chavot W1 NEW £70 ❷❸❸
41 Conduit St 7078 9577 3–2C
Eric Chavot is a chef with a long-term fan base, and it's turned out in force to acclaim the "spectacular", "classic" Gallic fare on offer at his new Mayfair dining room; the spacious interior – inherited from the Gallery (RIP) – is somewhere between "beautiful" and "blingy". / W1S 2YQ; www.brasseriechavot.com; @brasseriechavot; 10.30 pm, Sun 9 pm.

Brasserie Max
Covent Garden Hotel WC2 £73 ❹❹❸
10 Monmouth St 7806 1000 4–2B
An attractive hotel brasserie which offers a retreat from the hustle and bustle of Covent Garden; even foes concede it's a "buzzy spot", and even fans acknowledge it's "not the cheapest". / WC2H 9HB; www.coventgardenhotel.co.uk; 11 pm; set pre theatre £47 (FP).

Brasserie on St John Street EC1 £41 ❸❹❹
360-362 St John's St 7837 1199 8–3D
"Well situated for Sadler's Wells" – almost invariably the context in which reporters note this "noisy" brasserie; the food is not the main point, but it rarely seems to disappoint. / EC1V 4NR; www.the-brasserie.com; 11 pm, Fri-Sat 11.30 pm, Sun 10.30 pm; closed Mon.

Brasserie Toulouse-Lautrec SE11 £39 ❸❷❷
140 Newington Butts 7582 6800 1–3C
This wine bar offshoot of Kennington's nearby Lobster Pot is as "authentically Gallic" an affair as you'll find, and the food, say local supporters, is "better than ever" – "well worth supporting". / SE11 4RN; www.btlrestaurant.co.uk; 10.30 pm, Sat & Sun 11 pm.

BRASSERIE ZÉDEL W1 £38 ⑤❸❶
20 Sherwood St 7734 4888 3–2D
For an "opulently Parisian" experience on the cheap, you can't beat
Corbin & King's vast and "dazzling" Art Deco basement,
near Piccadilly Circus; views divide, however, on the overall verdict –
for a majority the "democratised" prices make it "remarkable value",
but a large minority finds the "clichéd" brasserie fare
"underwhelming". / W1F 7ED; www.brasseriezedel.com; @brasseriezedel;
11.45 pm; SRA-74%.

Brawn E2 £48 ❷❷❸
49 Columbia Rd 7729 5692 12–1C
"So different, so fresh, so quirky" – this "cool" East End offshoot
of the Terroirs empire has won renown with its "terrific, imaginative"
food, its "brilliant selection of really interesting wines", and its all-
round "attention to detail". / E2 7RG; www.brawn.co; @brawn49; 11 pm;
closed Mon L & Sun D; no Amex.

Bread Street Kitchen EC4 £62 ④④④
1 New Change 3030 4050 9–2B
"Warehouse-y", "cavernous" and "noisy", this City shopping mall
dining room gives no particular hint of being owned by the world-
famous Gordon Ramsay; the food – "nothing special" – likewise.
/ EC4M 9AF; www.breadstreetkitchen.com; 11 pm, Sun 8 pm.

Briciole W1 £39 ❸❸❸
20 Homer St 7723 0040 6–1D
"Wonderful ingredients are served very simply", at this "transformed"
former pub, in a "quiet Marylebone backwater" – now a "bustling",
"welcoming" and "good-value" Italian bar/deli. / W1H 4NA;
www.briciole.co.uk; @briciolelondon; 10.15 pm.

Brick Lane Beigel Bake E1 £7 ❶❷④
159 Brick Ln 7729 0616 12–1C
The "world-famous East End bakery", open 24/7; "you can't beat
a salt beef beigel from here, any time of day or night"… but
"they taste best at 2am!" / E1 6SB; open 24 hours; no credit cards;
no booking.

The Bright Courtyard W1 £55 ④④④
43-45 Baker St 7486 6998 2–1A
"Top dim sum" are a highlight at this grand and airy Marylebone
Chinese (part of a Shanghai-based chain); "the only problem is the
price"… especially with Royal China just over the road. / W1U 8EW;
www.lifefashiongroup.com; 10.45 pm, Thu-Sat 11.15 pm.

Brilliant UB2 £37 ❷❷❸
72-76 Western Rd 8574 1928 1–3A
An "amazing eatery", deep in the suburb of Southall, rightly
renowned for "authentic Punjabi food that's always first class".
/ UB2 5DZ; www.brilliantrestaurant.com; @BRILLIANTRST; 11 pm, Fri-Sat
11.30 pm; closed Mon, Sat L & Sun L.

Brinkley's SW10 £51 ⑤④❸
47 Hollywood Rd 7351 1683 5–3B
Home from home for the "Made in Chelsea crowd" –
this "atmospheric" stalwart wins a loyal following with its "great
value-for-money wines", and "lovely" garden; critics, however, dismiss
the "basic" scoff as "rah-rah rubbish". / SW10 9HX; www.brinkleys.com;
11 pm; closed weekday L.

Brinkley's Kitchen SW17 £51 ④④❸

35 Bellevue Rd 8672 5888 10–2C

"A fab local that never disappoints"; John Brinkley's Wandsworth brasserie is a "buzzy" sort of place offering a "really well chosen" and "good-value" wine list, plus "sensibly-priced" food that plays a bit of a supporting role. / SW17 7EF; www.brinkleys.com; @BrinkleysR; 11 pm; closed Mon & Sun D.

Brompton Bar & Grill SW3 £56 ❸②❸

243 Brompton Rd 7589 8005 5–2C

"Professional", "businesslike", "reliable", "relaxing", and "reasonably-priced"; this well-spaced bistro – on the Knightsbridge site which old-stagers will recall as the Brasserie St Quentin – attracts nothing but positive reports. / SW3 2EP; www.bromptonbarandgrill.com; 10.30 pm, Sun 10 pm.

The Brown Cow SW6 £42 ❸❸②

676 Fulham Rd 7384 9559 10–1B

Heart-of-Fulham locals are lucky that the Sands End team has taken over the former premises of Manson (RIP), which now trades as a "fun" gastroboozer, offering food that's "good, if not gastronomic". / SW6 5SA; www.thebrowncowpub.co.uk.

The Brown Dog SW13 £48 ❸❸②

28 Cross St 8392 2200 10–1A

A "hidden-away gem", in Barnes's super-cute Little Chelsea – a "really welcoming and cosy local pub" where the cooking is "a cut above standards gastropub pub fare"; "dog-friendly too!" / SW13 0AP; www.thebrowndog.co.uk; @browndogbarnes; 10 pm, Sun 9 pm.

(Hix at Albemarle)
Brown's Hotel W1 £78 ④❸❸

Albemarle St 7518 4004 3–3C

With its spacious layout, and its secluded tables and booths, this "discreet" Mayfair dining room is certainly "well-placed for business lunches"; despite Mark Hix's involvement, though, standards remain "ordinary, for a place of this price and type". / W1S 4BP; www.thealbemarlerestaurant.com; 11 pm, Sun 10.30 pm.

Browns £46 ⑤④④

2 Cardinal Pl, SW1 7821 1450 2–4B
47 Maddox St, W1 7491 4565 3–2C
82-84 St Martin's Ln, WC2 7497 5050 4–3B
9 Islington Grn, N1 7226 2555 8–3D
Butler's Wharf, SE1 7378 1700 9–4D
Hertsmere Rd, E14 7987 9777 11–1C
8 Old Jewry, EC2 7606 6677 9–2C

These "buzzy" English brasseries often occupy "fantastic" old buildings, and fans say they make "reliable" venues for many occasions; there are still too many reports, though, of meals where "every dish disappointed... and always in a different way!" / www.browns-restaurants.co.uk; most branches 10 pm-11 pm; EC2 closed Sat D & Sun; W1 closed Sun D.

Brula TW1 £52 ❷⓪❷

43 Crown Rd 8892 0602 1–4A

"Brula is brilliant!" – St Margaret's locals adore this "great little French-style neighbourhood restaurant"; it can get "noisy", though, and tables are "rather close". / TW1 3EJ; www.brula.co.uk; 10.30 pm; closed Mon & Sun D.

Brunswick House Cafe SW8   £42   ❸④❷

30 Wandsworth Rd   7720 2926   10–1D

You eat "surrounded by architectural salvage" at this "quirky" venue – a listed Georgian house packed with "bric-a-brac", right next to the "hideous" Vauxhall traffic system; it makes for a "wonderful, if unlikely" experience – surprisingly "comfortable", and with some "delicious" British grub. / SW8 2LG; www.brunswickhousecafe.co.uk; 10 pm; closed Sun D.

Bubbledogs W1   £30   ④❸❷

70 Charlotte St   7637 7770   2–1C

"Great champagne plus tasty hot dogs" – it's sure a "novel" concept, and the queues testify to the success of this unlikely Fitzrovia "dude food" hit… and critics duly insist that this is "the most overhyped place in town"; (see also Kitchen Table @ Bubbledogs). / W1T 4QG; www.bubbledogs.co.uk; 9 pm; closed Sun.

(Kitchen Table) Bubbledogs W1 NEW   £91   ❶❷❷

70 Charlotte St   7637 7770   2–1C

"My most exciting restaurant experience in years!" – enter via the hot dog place to eat at this horseshoe-shaped chef's table (19 seats), where James Knappett and his "brilliantly choreographed" chefs deliver a "stunning" 12-14 course dinner that's "full of invention", with wines from the "passionate" sommelier. / W1T 4QG; www.kitchentablelondon.co.uk; 9.30 pm (6 & & 7.30 pm seatings only); D only, closed Mon & Sun.

Buen Ayre E8   £51   ❶④④

50 Broadway Mkt   7275 9900   1–2D

"A small, humble, crowded and insanely popular Argentinian steakhouse, in the East End"; regulars say it "laughs in face of more sophisticated rivals like Hawksmoor", by serving "life-changing hunks of meat" (cooked on an open fire) at "great-value" prices. / E8 4QJ; www.buenayre.co.uk; 10.30 pm; no Amex.

Buenos Aires Cafe   £51   ❸④❸

86 Royal Hill, SE10   8488 6764   1–3D

17 Royal Pde, SE3   8318 5333   1–4D

"A steak-eater's delight"; this busy Argentinian – in an "atmospheric location overlooking the Heath" – is one of the best bets in Blackheath village; the Greenwich spin-off is more café-like. / www.buenosairesltd.com; SE3 10.30 pm; SE10 7 pm, Sat & Sun 6 pm; no Amex.

The Builders Arms SW3   £44   ④❸❸

13 Britten St   7349 9040   5–2C

"Good gastropub, very relaxing, not too noisy or packed" – all you need to know about this notably consistent Chelsea gastroboozer, hidden away behind Waitrose. / SW3 3TY; www.geronimo-inns.co.uk; 10 pm, Thu-Sat 11 pm, Sun 9 pm; no booking; SRA-60%.

Bull & Last NW5   £61   ❷❸❸

168 Highgate Rd   7267 3641   8–1B

"Setting the gastropub benchmark", this "perfect" Kentish Town phenomenon offers "quality food in a real pub setting"; OK, nowhere's actually perfect – it's "a bit too loud". / NW5 1QS; www.thebullandlast.co.uk; @thebullandlast; 10 pm, Sun 9 pm.

Bumpkin £51 ⑤⑤④

119 Sydney St, SW3   3730 9344   5–2B **NEW**
102 Old Brompton Rd, SW7   7341 0802   5–2B
209 Westbourne Park Rd, W11   7243 9818   6–1B
Westfield Stratford City, 105-106 The Street, E20   8221 9900   1–1D
This faux-"rustic" British chain has its fans, who praise its "freshly cooked fare" and "very relaxed" style; "well-meaning but incompetent" service, however, is a perennial bugbear – "it would have been comical, if they hadn't been charging for it!"
/ www.bumpkinuk.com; 11 pm.

Buona Sera £38 ④❸❸

289a King's Rd, SW3   7352 8827   5–3C
22 Northcote Rd, SW11   7228 9925   10–2C
"Reliable" and reasonably-priced, this Italian café in Battersea has quite a name as a "kid-friendly" destination (if sometimes a "hellishly noisy" one); its Chelsea spin-off, with its "perennially fascinating" two-level layout, is "hard to beat for impromptu pre-cinema dining".
/ midnight; SW3 11.30 pm, Sun 10 pm; SW3 closed Mon L.

Burger & Lobster £43 ❷❸❸

Harvey Nichols, SW1   7235 5000   5–1D **NEW**
29 Clarges St, W1   7409 1699   3–4B
36 Dean St, W1   7432 4800   4–2A
40 St John St, EC1   7490 9230   9–1B
Bow Bells Hs, 1 Bread St, EC4   7248 1789   9–2B **NEW**
"Dead simple" but "divine", a formula of lobster, lobster brioche or burger powers the growth of these "fun" and "casual" hang-out; they are "always packed" and "noisy", though, and waits can be "infuriating". / www.burgerandlobster.com; @Londonlobster; 10.30 pm; Clarges St closed Sun D, Bread St & St John St closed Sun.

Busaba Eathai £38 ❸❸❷

35 Panton St, SW1   7930 0088   4–4A
106-110 Wardour St, W1   7255 8686   3–2D
8-13 Bird St, W1   7518 8080   3–1A
22 Store St, WC1   7299 7900   2–1C
44 Floral St, WC2   7759 0088   4–2D
358 King's Rd, SW3   7349 5488   5–3B
Westfield, Ariel Way, W12   3249 1919   7–1C
Westfield Stratford, E20   8221 8989   1–1D
313-319 Old St, EC1   7729 0808   12–1B
"A lovely relaxed vibe" is created by the dark and "funky" decor at these large-communal-table 'Thai Wagamamas' (same creator, but better ratings) – "a great cheap eat", with dishes offering "lovely vivid flavours". / www.busaba.co.uk; 11 pm, Fri & Sat 11.30 pm, Sun 10 pm; W1 no booking; WC1 booking: min 10.

Bush Dining Hall W12 **NEW** £42 ❸④❸

304 Uxbridge Rd   8749 0731   7–1B
"A welcome addition to Shepherd's Bush" – this new "oasis" is an add-on to the characterful music venue, offering a "short" modern British menu, which critics find a touch "overpriced". / W12 7LJ; www.bushhalldining.co.uk; @BushHallDining; 10.30 pm, Fri-Sat 10 pm; closed Sun D.

Butcher & Grill SW11 £47 ④❸❸
39-41 Parkgate Rd   7924 3999   5–4C
A Battersea local restaurant with a deli and butcher attached; sceptics say there's "room for all-round improvement", but "the beef is of high standard", and the place has something of a reputation as a family brunch spot; the SW19 branch is no more. / SW11 4NP; www.thebutcherandgrill.com; 11 pm, Sun 4 pm; closed Sun D.

Butcher's Hook SW6 £41 ❸❷❸
477 Fulham Rd   7385 4654   5–4A
A "great local gastropub", opposite Stamford Bridge – "a top place for an interesting lunch before the footie". / SW6 1HL; www.thebutchershook.co.uk; 10.30 pm; no Amex.

Butlers Wharf Chop House SE1 £60 ④④④
36e Shad Thames   7403 3403   9–4D
Mixed views on this D&D group South Bank fixture – fans praise the "beautiful location by Tower Bridge", and the "meaty feasts" on offer, but critics find standards "variable", and caution that "the bar offers much better value than the restaurant". / SE1 2YE; www.chophouse.co.uk; 10.45 pm, Sun 9.45 pm; set weekday L £37 (FP); SRA-63%.

La Buvette TW9 £44 ❸❷❷
6 Church Walk   8940 6264   1–4A
"A treasure in the heart of Richmond", this "quietly hidden-away" and "cosy" ("cramped") bistro offers Gallic fare that's "old-fashioned" but "reliable"; for the summer, it has "lovely" tables in a leafy courtyard too. / TW9 1SN; www.labuvette.co.uk; @labuvettebistro; 10 pm.

Byron £35 ❸❸❸
11 Haymarket, SW1   7925 0276   4–4A
97-99 Wardour St, W1   7297 9390   3–2D
24-28 Charing Cross Rd, WC2   7557 9830   4–4B
33-35 Wellington St, WC2   7420 9850   4–3D
300 King's Rd, SW3   7352 6040   5–3C
242 Earl's Court Rd, SW5   7370 9300   5–2A
75 Gloucester Rd, SW7   7244 0700   5–2B
93-95 Old Brompton Rd, SW7   7590 9040   5–2B
Westfield, Ariel Way, W12   8743 7755   7–1C
222 Kensington High St, W8   7361 1717   5–1A
341 Upper St, N1   7704 7620   8–3D
46 Hoxton Sq, N1   3487 1230   12–1B
22 Putney High St, SW15   8246 4170   10–2B
Cabot Place East, E14   7715 9360   11–1C
7 Upper Cheapside Pas, One New Change, EC2   7246 2580   9–2B
"Not been to a bad'un yet!"; this phenomenal chain's growth remains "hectic", but it continues to impress with its "proper" burgers, its "fantastic" milkshakes, and its "attractive" (if sometimes "incredibly noisy") branches; can it last though? – ratings are, slowly, inching south. / www.byronhamburgers.com; -most branches 11 pm; SRA-63%.

C London W1 £97 ⑤⑤④
25 Davies St   7399 0500   3–2B
Even as a "fun" night out for rubbernecking the Eurotrash, this Mayfair Italian circus seems to be running out of steam – critics say food that's "inferior to your typical trattoria" comes at "insane" prices, and service is "catastrophic". / W1K 3DE; www.crestaurant.co.uk; 11.45 pm.

C&R Cafe £29 ❸④④
3-4 Rupert Ct, W1   7434 1128   4–3A
52 Westbourne Grove, W2   7221 7979   6–1B
Looking for a "cheap" but "inspiring" bite? – this "cramped" but "fun" Indonesian/Malaysian café, tucked-away in Chinatown, "consistently delivers the goods"; no feedback on the Bayswater branch. / www.cnrrestaurant.com; 11 pm.

The Cabin W4 £48 ④④④
148 Chiswick High Rd   8994 8594   7–2A
"Good grills, good seafood, good variety" – this solid (if perhaps "not spectacular") surf 'n' turf diner in Chiswick wins a steady local following. / W4 1PR; www.cabinrestaurants.co.uk; 10.30 pm, Fri & Sat 11 pm; No toddlers after 6pm.

The Cadogan Arms SW3 £48 ❸④❸
298 King's Rd   7352 6500   5–3C
"An underrated gem" – this King's Road corner boozer, handy for the UGC cinema, offers "simple but well cooked school food in a traditional pub atmosphere". / SW3 5UG; www.thecadoganarmschelsea.com; @TheCadoganArms; 10.30 pm, Sun 9 pm.

Café 209 SW6 £23 ④❸❶
209 Munster Rd   7385 3625   10–1B
Zany owner Joy ensures "it's always a hilarious experience" to dine at this tiny, squashed-in BYO caff in deepest Fulham, where the Thai chow is "inexpensive" but tasty. / SW6 6BX; 10.30 pm; D only, closed Sun, closed Dec; no Amex.

**Le Café Anglais
Whiteley's W2** £58 ❸④❷
8 Porchester Gdns   7221 1415   6–1C
"Like a cruise ship's main dining room" – Rowley Leigh's "light" and "well-spaced" Deco-ish brasserie (with oyster bar) floats serenely on the top floor of Whiteleys, and its cuisine is "very competent"; "inept" service can let it down (but they are "very kid friendly"); Monday nights BYO, no corkage! / W2 4DB; www.lecafeanglais.co.uk; 10.30 pm, Fri & Sat 11 pm, Sun 10pm.

Café Below EC2 £33 ④④❸
St Mary-le-Bow, Cheapside   7329 0789   9–2C
"Home-made food in the City", all "at very reasonable prices", underpins the appeal of this simple self-service café, which occupies the atmospheric crypt of St Mary le Bow. / EC2 6AU; www.cafebelow.co.uk; 3 pm; L only, closed Sat & Sun.

Café Bohème W1 £45 ❸❸❷
13 Old Compton St   7734 0623   4–2A
At "atmospheric" café/bar/brasserie at the heart of Soho – an ideal spot for a West End rendezvous, and offering pretty dependable food at "reasonable prices". / W1 5JQ; www.cafeboheme.co.uk; @CafeBoheme1; 2.45 am, Sun midnight; no reservations.

Café del Parc N19 £35 ❷❶❷
167 Junction Road   7281 5684   8–1C
"Superb hosts" win a devoted small fan club for this "tapas-with-a-twist" culinary oasis, "in the desert that is Tufnell Park". / N19 5PZ; www.delparc.com; 10.30 pm; open D only, Wed-Sun; no Amex.

Café des Amis WC2 £57 ④④④
11-14 Hanover Pl 7379 3444 4–2D
*With its "handy" location, down a cute alley near the Royal Opera
House, this "busy" Covent Garden landmark is well-known as a
"useful pre-theatre or post-opera" operation; the "overpriced" food
"could be better", though, and service too often "goes awry".
/ WC2E 9JP; www.cafedesamis.co.uk; 11.30 pm, Sun 7pm.*

Café du Marché EC1 £54 ❷❷❶
22 Charterhouse Sq 7608 1609 9–1B
*"Be transported from Clerkenwell to a village in France", at this
"side ally secret" – an "old faithful" that's "everything a French
restaurant ought to be"; "solid" bourgeois cuisine is "charmingly"
served in a "cosy and candle-lit" setting, that's business-friendly
at lunch, but seductive by night. / EC1M 6DX; www.cafedumarche.co.uk;
10 pm; closed Sat L & Sun.*

Cafe East SE16 £22 ❷④④
100 Redriff Rd 7252 1212 11–2B
*"The best pho in London" headlines the "very fresh" and "authentic"
menu on offer at this "basic" and "silly-cheap" Bermondsey café;
no wonder it's "always packed" (often "with Vietnamese people").
/ SE16 7LH; www.cafeeast.foodkingdom.com; 10.30 pm, Sun 10 pm;
closed Tue.*

Café in the Crypt
St Martin's in the Fields WC2 £31 ④④④
Duncannon St 7766 1158 2–2C
*"Reliable", "cheap" and "cheerful" – the self-service canteen below
Trafalgar Square's great church is no gourmet destination, but it's
a "useful" option in the very "heart" of town. / WC2N 4JJ;
www.smitf.org; 8 pm, Thu-Sat 9 pm, Sun 6 pm; no Amex; no booking.*

Café Japan NW11 £41 ❷④④
626 Finchley Rd 8455 6854 1–1B
*"Superb sushi in a busy part of Golders Green"; the setting may
be "cramped" and "sterile", but this very "authentic" and
"reasonably-priced" stalwart is "always full". / NW11 7RR; 10 pm,
Sun 9.30 pm; closed Mon; no Amex; only D.*

Café Pacifico WC2 £43 ④④❷
5 Langley St 7379 7728 4–2C
*"Loud and bustling", this Mexican cantina, in Covent Garden, dates
from long before the current Latino wave hit town; fans say it still
offers a good night out, with food that's "cheap and full of flavour".
/ WC2 9JA; www.cafepacifico-laperla.com; 11.45 pm, Sun 10.45 pm.*

Café Rouge £37 ⑤④④
Branches throughout London
*As a "reliable staple", some reporters do tip this formulaic Gallic
bistro chain, touting its good breakfasts, and its "suitability for
families"; as ever, though, the volume of feedback dissing it as
"horrific" is impressive – "why do we put up with it?"
/ www.caferouge.co.uk; 11 pm, Sun 10.30 pm.*

Café Spice Namaste E1 £54 ❷❷❸
16 Prescot St 7488 9242 11–1A
*Cyrus Todiwala "continues to weave his magic", at this "quirky" City-
fringe veteran – his trademark Parsee cooking is "sophisticated" and
"different", and it's charmingly served in a "funky" and "colourful"
high-ceilinged room. / E1 8AZ; www.cafespice.co.uk; 10.30 pm; closed
Sat L & Sun.*

Caffè Caldesi W1 £58 ❸❷❸

118 Marylebone Ln 7487 0754 2–1A
*For "straightforwardly good" meal, in "old-school, Italian fine dining"
style, fans think it worth seeking out this "friendly" and "respectful"
Marylebone stalwart.* / W1U 2QF; www.caldesi.com; 10.30 pm, Sun
10 pm; set weekday L £35 (FP).

Caffè Nero £13 ❹❸❸

Branches throughout London
*"You can taste the coffee, not an American facsimile" – and it's
"strong-tasting" and "universally good" – at this "staple" Italian
chain; "tasty wraps and paninis" too.* / most branches 7 pm; City branches
earlier; most City branches closed all or part of weekend; some branches
no credit cards; no booking.

Caffé Vergnano £31 ❹❸❷

Staple Inn, High Holborn, WC1 7242 7119 9–2A **NEW**
62 Charing Cross Rd, WC2 7240 3512 4–3B
Royal Festival Hall, SE1 7921 9339 2–3D
2 New Street Sq, EC4 7936 3404 9–2A
*"Exemplary coffee" is to be had from both branches of this Italian
café group, whose original outlet is in the heart of Theatreland;
the South Bank branch also serves "wonderful cakes", and more
substantial snacks too.* / www.caffevergnano1882.co.uk; EC4 11 pm;
SE1 midnight; WC2 8 pm, Fri & Sat midnight; EC4 Sat & Sun; no Amex.

La Cage Imaginaire NW3 £41 ❹❹❸

16 Flask Walk 7794 6674 8–1A
*A small Gallic bistro, with a "wonderful location" on a cute heart-of-
Hampstead lane; even those not thrilled by the food may find a visit
an "agreeable" experience overall.* / NW3 1HE;
www.la-cage-imaginaire.co.uk; 11 pm.

Cah-Chi £36 ❷❷❸

394 Garratt Ln, SW18 8946 8811 10–2B
34 Durham Rd, SW20 8947 1081 10–2B
*These buy Asian outlets in Earlsfield and Raynes Park, serve
up "delicious and fresh" fare at "cheap" prices; beware, though –
"we never know what to order, and the Koreans at the next table
always seem to have something more interesting!"; BYO.*
/ www.cahchi.com; SW20 11 pm; SW18 11 pm, Sat & Sun 11.30 pm;
SW20 closed Mon; cash only.

Il Calcio £55

33 North Audley St, W1 7629 7070 3–2A **NEW**
241 Old Brompton Rd, SW5 7835 0050 5–3A **NEW**
*A rather baffling new Romanian-backed Italian in a prime Mayfair
location (and also with a presence in Earl's Court); of the few early-
days reports, we agree with the one that says that – with its
"overpriced" food offer and its "erratic" service – it "feels like the
wrong venture in the wrong place".* / W1 10.45 pm.

Cambio de Tercio SW5 £61 ❷❷❷

161-163 Old Brompton Rd 7244 8970 5–2B
*Still "the star of London's Spanish restaurants" – this Earl's Court
fixture serves "deliciously inventive" cooking, plus a "breathtaking"
wine list, in a setting that's "noisy and exciting, and always full".*
/ SW5 0LJ; www.cambiodetercio.co.uk; 11.15 pm, Sun 11 pm; set weekday L
£41 (FP).

Camino N1 £46 ❸❷❷
3 Varnishers Yd, Regent Quarter 7841 7331 8–3C
"Tucked-away in a King's Cross courtyard", this "buzzy" and
"convivial" venue ("too noisy" at times) makes "a good find for tasty
Spanish tapas". / N1 9FD; www.camino.uk.com; 11 pm; closed Sun D;
SRA-70%.

Cannizaro House SW19 £62 ④④❷
West Side, Wimbledon Common 8879 1464 10–2A
"The new conservatory has added another dimension" to this
"charming" country house, by Wimbledon Common; its dining offer
is still inconsistent, though – fans say it's "first-class", but others talk
of "inexperienced" staff, "miserly portions" and "horrendous" prices.
/ SW19 4UE; www.cannizarohouse.com; 9.30 pm.

Canta Napoli £37 ❸❸④
9 Devonshire Rd, W4 8994 5225 7–2A
136 High St, TW11 8977 3344 1–4A
"Really cheerful" service and very "dependable" pizzas (plus other
staple dishes) underpin high local satisfaction with this Chiswick
Italian; there is also a branch in Teddington. / 10.30 pm; no Amex.

Canteen £41 ⑤⑤⑤
55 Baker St, W1 0845 686 1122 2–1A
Royal Festival Hall, SE1 0845 686 1122 2–3D
Park Pavilion, 40 Canada Sq, E14 0845 686 1122 11–1C
Crispin Pl, Old Spitalf'ds Mkt, E1 0845 686 1122 12–2B
As a breakfast staple, these "basic" cafés have their fans; ratings
remain at rock-bottom, though, as too many reporters find them
to be "bleak" places with "nondescript" food and "bad" service –
"there's no need to re-create '70s-retro as accurately as this!"
/ www.canteen.co.uk; 11 pm, E14 & W1 Sun 7 pm; no booking weekend L.

Cantina Laredo WC2 £52 ❸❷⑤
10 Upper St Martin's Ln 7420 0630 4–3B
This Covent Garden Mexican (part of an international chain) may
offer "authentic US-Mex" dishes, and "excellent margaritas", but it
looks and feels like a hotel brasserie. / WC2H 9FB;
www.cantinalaredo.co.uk; @CantinaLaredoUK; 11.30 pm, Sat midnight,
Sun 10.30 pm.

Cantina Vinopolis
Vinopolis SE1 £52 ④④❸
1 Bank End 7940 8333 9–3C
In atmospheric railway arches, within London's museum of wine,
this South Bank café has long given the impression of "trading on its
location"; it does, however, offer "a great selection of wines by the
glass". / SE1 9BU; www.cantinavinopolis.com; 10 pm; closed Sun.

Canton Arms SW8 £43 ❷❷❷
177 South Lambeth Rd 7582 8710 10–1D
"A privilege to have it in my 'hood"; with its "robust and delicious"
cooking, this sibling to the fabled Anchor & Hope has become the
brightest light of Stockwell gastronomy – it's "worth the trip".
/ SW8 1XP; www.cantonarms.com; 10 pm; closed Mon L & Sun D; no Amex;
no booking.

Cape Town Fish Market W1 £47 ④④❸
5 & 6 Argyll St   7437 1143   3–1C
Prominently-sited by the Palladium, a "no-nonsense" (and rather "touristy") fish and seafood outlet that some reporters find an "enjoyable destination before a show" (or "if you can get an offer"); service, though, can be "very slow". / W1F 7TE; www.ctfm.com; @ctfmlondon; 10.45 pm.

Capote Y Toros SW5 £43 ❷❸❸
157 Old Brompton Rd   7373 0567   5–2B
Cambio de Tercio's nearby "little sister" offers some "very good" tapas (albeit "a bit pricey"), and its South Kensington premises are quite "atmospheric" too. / SW5 0LJ; www.cambiodetercio.co.uk; @CambiodTercio; 11.15 pm; D only, closed Mon & Sun.

LE CAPRICE SW1 £71 ❸❷❷
Arlington Hs, Arlington St   7629 2239   3–4C
"Still with its old pizzazz and magic" – Richard Caring's '80s-minimalist "super-staple", behind the Ritz, "continues to deliver at a very high level"; old-timers, though, can't quite avoid the feeling that "standards have fallen" since yesteryear. / SW1A 1RJ; www.le-caprice.co.uk; midnight, Sun 11 pm; set pre theatre £47 (FP).

Caraffini SW1 £51 ❸❷❷
61-63 Lower Sloane St   7259 0235   5–2D
"Wonderfully reliable" and with "superlative" service, this "stalwart" Italian, near Sloane Square, is "almost like a club" – an "unpretentious", "fun" and "noisy" place where "many locals come to entertain their friends". / SW1W 8DH; www.caraffini.co.uk; 11.30 pm; closed Sun.

Caravan £45 ❸❸❷
1 Granary Sq, N1   7101 7661   8–3C
11-13 Exmouth Mkt, EC1   7833 8115   9–1A
"Amazing" brunches – with "hard-to-beat" coffee (roasted in-house) – is the highlight at these funky eateries, which at other times serve "a modern British/global take on tapas"; while still ultra "hip", the Exmouth original is nowadays eclipsed by the "exciting" King's Cross spin-off (housed in an "incredible" former grain store). / www.caravanonexmouth.co.uk; EC1 10.30 pm, Sun 4 pm; EC1 Sun D.

Carluccio's £41 ⑤⑤④
Branches throughout London
"We expected better" – too often the verdict on the "wishy-washy" food and "hit 'n' miss" service at this glossy, faux-Italian chain; staff can be "unbelievably helpful" where kids are concerned however, and "breakfasts are great value". / www.carluccios.com; most branches 11 pm, Sun 10.30 pm; no booking weekday L; SRA-62%.

Carob Tree NW5 £32 ❸❷❷
15 Highgate Rd   7267 9880   8–1B
"The closest you can get to a seaside Greek cafe in London!" – this "buzzy" and "friendly" Dartmouth Park spot has made quite a name with its "excellent" meze and its "wonderful" fish, all in "gigantic" portions. / NW5 1QX; 10.30 pm, Sun 9 pm; closed Mon; no Amex.

The Carpenter's Arms W6 £47 ❸❸❸
91 Black Lion Ln   8741 8386   7–2B
"A cut above your average gastropub", this "cute" and tucked-away Hammersmith spot offers "reliable" dishes in "relaxing" surroundings; "lovely" garden too. / W6 9BG; 10 pm, Sun 9 pm.

Carvosso's W4 £46 ④❸❷
210 Chiswick High Rd   8995 9121   7–2A
"There's something for everyone" at this large and rambling venture, in Chiswick's former police station, where the star feature is a "lovely summer courtyard"; the food, though is "variable". / W4 1PD; www.carvossosat210.co.uk; 11 pm.

Casa Brindisa SW7 £43 ④④④
7-9 Exhibition Rd   7590 0008   5–2C
"Superb" tapas draw quite a following to this "buzzing" and "chaotic" spot, by South Kensington tube; it also draws a fair amount of flak, though, from those who find its whole performance rather "unconvincing". / SW7 2HE; www.casabrindisa.com; 11 pm, Sun 10 pm.

Casa Malevo W2 £52 ❸❸❸
23 Connaught St   7402 1988   6–1D
"Good hearty fare" maintains the popularity of this "friendly" and "good-value" Bayswater Argentinian; "meat-eaters will love it!" / W2 2AY; www.casamalevo.com; @casamalevo; 10.30 pm.

Casse-Croute SE1 NEW £36
109 Bermondsey St   7407 2140   9–4D
We're really sorry we didn't get to visit this new Bermondsey bistro before this guide went to press – it's been widely reviewed as a top-value destination 'of the sort you don't get in France any more'. / SE1 3XB.

Cattle Grid £43 ❸④④
35-37 Battersea Rise, SW11   7228 4690   10–2C
1 Balham Station Rd, SW12   8673 9099   10–2C
Few reports on these Battersea and Balham steakhouses; fans proclaim "good quality belying the prices", but the experience can also seem rather "neutral". / www.cattlegridrestaurant.com; 10 pm, Fri & Sat 10.30 pm; no Amex.

Cây Tre £38 ❸④❸
42-43 Dean St, W1   7317 9118   4–2A
301 Old St, EC1   7729 8662   12–1B
"There's always a queue out of the door", at the original (and better) branch of this Vietnamese duo – a tiny café in Shoreditch, with "authentic and delicious" scoff; its more "polished" Soho sibling is slowly beginning to measure up. / www.vietnamesekitchen.co.uk; 11 pm, Fri-Sat 11.30 pm, Sun 10.30 pm.

Cecconi's W1 £73 ④④❷
5a Burlington Gdns   7434 1500   3–3C
"Hedgies wine and dine… for breakfast (especially), lunch and dinner", at this "entertaining", "slick" and "incredibly busy" all-day Mayfair corner linchpin; service needs to "sharpen" up, though, and the "simple" Italian fare has too often been an "anticlimax" of late. / W1S 3EP; www.cecconis.co.uk; @SohoHouse; 11.30 pm, Sun 10.30 pm.

Cellar Gascon EC1 £37 ❷❸❷
59 West Smithfield Rd   7600 7561   9–2B
A "wonderful" wine list complements the "delicious tapas style food from SW France" on offer at this offshoot from nearby Club Gascon; "slightly random" Gallic service "just adds to the atmosphere". / EC1A 9DS; www.cellargascon.com; midnight; closed Sat & Sun; set weekday L £20 (FP).

Le Cercle SW1 £54 ❸❷❸
1 Wilbraham Pl 7901 9999 5–2D
Hidden-away in a (deep) basement near Sloane Square, this Gallic venture is "a class act", serving "small plates with surprising flavour combinations"; the "subtle lighting and drapes" can make it "unbeatably romantic", but when it's "quiet" (perhaps more often of late?), the ambience can be rather "subdued". / SW1X 9AE; www.lecercle.co.uk; 10.45 pm; closed Mon & Sun.

Ceviche W1 £45 ❸❸❷
17 Frith St 7292 2040 4–2A
"Delicious" ceviche and other "interesting" Peruvian dishes help make this "bustling" Soho yearling "a great place to meet friends for casual eats"; it can, however, seem "pricey" for what it is. / W1D 4RG; www.cevicheuk.com; 11.30 pm, Sun 10.15 pm; SRA-56%.

Chabrot Bistrot d'Amis SW1 £59 ❸❷❸
9 Knightsbridge Grn 7225 2238 5–1D
"An antidote to more impersonal places"; this "traditional bistro", hidden-away in the heart of Knightsbridge, champions an approach that's less common than it should be – "very French", "simple", "unpretentious" and "fun". / SW1X 7QL; www.chabrot.co.uk; 10.45 pm, Sun 9.45 pm.

Chabrot Bistrot des Halles EC1 NEW £41 ❷❷❸
62-63 Long Ln 7796 4550 9–1B
"A straightforward menu, in an attractive room with pleasant service" – Chabrot's new offshoot, near the Barbican, does the whole 'Gallic bistro' thing properly – a trick which always seemed to elude its predecessor, St Julien (RIP). / EC1A 9EJ; www.chabrot.co.uk; @ChabrotSmith; 11 pm; closed Sun; set weekday L £27 (FP).

Chakra W11 £64 ❸④④
157-159 Notting Hill Gate 7229 2115 6–2B
Despite the "OTT" décor ("more club than restaurant"), the atmosphere can seem "a bit dull" at this Indian yearling in Notting Hill – "a pity, as the food tastes great" . / W11 3LF; www.chakralondon.com; 11 pm, Sun 10.30 pm.

Chamberlain's EC3 £70 ❸④④
23-25 Leadenhall Mkt 7648 8690 9–2D
A long-established fish restaurant, in the heart of Leadenhall Market, that's been winning more positive reviews of late; its "mainstream" food may come at decidedly "upmarket" prices, but fans proclaim this "one of the City's few reliable business lunch locations"! / EC3V 1LR; www.chamberlains.org; @chamberlainsldn; 9.15 pm; closed Sat & Sun.

Champor-Champor SE1 £49 ❷❸❶
62 Weston St 7403 4600 9–4C
"Tucked away near the Shard", a "weird-looking but fun" (and "romantic") little gem, where reporters are "knocked sideways" by the "interesting and different South East Asian cuisine". / SE1 3QJ; www.champor-champor.com; @ChamporChampor; 10 pm; D only, closed Sun.

The Chancery EC4 £51 ❸❸④
9 Cursitor St 7831 4000 9–2A
With its "professional" attitude and "beautifully presented" cuisine, this "hidden-away" spot, near Chancery Lane, often makes "a good quiet option for a business lunch"; some feedback, however, suggests a "slip in standards" of late. / EC4A 1LL; www.thechancery.co.uk; 10.30 pm; closed Sat L & Sun.

Chapters SE3 £49 ④❸④
43-45 Montpelier Vale 8333 2666 1—4D
*"West End, no thanks," say fans of this Blackheath brasserie,
who applaud its "very good all-day dining"; breakfasts apart, however,
the survey finds standards "nothing to write home about". / SE3 0TJ;
www.chaptersrestaurants.com; 11 pm, Sun 9 pm; set weekday L £29 (FP).*

Charles Lamb N1 £43 ❸❸❶
16 Elia St 7837 5040 8—3D
*Gallic ownership helps add a superb, "fun" dimension to this
"favourite" Islington gastropub, which serves a "small but perfectly
formed" menu of "utterly satisfying" pub grub "with a Gallic twist";
it can get "very crowded". / N1 8DE; www.thecharleslambpub.com;
@Thecharleslamb; 9.30 pm; closed Mon L & Tue L; no Amex; no booking.*

Charlotte's Bistro W4 £47 ❷❷❷
6 Turnham Green Ter 8742 3590 7—2A
*Fast becoming a "Chiswick staple", this "buzzy brasserie" is inspiring
ever-stronger support, thanks to its "well put-together" food and its
"friendly" service; kick off with a cocktail in the "stylish bar".
/ W4 1QP; www.charlottes.co.uk; @CharlottesW4; 10 pm, Fri-Sat 10.30 pm,
Sun 9 pm; SRA-56%.*

Charlotte's Place W5 £47 ❸❷❸
16 St Matthew's Rd 8567 7541 1—3A
*"Back on top form", this mega-popular bistro, on the Common,
"definitely offers the best food in Ealing"; even fans may concede,
though, that it's "probably not a 'destination'". / W5 3JT;
www.charlottes.co.uk; 10.30 pm, Fri & Sat 11 pm, Sun 9 pm; SRA-56%.*

Chelsea Bun Diner SW10 £29 ❸④④
9a Lamont Rd 7352 3635 5—3B
*A "workman's café"-style operation, by a bus stop, offering "massive
portions for minimum cost in an area of fabulous wealth" (Chelsea,
that is); not least as a hangover cure, the famous all-day
breakfast is "hard to beat"; BYO. / SW10 0HP; www.chelseabun.co.uk;
6 pm; L only; no Amex; no booking, Sat & Sun; set weekday L £19 (FP).*

The Chelsea Kitchen SW10 £28 ④④❸
451 Fulham Rd 3055 0088 5—3B
*"For nostalgia alone" fans of this re-located "no-frills" '50s veteran,
nowadays near Brompton Cemetry, are "glad it was revived"; it can,
however, also seem "lame" — "it's cheap, with lots of choice, but I'd
rather pay more, for something a bit nicer!" / SW10 9UZ;
www.chelseakitchen.com; 11.30 pm, Sun 11 pm.*

The Chelsea Ram SW10 £40 ④❸❷
32 Burnaby St 7351 4008 5—4B
*A characterful gastroboozer that's nowadays part of the Geronimo
Inns portfolio — "a useful outpost on the Chelsea borders".
/ SW10 0PL; www.chelsearam.com; 10 pm, sun 8 pm; no Amex; SRA-60%.*

Chettinad W1 £31 ❸❸④
16 Percy St 3556 1229 2—1C
*The "café-like" decor may be "quite bland", but you couldn't say the
same about the "real South Indian dishes" on offer at this Fitzrovia
yearling; a "great-value lunch thali" is especially worth seeking out.
/ W1T 1DT; www.chettinadrestaurant.com.*

Cheyne Walk Brasserie SW3 £69 ④④❸
50 Cheyne Walk 7376 8787 5–3C
A bit of a missed opportunity, this attractive Thames-side pub-conversion is nowadays a Gallic brasserie for Chelsea plutocrats; the style is "convivial", and the wood-fired grill produces some delicious dishes, but "the quality doesn't begin to live up to the prices". / SW3 5LR; www.cheynewalkbrasserie.com; 10.30 pm, Sun 9.30 pm; closed Mon L.

CHEZ BRUCE SW17 £68 ❶❶❷
2 Bellevue Rd 8672 0114 10–2C
For the 9th year, Bruce Poole's formidably consistent neighbourhood legend, by Wandsworth Common, is the survey's No 1. favourite – its straightforward but unbeatable formula combines "incredible-value" cooking, "amazing" wine and "helpful and welcoming" service. / SW17 7EG; www.chezbruce.co.uk; 10 pm, Fri & Sat 10.30 pm, Sun 9.30 pm.

Chez Marcelle W14 £32 ❶⑤④
34 Blythe Rd 7603 3241 7–1D
Friendly proprietor Marcelle provides "tremendous" dishes – "some of the best Lebanese food anywhere" – at her "jolly" café, behind Olympia; be braced, though, for "incredibly slow" service... so "just chill, and have a good time". / W14 0HA; 10 pm; closed Mon, Tue-Thu D only, Fri-Sun open L & D; no credit cards.

Chez Patrick W8 £46 ❸❶❸
7 Stratford Rd 7937 6388 5–2A
"Patrick continues to charm and amuse", at his "quirky" and "cramped" Gallic stalwart, hidden away in Kensington; it remains ever popular with a loyal fan club for its "sound" cooking ("especially of fish"). / W8 6RF; www.chez-patrick.co.uk; 10.30 pm; closed Sun D; set weekday L £30 (FP).

Chicken Shop NW5 £30 ❸❷❷
79 Highgate Rd 3310 2020 8–1B
"Chirpy chirpy... cheap cheap!"; this "vibrant" Kentish Town yearling – a sort of "upmarket Nando's" – is "a great idea, well-executed"; "go early to avoid the queues". / NW5 1TL; www.chickenshop.com; SRA-60%.

Chilango £15 ❷❷❸
76 Chancery Ln, WC2 7430 1323 2–1D
27 Upper St, N1 7704 2123 8–3D
32 Brushfield St, E1 3246 0086 12–2B **NEW**
64 London Wall, EC2 7628 7663 9–2C **NEW**
142 Fleet St, EC4 7353 6761 9–2A
"Totally addictive" burritos "bursting with flavour" underpin the high esteem of these "great alternatives to sandwich tedium". / www.chilango.co.uk; @Chilango_uk; EC4, EC2, EC1 9 pm; N1 10 pm, Fri & Sat midnight; EC4, EC2, E1 closed Sat & Sun; no booking.

Chilli Cool WC1 £30 ❸⑤⑤
15 Leigh St 7383 3135 2–1D
"Most of the clientèle are Chinese", at this Bloomsbury café, which offers "proper hot and oily Sichuanese cooking" to "blow your socks off" – almost makes it worthwhile braving the dingy décor and sometimes "rude" service. / WC1H 9EW; www.chillicool.com; 10.15 pm.

China Tang
Dorchester Hotel W1   £72   ④④❸
53 Park Ln   7629 9988   3–3A
*"There are dozens of oriental eateries better than this!" – David
Tang's "self-important" Mayfair hotel basement offers "bland"
cooking at "top dollar" prices; the lavishly styled bar, though,
is undoubtedly "great". / W1K 1QA; www.thedorchesterhotel.com;
11.45 pm; set weekday L £29 (FP).*

Chinese Cricket Club EC4   £54   ④④⑤
19 New Bridge St   7438 8051   9–3A
*A potentially handy business-restaurant, in a hotel by Blackfriars
Bridge; recent reports, however, range quite irreconcilably –
from "brilliant cooking and good value" to "my very worst meal of the
year"! / EC4V 6DB; www.chinesecricketclub.com; 10 pm; closed Sat & Sun L.*

Chipotle   £17   ❸❸④
101-103 Baker St, W1   7935 9881   2–1A
181-185 Wardour St, W1   7494 4156   3–1D
114-116 Charing Cross Rd, WC2   7836 8491   4–1A
92-93 St Martin's Ln, WC2   7836 7838   4–4B
334 Upper St, N1   7354 3686   8–3D **NEW**
40 Wimbledon Hill, SW19   8946 6360   10–2B **NEW**
*"The best burritos", and other "distinct and tangy" Mexican dishes,
help win consistent support for this "fairly authentic" chain; oddly,
though, it's never become big news here, as it is in the US.
/ www.chipotle.com; 10 pm - 11 pm.*

Chisou   £50   ❷❸④
4 Princes St, W1   7629 3931   3–1C
31 Beauchamp Pl, SW3   3155 0005   5–2D
1-4 Barley Mow Pas, W4   8994 3636   7–2A
*"Authentic" Japanese dishes (including "top-notch sushi") and
a "comprehensive sake list" all reward "adventurous selection" at this
small chain; the "utilitarian" Mayfair original is still top for food,
with Knightsbridge more atmospheric; Chiswick is the "cute" one.
/ www.chisourestaurant.com; Mon-Sat 10.30 pm, Sun 9.30 pm.*

Chiswell Street Dining Rooms EC1   £60   ④❸④
56 Chiswell St   7614 0177   12–2A
*The name says it all – this relatively ambitious gastropub-style
operation, near the Barbican, makes a handy business rendezvous,
from breakfast onwards. / EC1Y 4SA; @chiswelldining; 11 pm; closed
Sat & Sun.*

Cho-San SW15   £41   ❷❷❸
292 Upper Richmond Rd   8788 9626   10–2A
*"Just like being in Tokyo!"; this Putney stalwart offers "freshly-
prepared", "homely" and "delicious" Japanese food from a "wide and
interesting" menu (including excellent sushi); "hopefully it will keep its
character after a recent refurb". / SW15 6TH; 10.30 pm; closed Mon.*

Chop Shop SW1 **NEW**   £49   ❸❸④
66 Haymarket   7842 8501   4–4A
*In the heart of Theatreland, a new steakhouse concept from an outfit
based in NYC; it might be useful enough pre-show, but our early-days
visit hinted at no positive reason actively to seek it out. / SW1Y 4RF;
www.chopshopuk.com.*

Chor Bizarre W1 £57 ❷❷❷
16 Albemarle St 7629 9802 3–3C
"Terrific thalis" are a menu highlight at this "pleasantly surprising"
Mayfair Indian – a "posh" but "unstuffy" venue, packed with bric-à-
brac, which deserves to be better-known. / W1S 4HW;
www.chorbizarre.com; 10.45 pm, Sun 10.15 pm; set weekday L £40 (FP).

Chotto Matte W1 NEW £55
11 Frith St 7042 7171 4–2A
From the man behind Ping Pong, an ambitious, multi-level Soho
newcomer, where the fare is Japanese/Peruvian, and for rather less
than it costs at Nobu – sounds as if it could be interesting. / W1D 4RB;
www.chotto-matte.com.

Choys SW3 £46 ④❸④
172 King's Rd 7352 9085 5–3C
The 'Last Emperor' of the Chelsea Chinese dining scene? –
this "bright" King's Road classic (est. 1952) can seem "a little
expensive for what it is", but remains a valued standby for
most reporters who comment on it. / SW3 4UP; 11 pm.

Christopher's WC2 £70 ❸❸❷
18 Wellington St 7240 4222 4–3D
The recent refit "has added glamour and a sense of space" to this
"delightful" (and business-friendly) Covent Garden townhouse; early
reports suggest that, as ever, it's "not cheap", but that realisation
of the surf 'n' turf cuisine has improved since the re-launch.
/ WC2E 7DD; www.christophersgrill.com; @christopherswc2; 11.30 pm,
Sun 10.30 pm; booking: max 14; set pre theatre £39 (FP).

Chuen Cheng Ku W1 £37 ❸④④
17 Wardour St 7437 1398 4–3A
"Ever-circling" dim sum trolleys are the key feature of a "cracking-
value" lunchtime visit to this "old Chinatown warhorse" –
a particularly good experience "with kids"; à la carte, however,
the food is "very average". / W1D 6DJ; www.chuenchengku.co.uk;
11.45 pm.

Churchill Arms W8 £34 ❸❷⓿
119 Kensington Church St 7792 1246 6–2B
"At the back of a truly original, quirky pub, off Notting Hill Gate",
a "really fun", "plant-filled" conservatory, where the Thai dishes
on offer are "the very definition of cheap and cheerful". / W8 7LN;
10 pm, 9.30 pm.

Chutney SW18 £31 ❷❸❸
11 Alma Rd 8870 4588 10–2B
"A great local Indian with its own unique style of cooking and some
fantastic deals" – the worst thing any reporter has to say about this
"friendly" Wandsworth fixture! / SW18 1AA; www.chutneyrestaurant.co.uk;
11.30 pm; D only.

Chutney Mary SW10 £55 ❷⓿❷
535 King's Rd 7351 3113 5–4B
"A real aristocrat of the Indian restaurant world" – this "long-term
favourite", at the far end of Chelsea, boasts a "very atmospheric
conservatory", and is a "totally charming" destination, offering
"wonderfully aromatic" dishes, and "tip top" service too. / SW10 0SZ;
www.realindianfood.com; 11.45 pm, Sun 10.45 pm; closed weekday L; booking:
max 8.

Chutneys NW1 £30 ④❸④
124 Drummond St 7388 0604 8–4C
"The lunchtime and weekend buffet is very tasty and truly excellent value", say fans of this "airy" café – long a "cheap 'n' cheerful" staple of the Little India, near Euston; you can BYO too. / NW1 2PA; www.chutneyseuston.co.uk; 11 pm; no Amex; need 5+ to book.

Ciao Bella WC1 £41 ④❷❷
86-90 Lamb's Conduit St 7242 4119 2–1D
It's not just the "back-to-the-70s" time warp experience that wins fans for this "buzzy", "no-frills" family-run Bloomsbury Italian – its "solid" scoff comes at "value-for-money" prices. / WC1N 3LZ; www.ciaobellarestaurant.co.uk; 11.30 pm, Sun 10.30 pm.

Cibo W14 £51 ❷0❸
3 Russell Gdns 7371 6271 7–1D
"The forgotten star of west London" – this "marvellous local Italian", on the Kensington/Olympia border, is an "authentic" and "unassuming" stalwart, where the cooking is still often "superb". / W14 8EZ; www.ciborestaurant.net; 11 pm; closed Sat L & Sun D.

Cigala WC1 £49 ❸❸④
54 Lamb's Conduit St 7405 1717 2–1D
With its "genuine" Spanish food (plus "a very good wine list"), this "bustling" operation, on a quiet Bloomsbury street, impresses many reporters; the decor is a touch "sterile", though, and service can be erratic. / WC1N 3LW; www.cigala.co.uk; 10.45 pm, Sun 9.45 pm.

Le Cigalon WC2 £47 ❸❷❷
115 Chancery Ln 7242 8373 2–2D
Built as a Victorian auction house, these "very bright and airy" premises, now specialising in the cuisine of Provençe, are "something of an oasis in the restaurant-starved legal district" – "great for a business lunch", obviously, but equally suited to "dinner with friends". / WC2A 1PP; www.cigalon.co.uk; 10 pm; closed Sat & Sun.

THE CINNAMON CLUB SW1 £69 ❷❸❷
Old Westminster Library, Great Smith St 7222 2555 2–4C
In the "beautiful" setting of Westminster's former library, near the Abbey, Iqbal Wahhab's "outstanding" venture is one of London's most impressive destinations; its "haute take" on Indian cuisine often achieves an "absolutely sublime" standard. / SW1P 3BU; www.cinnamonclub.com; @CinnamonClub; 10.30 pm; closed Sun; no trainers; set weekday L & pre-theatre £48 (FP); SRA-68%.

Cinnamon Kitchen EC2 £55 ❷❷❸
9 Devonshire Sq 7626 5000 9–2D
"Exciting" Indian fusion cuisine combines with "attentive" service and an "elegant" setting (with airy seating in the atrium) to make the Cinnamon Club's "business-like" spin-off a top City destination – it even offers a "good-value set lunch". / EC2M 4YL; www.cinnamon-kitchen.com; @cinnamonkitchen; 11 pm; closed Sat L & Sun; set weekday L £34 (FP); SRA-61%.

Cinnamon Soho W1 £43 ④④④
5 Kingly St 7437 1664 3–2D
Soho's "stripped-down version of the Cinnamon Club" pleases most reporters with its "small menu of well-spiced Indian dishes" (and its "fantastic-value" set lunch deals too); for a voluble minority, though, the whole performance is "a bit lacklustre". / W1B 5PE; www.cinnamon-kitchen.com/soho-home; @cinnamonsoho; 11 pm, Sun 4.30 pm; closed Sun D; set weekday L & pre-theatre £32 (FP).

Circus WC2 £65 ④④❷
27-29 Endell St 7420 9300 4–2C
OK, it's "the unique ambience" and "enjoyable showmanship" you
go for, but this Covent Garden cabaret wins surprisingly upbeat
feedback on its "high-quality Asian food". / WC2H 9BA;
www.circus-london.co.uk; @circus_london; midnight, Fri-Sat 2 am; D only,
closed Mon & Sun.

City Càphê EC2 £14 ❶❸⑤
17 Ironmonger St no tel 9–2C
"Get there by noon", to nab a seat at this "great little
restaurant/take-away" – the quality of its "fabulous" and "great
value" Vietnamese dishes (in particular the bánh mi) has become the
stuff of local City legend. / EC2V 8EY; www.citycaphe.com; 3 pm; L only,
closed Sat & Sun.

City Miyama EC4 £52 ❸④⑤
17 Godliman St 7489 1937 9–3B
This City stalwart attracts a steady "Japanese-corporate" clientele,
thanks to its very decent cuisine (particularly sushi), and in spite of its
"tired décor and lack of atmosphere". / EC4 5BD;
www.miyama-restaurant.co.uk; 9.30 pm; closed Sat & Sun.

Clarke's W8 £69 ❸❷–
124 Kensington Church St 7221 9225 6–2B
Preparing to celebrate 30 years in business in 2014, Sally Clarke's
"civilised" Californian-inspired Kensington fixture had a major
refurbishment after our survey for the year had concluded;
the restaurant was path-breaking in its day, so here's hoping that the
revamp marks an era of renewed vigour. / W8 4BH; www.sallyclarke.com;
10 pm; closed Sun D; booking: max 14.

The Clissold Arms N2 £49 ④❸❸
Fortis Grn 8444 4224 1–1C
This Muswell Hill boozer (known for its associations with The Kinks)
is one of the better gastropubs in these parts, and consistently well-
rated; "the garden is wonderful in summer". / N2 9HR; @ClissoldArms;
10 pm, Sat 10.30 pm, Sun 9 pm.

CLOS MAGGIORE WC2 £59 ❷❶❶
33 King St 7379 9696 4–3C
"So romantic, you could say yes to anyone!"; this "womb-like" Covent
Garden wonderland is again London's No.1 passion-magnet –
"the best tables are in the conservatory"; the food is often
"excellent", but it's eclipsed by the "encyclopaedic" wine list.
/ WC2E 8JD; www.closmaggiore.com; @ClosMaggioreWC2; 11 pm,
Sun 10 pm.

The Clove Club EC1 NEW £65 ❷❶❷
Shoreditch Town Hall, 380 Old St 7729 6496 12–1B
"Stunning" food ("a real adventure for the senses!") twinned with
"really knowledgeable" service has made an instant hit of the former
Ten Bells pop-up, now translated to an "exciting and buzzing" setting
in Shoreditch's erstwhile town hall – "definitely worth the hype".
/ EC1V 9LT; www.thecloveclub.com; 9.30 pm.

Club Gascon EC1 £71 ❷❸❸
57 West Smithfield 7600 6144 9–2B
"Unusual" SW French regional cuisine is prepared with "imagination
and verve" – and "fabulous wine to match" – at this very "classy"
City-fringe haven, renowned for "London's best foie gras". / EC1A 9DS;
www.clubgascon.com; @club_gascon; 10 pm, Fri-Sat 10.30 pm; closed
Sat L & Sun; set weekday L £45 (FP).

Cocum SW20 £30 ❷❷❸
9 Approach Rd   8540 3250   10–2B
An "authentic" and "reliable" Raynes Park south Indian… "not much
else to say, really!" / SW20 8BA; www.cocumrestaurant.co.uk; 10.30 pm;
closed Fri L.

Colbeh W2 £26 ❷④④
6 Porchester Pl   7706 4888   6–1D
It's nothing to look at, and the menu never changes, but this pint-
sized Bayswater Iranian majors in "spicy kebabs" and
"the best flatbread in town". / W2 2BS; 11 pm.

Colbert SW1 £60 ④④❸
51 Sloane Sq   7730 2804   5–2D
Come back Oriel (RIP), all is forgiven? – the Wolseley team really
needs to "get a grip" on their long-awaited Belgravia brasserie
project; it has its fans, but the proportion of reporters who find
it "charmless, overblown and overpriced" is little short of astonishing.
/ SW1W 8AX; www.colbertchelsea.com.

Colchis W2 £55 ❷❸❸
39 Chepstow Pl   7221 7620   6–1B
"A real eye-opening experience"; the ground floor of this former
Bayswater boozer (of which the upstairs is Assaggi) is still little-known,
but it offers some "very interesting" Georgian dishes, and some
intriguing Georgian wines to go with them. / W2 4TS;
www.colchisrestaurant.co.uk; 11 pm, Sun 10 pm; closed weekday L.

La Collina NW1 £54 ❸❸❷
17 Princess Rd   7483 0192   8–3B
"A small gourmet Italian in a Primrose Hill side street", where the
food (Piedmontese) is "unusual and always good"; summer visits are
best, as you can sit in the garden. / NW1 8JR;
www.lacollinarestaurant.co.uk; 10.15 pm, Sun 9.45 pm, Mon 9.30 pm; closed
Mon L; set weekday L £35 (FP).

Le Colombier SW3 £59 ❸❷❷
145 Dovehouse St   7351 1155   5–2C
"The perfect formula for a super-agreeable dining experience",
say fans, this "uncomplicated" Chelsea Gallic "classic" is a
"warm and personal" sort of place in a "smart", rather "old-
fashioned" style; "it helps if your French is adequate!" / SW3 6LB;
www.le-colombier-restaurant.co.uk; 10.30 pm, Sun 10 pm; set weekday L £40
(FP), set Sun L £46 (FP).

Como Lario SW1 £47 ④④❸
18-22 Holbein Pl   7730 2954   5–2D
This "jolly" and "reasonably-priced" Italian used to be quite a Sloane
Square staple; nowadays, its "old-fashioned" charms inspire few
reports, but all are reasonably positive. / SW1W 8NL;
www.comolario.co.uk; 11.30 pm, Sun 10 pm; set Sun L £31 (FP).

Comptoir Gascon EC1 £44 ❸④❸
63 Charterhouse St   7608 0851   9–1A
The "duck burger de luxe is not to be missed", if you visit this "no-
fuss" (but quite "romantic") bistro, by Smithfield Market; it offers
a "simple" but "interesting" French (SW) menu, and "excellent
wines" too. / EC1M 6HJ; www.comptoirgascon.com; 10 pm, Thu-Fri
10.30 pm; closed Mon & Sun.

Comptoir Libanais £28 ④④❸

59 Broadwick St, W1 7434 4335 3–2C
65 Wigmore St, W1 7935 1110 3–1A
1-5 Exhibition Rd, SW7 7225 5006 5–2C
Westfield, The Balcony, W12 8811 2222 7–1C
Westfield Stratford City, 2 Stratford Pl, E20 8555 6999 1–1D
A "cosmopolitan" atmosphere (at South Kensington in particular) –
plus "a great range of Lebanese staples" (meze, wraps, juices)
at "decent prices" – win many recommendations for this "useful"
chain. / www.lecomptoir.co.uk; W12 9 pm, Thu & Fri 10 pm, Sun 6 pm;
W1 9.30 pm; W12 closed Sun D; no bookings.

Constancia SE1 £49 ❸❸❸

52 Tanner St 7234 0676 9–4D
A "cosy and bustling" Argentinian, near Tower Bridge, which serves
"fantastic steaks, cooked on an open grill", and "great wines" to go
with 'em too. / SE1 3PH; www.constancia.co.uk; 10.30 pm; D only; no Amex.

Il Convivio SW1 £55 ❷❷❸

143 Ebury St 7730 4099 2–4A
"Stylish, quiet and agreeable", this "hidden treasure", in Belgravia,
offers "consistently good" Italian cooking, and "impeccable" service
too; so why isn't it better known? – "the atmosphere doesn't match
the rest of the experience". / SW1W 9QN; www.etruscarestaurants.com;
10.45 pm; closed Sun.

Coopers Restaurant & Bar WC2 £49 ❸❸④

49a Lincolns Inn Fields 7831 6211 2–2D
Hidden away in Lincoln's Inn Fields, a "reasonably-priced" midtown
standby that's especially useful as a lunchtime rendezvous, "popular
with local lawyers, and university academics too"; upstairs is slightly
grander. / WC2A 3PF; www.coopers-restaurant.com; 11 pm; closed Sat & Sun.

Copita W1 £43 ❸④❸

27 D'Arblay St 7287 7797 3–1D
"Why isn't this place rammed?", say fans of the "novel flavours and
combinations" on offer at this Soho tapas yearling; the results are
"not universally outstanding", however, and "pricey" too. / W1F 8EP;
www.copita.co.uk; 10.30 pm; closed Sun.

Le Coq N1 NEW £39

292-294 St Paul's Rd 7359 5055 8–2D
A new Islington rôtisserie chicken specialist; sadly, we didn't have the
opportunity to visit before this guide went to press, but some media
commentary has been very positive indeed. / N1 2LH; www.le-coq.co.uk.

Coq d'Argent EC2 £60 ④④❸

1 Poultry 7395 5000 9–2C
The "fantastic" top-floor location, complete with a "great summer
terrace", makes this "slick" D&D group restaurant a perennial
favourite for City dining (and for breakfast too); critics dismiss the
cooking as "by numbers", though, and the wine list can seem
"insanely overpriced". / EC2R 8EJ; www.coqdargent.co.uk; 9.45 pm; closed
Sun D; SRA-65%.

Cork & Bottle WC2 £48 ④④❷
44-46 Cranbourn St 7734 7807 4–3B
So retro it's now "cool", this "hidden gem" of a wine bar, in a seedy corner of Leicester Square, manages "never to be overrun with tourists"; it's "the wide and exciting wine list", though, which draws the locals – the scoff doesn't have much to do with it. / WC2H 7AN; www.thecorkandbottle.co.uk; @corkbottle1971; 11.30 pm, Sun 10.30 pm; no booking after 6.30 pm.

Corner Room E2 £48 ❶❷❸
Patriot Sq 7871 0461 1–2D
Fans are "blown away" by the "weird but perfect flavour combinations" on offer at this "quirky" spin-off from Viajante; "much cosier" than big brother, and "tremendous value" to boot, it's "well worth the trip to Bethnal Green!" / E2 9NF; www.viajante.co.uk/corner-room/; @townhallhotel; 10.30 pm.

Corrigan's Mayfair W1 £86 ④④④
28 Upper Grosvenor St 7499 9943 3–3A
Fans still find Richard Corrigan's Mayfair dining room "an absolute British gem", but its performance slid dramatically this year; "heavy-handed" cooking and "eye-watering" prices were key complaints, but "shambolic" service, and a "subdued" ambience also played their part; Monday nights BYO, no corkage! / W1K 7EH; www.corrigansmayfair.com; 10.45 pm, Sun 9.30 pm; closed Sat L; booking: max 10; set weekday L £54 (FP).

Côte £43 ④❸④
124-126 Wardour St, W1 7287 9280 3–1D
17-21 Tavistock St, WC2 7379 9991 4–3D
45-47 Parsons Green Ln, SW6 7736 8444 10–1B
98 Westbourne Grove, W2 7792 3298 6–1B
50-54 Turnham Green Ter, W4 8747 6788 7–2A
47 Kensington Ct, W8 7938 4147 5–1A
Hays Galleria, Tooley St, SE1 7234 0800 9–4D
8 High St, SW19 8947 7100 10–2B
26 Ludgate Hill, EC4 7236 4399 9–2A
"Usually reliable", this "accommodating" and "buzzy" Gallic brasserie chain makes an ideal "standby", and one offering "value for money" too, especially at lunch (and early-evening); Richard Caring, le patron, has just made a(nother) mint, selling the business to a private equity firm. / www.cote-restaurants.co.uk; 11 pm.

Cotidie W1 £78
50 Marylebone High St 7258 9878 2–1A
This ambitious Marylebone Italian was relaunched, with a new chef, in the summer of 2013; let's hope he can improve on the formerly "hit-and-miss" standards! / W1U 5HN; www.cotidierestaurant.com; 11.30 pm, Sun 11 pm; set weekday L £52 (FP).

The Courtauld Gallery Café
The Courtauld Gallery WC2 £30 ④❸❸
Somerset Hs, Strand 7848 2527 2–2D
"Convenient", if too often crowded, this café on Somerset House's main courtyard is of note for a lower-level al fresco dining area all of its own – a surprise 'find' just a few metres from the Strand. / WC2R 0RN; L only; no Amex.

The Cow W2 £54 ❸❸❶
89 Westbourne Park Rd 7221 0021 6–1B
*"Great Guinness and oysters" headline the menu at Tom Conran's hip
Notting Hill-fringe boozer (which has a marginally grander dining
room upstairs); on the downside, it's "quite pricey for a non-booking
establishment with small and slightly cramped tables". / W2 5QH;
www.thecowlondon.co.uk; 10.30 pm, Sun 10 pm; no Amex.*

Coya W1 NEW £70 ❷❷❶
118 Piccadilly 7042 7118 3–4B
*"Suitable for romance, a celebration, or a big table with friends",
this "excellent" ("and expensive") new Mayfair Peruvian is not
just a "fun" place, but offers "fabulous food" as well; "cool" bar too.
/ W1J 7NW; www.coyarestaurant.com; @coyarestaurant.*

Crazy Bear W1 £62 ❸④❷
26-28 Whitfield St 7631 0088 2–1C
*With its sexy basement bar and mega-lavish decor, this ever-"trendy"
Fitzrovia haunt still pleases most reporters, and its "pricey" pan-Asian
fare generally hits the spot too; service, however, can be somewhat
"idiosyncratic". / W1T 2RG; www.crazybeargroup.co.uk; 10.30 pm; closed
Sat L & Sun; no shorts.*

Criterion W1 £69 ④④❶
224 Piccadilly 7930 0488 3–3D
*"Spectacular", "truly magnificent", "beautiful" – it's the architecture
and ambience of this extraordinary neo-Byzantine "oasis", right
on Piccadilly Circus, that "makes a visit worthwhile"; the food,
however, can be a touch "institutional". / W1J 9HP;
www.criterionrestaurant.com; 11.30 pm, Sun 10.30 pm; set weekday L &
pre-theatre £48 (FP).*

The Crooked Well SE5 £47 ❷❷❷
16 Grove Ln 7252 7798 1–3C
*"A neighbourhood joint that's a real favourite"; this "large" but
"friendly" Camberwell two-year-old is an all-round hit, thanks not
least to its "succulent" British fare. / SE5 8SY; www.thecrookedwell.com;
@crookedwell; 10.30 pm; closed Mon L; no Amex.*

Crussh £17 ❸❷④
Branches throughout London
*"A great place for a healthy lunch of soup, wraps or salads, and the
juices are very good too" – this "extremely helpful" chain pulls off the
hard act of being "virtuous without being dull". / www.crussh.com;
4.30 pm-8 pm; many branches closed all or part of weekend; no credit cards
in many branches.*

Cumberland Arms W14 £42 ❷❷❸
29 North End Rd 7371 6806 7–2D
*"Really good food every time" – reason to seek out this pleasing,
if no-frills, pub in the no man's land near Olympia (run by the same
team as The Atlas). / W14 8SZ; www.thecumberlandarmspub.co.uk;
@thecumberland; 10 pm, Sun 9.30 pm.*

Cut
45 Park Lane W1 £98 ⑤⑤⑤
45 Park Ln 7493 4545 3–4A
*"Smell the money!"; the steaks may often be "indulgent", but prices
(especially of wine) at LA restaurateur Wolfgang Puck's steakhouse
are so "stupefying" that the whole operation strikes critics as plain
"vulgar"; the view – "Park Lane traffic" – is no great plus either.
/ W1K 1PN; www.45parklane.com; 10.30 pm; set weekday L £68 (FP).*

Cyprus Mangal SW1 £31 ❷❸④
45 Warwick Way 7828 5940 2–4B
"OK it's cheap, OK it's not luxurious, but the food is extraordinary value", say fans of the "good fresh grills and salads" on offer at this "cramped and dive-y" Pimlico BBQ; BYO. / SW1V 1QS; 10.45 pm, Fri & Sat 11.45 pm.

Da Mario SW7 £41 ❸❸❸
15 Gloucester Rd 7584 9078 5–1B
A "friendly" and "lively" South Kensington pizzeria veteran, where "children are always given a typically Italian welcome"; "great pre-Albert Hall". / SW7 4PP; www.damario.co.uk; 11.30 pm.

Da Mario WC2 £45 ❸❷❸
63 Endell St 7240 3632 4–1C
This "lovely, neighbourhood, family-run Italian" makes a rather "unusual" find, slap bang in the middle of Covent Garden – "always good value", and always offering "a welcoming reception for returning customers". / WC2H 9AJ; www.da-mario.co.uk; 11.15 pm; closed Sun.

DABBOUS W1 £63 ❶❶❸
39 Whitfield St 7323 1544 2–1C
A tiny minority may proclaim "the emperor's new clothes", but – for a crushing majority – Ollie Dabbous's "industrial"-style foodie Fitzrovia sensation fully "lives up to the hype" – service may be "with the minimum of fuss", but "every magical mouthful is a wonder"; book for next year now. / W1T 2SF; www.dabbous.co.uk; @dabbous; 11.30 pm; closed Mon & Sun; set weekday L £47 (FP).

Daddy Donkey EC1 £16 ❷❸–
100 Leather Ln 448448 9–2A
A grand-daddy of the streetfood world, this "cool" Clerkenwell outfit specialises in "burritos as they should be served"; let's hope they don't spoil it all, now they have an actual shop! / EC1N 7TE; www.daddydonkey.co.uk/.

The Dairy SW4 NEW £39
15 The Pavement 7622 4165 10–2D
Oddly located on a busy corner of Clapham Common tube, this wine-bar-style newcomer – whose chef used to work at Raymond Blanc's 'Manoir' – has been a 'rave' for almost all of the many press critics who have visited. / SW4 0HY; www.the-dairy.co.uk.

Dalchini SW19 £36 ④❸④
147 Arthur Rd 8947 5966 10–2B
The "interesting" menu at this "charming spot", opposite Wimbledon Park tube, features Hakka (Indian/Chinese) cuisine; not everyone's wowed, but fans insist this is "a great local". / SW19 8AB; www.dalchini.co.uk; 10.30 pm, Fri & Sat 11 pm, Sun 10 pm; no Amex.

Dans le Noir EC1 £77 ④④④
29 Clerkenwell Grn 7253 1100 9–1A
"A mystery menu, eaten in total darkness, how exciting can you get?" – that's the more positive view on this bizarre Farringdon venture; others, though, dismiss it as a "gimmick" – "the pitch black supposedly heightens your senses… but it certainly heightens the bill!" / EC1R 0DU; www.danslenoir.com; 9.30 pm, Sun 7.30 pm; closed weekday L.

Daphne's SW3 £68 ④❷❷

112 Draycott Ave 7589 4257 5–2C

"A perennial favourite"; this "elegant and comfortable" ("slightly '80s") Chelsea stalwart – with its "personal" service – is "always busy and lively"; no one really minds that its "comfort-Italian" dishes are rather middle of the road. / SW3 3AE; www.daphnes-restaurant.co.uk; 11.30 pm, Sun 10.30 pm.

Daquise SW7 £45 ④❸④

20 Thurloe St 7589 6117 5–2C

"New owners have done a brilliant job", at this revived Polish bistro, by South Kensington tube, which "has gone up in the world since its days as a '50s café"; it serves us "solid, authentic cooking" at "reasonable prices". / SW7 2LT; daquise.co.uk; 11 pm; no Amex; set weekday L £26 (FP).

The Dartmouth Arms SE23 £37 ④❸❸

7 Dartmouth Rd 8488 3117 1–4D

A "very cosy" gastropub in Forest Hill; there is the occasional suggestion that it has "gone slightly downhill this year", but it still attracts mainly positive reports. / SE23 3HN; www.thedartmoutharms.com; 10 pm, Sun 9 pm; no Amex.

The Dartmouth Castle W6 £42 ④❸❸

26 Glenthorne Rd 8748 3614 7–2C

"A great little find in Hammersmith" – an atmospheric and "busy" pub, north of King Street, offering "good, solid" cooking. / W6 0LS; www.thedartmouthcastle.co.uk; 10 pm, Sun 9.30 pm; closed Sat L.

Daylesford Organic £42 ④⑤④

44b Pimlico Rd, SW1 7881 8060 5–2D

208-212 Westbourne Grove, W11 7313 8050 6–1B

More even standards of late at this "bright" and "airy" deli/café de luxe, five minutes' walk from Sloane Square; it's often hailed as a "really good" venue for breakfast or for brunch. / www.daylesfordorganic.com; SW1 & W11 7 pm, Sun 4 pm; W1 9 pm, Sun 6.15 pm; W11 no booking L.

Dean Street Townhouse W1 £56 ④④❷

69-71 Dean St 7434 1775 4–2A

"Slick" and happening, this Soho brasserie seduces the punters with its "comfortable" gent's-club décor, which "harks back to a bygone era of luxury"; the food, though, is decidedly "ordinary" – only the "fabulous" brunch really stands out. / W1D 3SE; www.deanstreettownhouse.com; 11.30 pm, Fri & Sat midnight, Sun 10.30 pm; set pre theatre £37 (FP).

Defune W1 £63 ❷❸⑤

34 George St 7935 8311 3–1A

This "old-school" Japanese ("a world away from the glitz of Nobu or Zuma") is "as cold as ice" on the decor front, but fans feel its "incredible" sushi and "terrific" other fare "makes it all worthwhile"; critics, though, can find bills "outrageous". / W1U 7DP; www.defune.com; 10.45 pm, Sun 10.30 pm.

Dehesa W1 £49 ❶❷❷

25 Ganton St 7494 4170 3–2C

"Truly heavenly" tapas and an "excellent wine list" fuel the "busy buzz" of this stylish haunt, a sibling to Salt Yard, just off Carnaby Street; "despite its initial pokey appearance", it's "a lovely place to spend a long afternoon". / W1F 9BP; www.dehesa.co.uk; @SaltYardGroup; 10.45 pm; closed Sun D; SRA-63%.

THE DELAUNAY WC2   £60   ❸❷❶
55 Aldwych   7499 8558   2–2D
"Like The Wolesley, only smaller" – this *"beautiful"* Aldwych celeb-
magnet is *"another triumph"* for Corbin & King (and likewise
a business and power breakfast mainstay); the food –
"Viennese/Alsatian cooking with a smattering of British dishes" –
is *"good, but always a secondary attraction"*. / WC2B 4BB;
www.thedelaunay.com; @TheDelaunayRest; midnight, Sun 11 pm; SRA-66%.

Delfino W1   £51   ❷❸④
121 Mount St   7499 1256   3–3B
A Mayfair Italian claimed by fans to offer *"the best pizza in central
London"* (with a *"thin base and crust, and very flavourful toppings"*),
and *"efficient and charming"* service too – the consistency of the
many reports is impressive. / W1K 3NW; www.finos.co.uk; 11 pm;
closed Sun.

Delhi Grill N1   £33   ❷❷❸
21 Chapel Mkt   7278 8100   8–3D
"Zingy flavours... amazing kebabs... terrific value" – that's the deal
at this *"addictive"* little *"gem"* of a curry shop, near Angel tube,
and *"so easy on the wallet"* too. / N1 9EZ; www.delhigrill.com; 10.30 pm.

La Delizia Limbara SW3   £39   ❸④④
63-65 Chelsea Manor St   7376 4111   5–3C
The thin-crust pizza at this *"busy"* Chelsea side street stalwart are
amongst *"the most authentic"* in town; the *"no-frills"* setting, however,
can seem a little too *"clinical"*. / SW3 5RZ; 11 pm, Sun 10.30 pm;
no Amex.

Department of Coffee EC1   £15   ❸❷❷
14-16 Leather Ln   7419 6906   9–2A
"The coffee and the feel are excellent"; the food may not excite,
but fans still insist this City spot *"leads the coffee-shop pack"*.
/ EC1N 7SU; www.departmentofcoffee.co.uk; 6 pm, Sat-Sun 4 pm; L only.

The Depot SW14   £41   ❸❷❷
Tideway Yd, Mortlake High St   8878 9462   10–1A
"Perfect, if you get a table by the river" – this *"spacious"* and
"informal" Barnes haunt can be *"magical when the sun sets"*, and is
a major family favourite at weekends; the food's never been the main
event, but is currently on something of a high. / SW14 8SN;
www.depotbrasserie.co.uk; @TheDepotBarnes; 10 pm, Sun 9.30 pm.

Les Deux Salons WC2   £50   ④④❸
40-42 William IV St   7420 2050   4–4C
"A wonderful take on a posh Parisian brasserie", say fans of Will
Smith & Anthony Demetre's *"useful"* and *"vibrant"* Theatreland spot;
others think that – while it *"seems to tick all the boxes"* – the food
is *"uninspired"*, the decor *"boring"*, and the service so-so.
/ WC2N 4DD; www.lesdeuxsalons.co.uk; 10.45 pm, Sun 5.45 pm; closed
Sun D; set weekday L £35 (FP).

Le Deuxième WC2   £57   ④④⑤
65a Long Acre   7379 0033   4–2D
An *"always reliable"* standby, handy for the Royal Opera House –
a *"popular"* and *"busy"* spot, especially pre-theatre and for lunch;
the décor is *"rather sparse"*, though, and the food is *"reasonable,
rather than exciting"*. / WC2E 9JH; www.ledeuxieme.com; Mon-Thu 11 pm,
Fri-Sat 11.30 pm, Sun 10 pm; set weekday L & pre-theatre £28 (FP).

dim T £34 ④④④
56-62 Wilton Rd, SW1   7834 0507   2–4B
32 Charlotte St, W1   7637 1122   2–1C
1 Hampstead Ln, N6   8340 8800   8–1B
3 Heath St, NW3   7435 0024   8–2A
Tooley St, SE1   7403 7000   9–4D
A modern, pan-Asian chain whose performance is "not ground breaking in any way"; the SE1 branch, however, boasts "a nice upstairs with views of Tower Bridge and the Thames". / www.dimt.co.uk; @dim_t; most branches 11 pm, Sun 10.30 pm.

Diner £33 ④❸❷
18 Ganton St, W1   7287 8962   3–2C
190 Shaftesbury Ave, WC2   3551 5225   4–1C
105 Gloucester Rd, SW7   7244 7666   5–2B NEW
21 Essex Rd, N1   7226 4533   8–3D
64-66 Chamberlayne Rd, NW10   8968 9033   1–2B
2 Jamestown Rd, NW1   7485 5223   8–3B
128 Curtain Rd, EC2   7729 4452   12–1B
"My US friends thought I'd flown them home!" – these "buzzy" hang-outs offer "a decent slice of Americana", including all the "classic" dishes (burgers, ribs, chilli dogs, shakes…). / www.goodlifediner.com; most branches 11 or 11.30 pm; booking: max 10.

Dinings W1 £53 ❶❷⑤
22 Harcourt St   7723 0666   8–4A
"An odd, even ugly place but WOW!!"; the sushi Tomonari Chiba offers at this Marylebone bunker is "off-the-scale-good" (and rivalled only by Sushi Tetsu for the crown as 'best in London'); shame about the "dark and uncomfy" interior. / W1H 4HH; www.dinings.co.uk; 10.30 pm; closed Sun.

DINNER
MANDARIN ORIENTAL SW1 £94 ❸❸❸
66 Knightsbridge   7201 3833   5–1D
"Heston's done it again", say fans of his Knightsbridge production, extolling "incredible" dishes, with an "amusing" and "superbly inventive" olde-English twist; but not everyone's dazzled – to sceptics its merely "a smart hotel place", with nice park views and "ludicrous" bills. / SW1X 7LA; www.dinnerbyheston.com; 10.30 pm; set weekday L £65 (FP).

Dirty Burger £14 ❷❸❸
78 Highgate Rd, NW5   3310 2010   8–2B
Arch 54, 6 South Lambeth Rd, SW8   7074 1444   2–4D NEW
"Don't be fooled by the downtrodden exterior"; this "not-so-secret-burger shack", in Kentish Town, is one of the best "no-nonsense" burger joints in town – "lip-smackingly good" scoff, and "a lot of fun" too; now with a new Vauxhall sibling. / www.eatdirtyburger.com; NW5, Mon-Thu midnight, Fri & Sat 1 am, Sun 11 pm – SW8 Mon-Thu 11 pm, Fri & Sat 2 am, Sun 8 pm.

Dishoom £40 ❸❸❶
12 Upper St Martins Ln, WC2   7420 9320   4–3B
7 Boundary St, E2   7420 9324   12–1B NEW
"A real change from most Indians"; this "vibrant" Covent Garden café – a superb "recreation of the numerous Parsi cafés in Mumbai" – has many fans for its unusually "cool" ambience, and "delicious contemporary cuisine"; now in Shoreditch too. / www.dishoom.com; @Dishoom; 11 pm, Sun 10 pm.

Diwana Bhel-Poori House NW1 £30 ④④⑤
121-123 Drummond St   7387 5556   8–4C
The characterfully knackered canteen decor may evoke "a '70s sauna", but this "marvellous" survivor, near Euston is still celebrated for its "cheap lunchtime buffet" and "great dosas" – twin highlights of its "delicious veggie Indian menu", which is priced "as cheap as chips"; BYO. / NW1 2HL; 11.45 pm, Sun 11 pm; no Amex; need 10+ to book.

The Dock Kitchen
Portobello Dock W10 £54 ❸❸❶
344 Ladbroke Grove, Portobello Dock   8962 1610   1–2B
"An extraordinary variety of cuisines delivered with great panache" wins fans for Steve Parle's "exciting" venture, in an "urban-romantic" canalside setting in deepest Notting Hill; it does have its critics, though, who feel "it's too eclectic to get any one thing particularly right". / W10 5BU; www.dockkitchen.co.uk; @TheDockKitchen; 10 pm; closed Sun D.

Dockmaster's House E14 £53 ❷❸④
1 Hertsmere Rd   7345 0345   11–1C
"Unexpected and under-utilised", this "posh" Indian, in an "historic" Georgian building near West India Quay, is well worth seeking out for its "tasty, well-balanced and different" dishes, "efficiently" served too. / E14 8JJ; www.dockmastershouse.com; @DockmastersHous; 10.30 pm; closed Sat L & Sun.

The Don EC4 £64 ❸❷❸
20 St Swithin's Ln   7626 2606   9–3C
This "City oasis", tucked-away near Bank, remains one of the Square Mile's top lunch spots – it's "that rare spot where business can be done in attractive surroundings" (especially in the "fun" basement wine "caves"); the cuisine, though, risks "resting on its laurels" a bit. / EC4N 8AD; www.thedonrestaurant.com; @thedonlondon; 9.45 pm; closed Sat & Sun; no shorts.

don Fernando's TW9 £43 ④❷④
27f The Quadrant   8948 6447   1–4A
"Unchanging, but always popular"; this "efficient" tapas bar is a "jolly" and "bustling" fixture, where the food comes in "hearty" portions; handy for the Richmond Theatre too. / TW9 1DN; www.donfernando.co.uk; 11pm, Sun 10pm; no Amex; no booking.

Donna Margherita SW11 £42 ❷❸④
183 Lavender Hill   7228 2660   10–2C
"Naples on a plate"; "the pizzas are to die for", at this "chilled" and "authentic" Battersea spot; it's a "family-friendly" destination, naturally, "but even babies who arrive crying are soothed by the joyful welcome!" / SW11 5TE; www.donna-margherita.com; 10.30 pm, Fri-Sat 11 pm; Mon-Thu D only, Fri-Sun open L & D.

Donostia W1 £44 ❸❷❷
10 Seymour Pl   3620 1845   2–2A
For many reporters, this popular yearling near Marble Arch offers "tapas with a Basque influence" which are "far superior to that of most rivals"; the occasional sceptic, though, tends to the view that it's "not worth a special trip". / W1H 7ND; www.donostia.co.uk; @DonostiaW1; 11 pm; closed Mon L.

Dorchester Grill
Dorchester Hotel W1   £95   ❸❷④
53 Park Ln   7629 8888   3–3A
This grand Mayfair hotel's grill-room has been dishing up some
"outstanding" dishes of late... so it's a shame about the "OTT" décor
("odd having all that tartan!") and "outrageous" prices. / W1K 1QA;
www.thedorchester.com; 10.15 pm, Sat 10.45 pm, Sun 10.15 pm; no trainers;
set weekday L £37 (FP).

Dose EC1   £13   ❷❸④
70 Long Ln   7600 0382   9–1B
A "fantastic" caffeine high, plus a sandwich that's "worth a journey"
– this Antipodean coffee shop, in Smithfield, still gets an enthusiastic
thumbs-up from its small fan club. / EC1A 9EJ; www.dose-espresso.com;
L only, closed Sun; no Amex.

Dotori N4   £28   ❷④④
3 Stroud Green Rd   7263 3562   8–1D
A "tiny" Finsbury Park Asian that "always rammed to the rafters";
your order can take "ages" to come, but it's "worth the wait", as the
Korean/Japanese fare is "always tasty" and "definitely good value for
money". / N4 2DQ; 10.30 pm; closed Mon; no Amex.

Downtown Mayfair W1   £92   ④④④
15 Burlington St   3056 1001   3–2C
This Mayfair Italian lacks even the 'charm' some discern in its elder
sibling, C London; reports, few, suggest it's a "cold" and "soulless"
sort of place, that's "very overpriced for the food it offers".
/ W1S 2HX; www.downtownmayfair.com; @downtownmayfair; 11.45 pm;
closed Fri D, Sat D & Sun.

Dragon Castle SE17   £37   ❷❸④
100 Walworth Rd   7277 3388   1–3C
It may sometimes seem a bit of a "cavern", but this Elephant
& Castle fixture is, for some reporters, "still the best Chinese
restaurant in London", with "really good" dim sum a highlight of the
often-"memorable" cooking. / SE17 1JL; www.dragon-castle.com; 11 pm.

The Drapers Arms N1   £46   ❸❸❸
44 Barnsbury St   7619 0348   8–3D
An "excellent neighbourhood pub", in Islington, that's "still going
strong"; it's a "friendly" sort of place, whose attractions include
"seasonal" British menus, and "great craft ales". / N1 1ER;
www.thedrapersarms.com; @DrapersArms; 10.30 pm; no Amex.

Duck & Waffle EC2   £68   ④④❶
110 Bishopsgate   3640 7310   9–2D
With its "incredible" 40th-floor views (plus a "terrifying" lift ride
to get there), this City yearling would have made quite a splash
anyway, so it's surprising how many reporters also applaud its
"unexpectedly great" British food... especially when it's served 24/7.
/ EC2N 4AY; www.duckandwaffle.com.

Ducksoup W1   £50   ④④④
41 Dean St   7287 4599   4–2A
"So cool it hurts"; this "narcissistic" bare-bones Soho bistro is a
"cramped" but "expensive" venue, where the food is "not bad...
just not as good as they think it is!" / W1D 4PY; www.ducksoupsoho.co.uk;
@ducksoup.

The Duke of Cambridge N1 £50 ❸❸❷
30 St Peter's St 7359 3066 1–2C
"Creative organic cooking" ("from an ever-changing blackboard menu") has made quite a name for this "lovely" Islington back street boozer, which inspires impressively consistent reviews all-round. / N1 8JT; www.dukeofcambridge.com; 10.30 pm, Sun 10 pm; no Amex.

Duke of Sussex W4 £44 ❸❹❷
75 South Pde 8742 8801 7–1A
On the Chiswick/Acton border, an "airy" and "appealing" Victorian pub (with "a lovely garden tucked away at the back"), serving an "interestingly different menu with a Spanish bias"; "always buzzing", it gets "rammed" at peak times. / W4 5LF; @thedukew4; 10.30 pm, Sun 9.30 pm.

Duke's Brew & Que N1 NEW £43 ❷❸④
33 Downham Rd 3006 0795 1–2D
"Amazing, huge and tasty beef ribs", "incredible burgers" and "an excellent choice of beers" (they brew their own) – all star dishes at this "cool BBQ", in Dalston. / N1 5AA; www.dukesbrewandque.com; @DukesJoint; 10.30 pm, Sun 9.30 pm.

Durbar W2 £32 ❷❷❷
24 Hereford Rd 7727 1947 6–1B
"Top-quality Indian food, at decent prices" – it may be prehistoric in origin (1956), but this Bayswater veteran still draws a "loyal crowd" with its "refined but unfussy" cuisine. / W2 4AA; www.durbartandoori.co.uk; 11.30 pm; closed Fri L.

E&O W11 £52 ❷❸❶
14 Blenheim Cr 7229 5454 6–1A
"After 10 years, I still get excited!" – this "social, buzzy and groovy" Notting Hill hang-out is still serving "Asian-fusion dishes at their finest", and still "always fun". / W11 1NN; www.rickerrestaurants.com; 11 pm, Sun 10.30 pm; booking: max 6.

E11even Park Walk SW10 £59 ❸❸④
11 Park Wk 7352 3449 5–3B
"Calm", "nice", perhaps "a bit bland" – this contemporary Chelsea Italian doesn't always set the pulse racing, but its "traditional food with a modern twist" is prepared to a very "steady" standard. / SW10 0AJ; www.atozrestaurants.com/11parkwalk; midnight; set weekday L £33 (FP), set dinner £41 (FP).

The Eagle EC1 £32 ❸④❷
159 Farringdon Rd 7837 1353 9–1A
"The first, and still among the best"; this "vibe-filled" Farringdon boozer helped coin the term 'gastropub', and still offers "imaginative" Med-inspired dishes from its blackboard menu. / EC1R 3AL; 10.30 pm; closed Sun D; no Amex; no booking.

Earl Spencer SW18 £46 ❸④❸
260-262 Merton Rd 8870 9244 10–2B
It may look "like a roadhouse" (and "on a busy road" too), but this Wandsworth fixture is really "a pub in name only" nowadays – the food is "consistently good" and sometimes "excellent". / SW18 5JL; www.theearlspencer.co.uk; 11 pm; Mon-Thu D only, Fri-Sun open L & D; no booking Sun.

Eat   £14   ④❸④
Branches throughout London
*"A fab selection of interesting soups" remains a highlight at this grab-
and-go chain; as always, fans say it's "taken on Pret and won", but, as
ever, survey ratings still lag its arch-rival's. / www.eat.co.uk; 4 pm-8 pm;
most City branches closed all or part of weekend; no credit cards; no booking.*

Eat Tokyo   £23   ❸❸④
50 Red Lion St, WC1   7242 3490   2–1D
15 Whitcomb St, WC2   7930 6117   4–4A
169 King St, W6   8741 7916   7–2B NEW
18 Hillgate St, W8   7792 9313   6–2B
14 North End Rd, NW11   8209 0079   1–1B NEW
*The "intimate and stylish" new Holborn branch (on the former site
of Eddoko, RIP) is a highlight of this small Japanese chain, where the
food is "inexpensive but high on quality and authenticity".*

Ebury Restaurant & Wine Bar SW1   £53   ④④④
139 Ebury St   7730 5447   2–4A
*This "old-time" (1959) Belgravia wine bar-cum-restaurant is never
going to set the world on fire, but its "reliable" food – and, more
particularly, its "superb" and "good-value" wines – can still make
it "a good destination for a reasonably-priced meal". / SW1W 9QU;
www.eburyrestaurant.co.uk; 10.15 pm.*

Eco SW4   £34   ❷❸❷
162 Clapham High St   7978 1108   10–2D
*"Improved" by its recent major refurbishment, this perennially trendy
Clapham haunt remains a "friendly" outfit that's "always reliable" for
an "excellent pizza". / SW4 7UG; www.ecorestaurants.com;
@ecopizzaLDN; 11 pm, Fri & Sat 11.30 pm.*

Ed's Easy Diner   £31   ④④❸
12 Moor St, W1   7434 4439   4–2A
Trocadero, 19 Rupert St, W1   7287 1951   3–3D
Sedley Pl, 14 Woodstock St, W1   7493 9916   3–2B
*London's original US diner chain is a riot of '50s kitsch; a visit can still
be "great fun" (especially with kids), even if there's no doubt "you can
find a better burger in town these days". / www.edseasydiner.co.uk;
Rupert St 10.30 pm, Fri & Sat 11.30 pm, Sun 10 pm; Moor St 11.30 pm,
Thu-Sat midnight, Sun 10 pm, Sedley Place 9 pm, Thu-Sat 10 pm,
NW1 Mon-Sat 10 pm, Sun 9 pm; Moor St no booking.*

Edera W11   £61   ❷0④
148 Holland Park Ave   7221 6090   6–2A
*"First-rate" Sardinian food and notably "charming" service win very
solid support for this "reliable" Holland Park fixture; it's no bargain,
though, and "the menu seems slow to change". / W11 4UE;
www.atoz.co.uk; 11 pm, Sun 10 pm.*

Eight Over Eight SW3   £57   ❸❷❸
392 King's Rd   7349 9934   5–3B
*A "humming star of Chelsea"; Will Ricker's hang-out at World's End
is always "vibrant and fun", and it offers some "excellent" pan-Asian
nibbles; no denying, though, that it's "pricey, for what you get".
/ SW3 5UZ; www.rickerrestaurants.com; 11 pm, Sun 10.30 pm.*

Elena's L'Etoile W1   £52   ④④④
30 Charlotte St   7636 7189   2–1C
*Traditionalists still warm to the "good old-fashioned French fare" and
"uncorporate" vibe at this faded Fitzrovia fixture (est 1896); since
Elena retired, however, it seems rather to have lost its way.
/ W1T 2NG; www.elenasletoile.co.uk; 10.30 pm; closed Sat L & Sun.*

Elephant Royale
Locke's Wharf E14 £49 ❸④❸
Westferry Rd 7987 7999 11–2C
"A lovely location by the river" (nice terrace too, with stunning views of Greenwich) helps ensure that this remote Thai, on the Isle of Dogs, is "always busy"; it's on the pricey side, but the food is of a "high standard". / E14 3WA; www.elephantroyale.com; 10.30 pm, Fri & Sat 11 pm, Sun 10 pm.

Elliot's Cafe SE1 £51 ❸④④
12 Stoney St 7403 7436 9–4C
"A welcome addition to Borough Market" – this "casual" café yearling wins much praise for its "inventive" and "seasonal" cooking, and its "welcoming style"; consistency can be an issue, though, and the odd "disappointing" meal is not unknown. / SE1 9AD; www.elliotscafe.com; @elliotscafe; 10 pm; closed Sun.

Emile's SW15 £44 ❸❷④
96-98 Felsham Rd 8789 3323 10–2B
"Tucked away" in a Putney back street, a "friendly" and "romantic" stalwart bistro, where the beef Wellington (in particular) is the stuff of local legend. / SW15 1DQ; www.emilesrestaurant.co.uk; 11 pm; D only, closed Sun; no Amex.

The Empress E9 £44 ❷❸❷
130 Lauriston Rd 8533 5123 1–2D
"A stone's throw from beautiful Victoria Park", this "atmospheric" boozer is one of East London's top gastropubs; the menu is divided into small plates and more standard options, and results are often "excellent". / E9 7LH; www.empresse9.co.uk; @elliottlidstone; 10 pm, Sun 9.30 pm; closed Mon L; no Amex.

Empress of Sichuan WC2 £36 ❷❸❷
6 Lisle St 7734 8128 4–3A
"Spicy treats in the heart of Chinatown!" – this "authentic" Sichuanese is well worth seeking out… assuming you like your dishes hot, of course. / WC2H 7BG; 11 pm; set weekday L £23 (FP).

The Engineer NW1 £58 ④④❸
65 Gloucester Ave 7722 0950 8–3B
"It's everything a gastropub should be", say devotees of this "lovely" Primrose Hill boozer, especially known for its "great garden"; since it changed hands a year or two ago, however, some reporters feel "it's not what it was". / NW1 8JH; www.the-engineer.com; 10.30 pm, Sun 10 pm; no Amex.

Enoteca Turi SW15 £56 ❷0❸
28 Putney High St 8785 4449 10–2B
The "rustic" cooking is eclipsed only by the "spellbinding" all-Italian wine list at Giuseppe and Pamela Turi's "hidden gem", near Putney Bridge – a "welcoming" stalwart, run in "convivial" family-run style. / SW15 1SQ; www.enotecaturi.com; 10.30 pm, Fri-Sat 11 pm; closed Sun.

The Enterprise SW3 £57 ④❸❷
35 Walton St 7584 3148 5–2C
The food is "never spectacular", but that does little to dent the appeal of this "long-term-favourite" Chelsea local – a "tightly-packed" but "fun" haunt that "appeals to all age-groups". / SW3 2HU; www.theenterprise.co.uk; 10 pm, Sat 10.30 pm; no booking, except weekday L; set weekday L £36 (FP).

Entrée SW11
£52　❸❷❷
2 Battersea Rise　7223 5147　10–2C
"A cracking little basement cocktail bar" adds life to this "small but well-conceived" Battersea venue – "a step up from other locals", with "cheerful" staff and an "interesting and varied" menu.
/ SW11 1ED; www.entreebattersea.co.uk/; 10.30 pm; closed weekday L.

Eriki NW3
£39　❷❸④
4-6 Northways Pde, Finchley Rd　7722 0606　8–2A
"The hidden gem of Swiss Cottage!" – this ambitious Indian serves an "interesting" menu of "fresh"-tasting, dishes of high quality; despite their best efforts on the décor front, however, the atmosphere "does not hum". / NW3 5EN; www.eriki.co.uk; 10.45 pm; closed Sat L.

Esarn Kheaw W12
£33　❷❸⑤
314 Uxbridge Rd　8743 8930　7–1B
"Authentic Esarn (North Eastern) Thai cuisine" has long been a feature of this family-run shop-conversion in Shepherd's Bush... but "don't go in search of atmosphere". / W12 7LJ; www.esarnkheaw.co.uk; @esarn_kheaw; 11 pm; closed Sat L & Sun L; no Amex.

L'Escargot W1
£59　❸❷❷
48 Greek St　7439 7474　4–2A
This Soho "classic" is certainly well suited to a "delightful set lunch", and it offers a "good-value pre-theatre menu" too; some reporters also tip it for romance or as a top foodie destination, but the volume of feedback of late has been surprisingly limited. / W1D 4EF; www.whitestarline.org.uk; 11.15 pm; closed Sat L & Sun; set pre theatre £36 (FP).

Essenza W11
£57　❸❸④
210 Kensington Park Rd　7792 1066　6–1A
A "casual" and "friendly" Notting Hill spot fans like for being "not quite as heaving as some other places" nearby; it offers "consistent" cooking, too, at prices that are "very reasonable, for the area". / W11 1NR; www.essenza.co.uk; 11.30 pm; set weekday L £36 (FP).

L'Etranger SW7
£69　❸④❸
36 Gloucester Rd　7584 1118　5–1B
"Very interesting French-Asian fusion cuisine" is twinned with "astonishing" (if "extraordinarily expensive") wine list at this "sexily lit" (but somewhat "subdued") South Kensington fixture. / SW7 4QT; www.etranger.co.uk; 11 pm, Sun 10 pm; set weekday L £38 (FP), set pre-theatre £42 (FP).

Euphorium Bakery N1
£13　❸④❸
26a Chapel Mkt　7837 7010　8–3D
"The antidote to high street coffee chains" – this "genuinely Continental" café/bakery offers "fine sarnies and cakes at fair prices". / N1 9EN; www.euphoriumbakery.com; 6.15 pm; L only; no Amex.

Everest Inn SE3
£34　❷❷❸
41 Montpelier Vale　8852 7872　1–4D
"Fresh", "innovative" and "big-flavoured" north Indian cuisine – with some "outstanding Nepalese dishes" – wins more-than-local applause for this "helpful and efficient" Blackheath fixture. / SE3 0TJ; www.everestinn.co.uk; midnight, Sun 11 pm.

Eyre Brothers EC2   **£57**   ❸❸❸
70 Leonard St   7613 5346   12–1B
A "sophisticated" Hispanic venture, which was launched long before
anyone ever called this area 'Silicon Roundabout'; it draws a steady
business following, but – thanks not least to its "expertly assembled"
wine list – arguably "deserves to be busier". / EC2A 4QX;
www.eyrebrothers.co.uk; 10 pm; closed Sat L & Sun.

Faanoos   **£27**   ❸④❸
472 Chiswick High Rd, W4   8994 4217   7–2A
481 Richmond Road, SW14   8878 5738   1–4A
"Amazing" flatbread, straight from the oven, is a highlight of dining
at these "accommodating" west London Persians – a top cheap 'n'
cheerful choice, where the cooking is "always fresh"; BYO. / SW14
11 pm; W4 11 pm; Fri & Sat midnight.

Fabrizio EC1   **£52**   ❷⓿⑤
30 Saint Cross St   7430 1503   9–1A
"Fabrizio the charming and genial patron keeps up high standards",
at this "unpretentious" trattoria, near Hatton Garden, which serves
up "comforting" and "unfussy" dishes ("like your Sicilian grandma
might make") at "top-value" prices. / EC1N 8UH;
www.fabriziorestaurant.co.uk; 10 pm; closed Sat L & Sun.

Fabrizio N19   **£31**   ❸❷④
34 Highgate Hill   7561 9073   8–1C
Fabrizio "is such a welcoming host", at this "no-frills" neighbourhood
Italian, "in the leafy environs of Highgate Hill"; it serves "delicious
and straightforward pizza and pasta". / N19 5NL.

Fairuz W1   **£49**   ❸❷❸
3 Blandford St   7486 8108   2–1A
"Possibly Marylebone's best-kept secret"; the Lebanese fare at this
popular spot is "a cut above", and "reasonably priced" too (especially
at lunch); the only real complaint? – some tables are a touch
"cramped". / W1H 3DA; www.fairuz.uk.com; 11 pm, Sun 10.30 pm.

La Famiglia SW10   **£60**   ④④❸
7 Langton St   7351 0761   5–3B
"Retaining some of its old magic", this long-established trattoria "all-
rounder" (with legendary garden) still pleases the faithful with its
"comfortable" charms; critics, though, say it's "overpriced, even for
Chelsea", and find standards "very average" nowadays. / SW10 0JL;
www.lafamiglia.co.uk; 11.45 pm.

Fat Boy's   **£34**   ④④❸
10a-10b Edensor Rd, W4   8994 8089   10–1A
33 Haven Grn, W5   8998 5868   1–2A
201 Upper Richmond Rd, SW14   8876 0644   1–4A
431 Richmond Rd, TW1   8892 7657   1–4A
68 High St, TW8   8569 8481   1–3A
A "reliable" chain of neighbourhood Thais, where the food's
"consistently good", if "not exciting". / www.fatboysthai.co.uk; 11 pm.

Faulkner's E8   **£29**   ❷④④
424-426 Kingsland Rd   7254 6152   1–1D
A long-standing Dalston chippy, still winning praise for its "wonderful,
traditional fried fish". / E8 4AA; 10 pm, Fri-Sun 11 pm; no Amex; need 8+
to book.

The Fellow N1 £45 ❸④④

24 York Way   7833 4395   8–3C

"Just around the corner from King's Cross", this "solid" gastropub is certainly "a boon for travellers", and in a still "pretty barren area"; "throw in the roof terrace, and you have to call it a hidden gem!" / N1 9AA; www.thefellow.co.uk; @24yorkway; 9.45pm.

The Fentiman Arms SW8 £46 ❸❸❷

64 Fentiman Rd   7793 9796   10–1D

One of the best of the Geronimo Inns, this "pleasant" Kennington gastroboozer is a notably consistent performer; it particularly benefits from its "great" garden (which offers an "excellent" summer BBQ). / SW8 1LA; www.geronimo-inns.co.uk; @fentmanarms; 10 pm, Sun 9 pm; SRA-60%.

Fernandez & Wells £33 ❸❸❷

16a, St Anne's Ct, W1   7494 4242   3–1D
43 Lexington St, W1   7734 1546   3–2D
73 Beak St, W1   7287 8124   3–2D
Somerset Hs, Strand, WC2   7420 9408   2–2D

"A brilliant little chain", whose artfully "scruffy" Soho origins are somewhat at odds with the "light and airy" branch in Somerset House; all are "bustling and fun", serving "outstanding coffee, sandwiches and cake", plus other "well-sourced" bites, and "interesting" wines. / www.fernandezandwells.com; Lexington St & St Anne's court 10 pm; Beak St 6 pm; Somerset House 11 pm; St Anne's Court closed Sun.

Fez Mangal W11 £22 ❶❷❸

104 Ladbroke Grove   7229 3010   6–1A

"Not fancy, but the food is excellent"; this "honest" Turkish charcoal grill, in Notting Hill, inspires impressively consistent reports; BYO. / W11 1PY; www.fezmangal.co.uk; 11.30 pm; no Amex.

Ffiona's W8 £53 ④❸❸

51 Kensington Church St   7937 4152   5–1A

Fiona presides with aplomb over this "dinner-party-like" Kensington bistro veteran, where the food is "relatively simple" but "consistent", and "a great night out is guaranteed"; recent innovation – a "fab" brunch. / W8 4BA; www.ffionas.com; @ffionasnotes; 11 pm, Sun 10 pm; closed Mon; no Amex.

Fifteen N1 £61

15 Westland Pl   3375 1515   12–1A

Jamie's philanthropic Hoxton bistro may do its trainees a favour, but the poor old punters have been paying through the nose for its often "unattractive" and "poorly cooked" dishes; the first report of the spring 2013 relaunch, however, relates "improvements all round" – about time! / N1 7LP; www.fifteen.net; 10 pm; booking: max 12.

The Fifth Floor Restaurant
Harvey Nichols SW1 £57 ❸❸❸

109-125 Knightsbridge   7235 5250   5–1D

It's surprising the way this late-'90s-hotspot, up above Knightsbridge, has faded from view in recent times... especially as the very modest feedback it inspires is all positive, praising an airy "oasis", with "surprisingly good food and service", and an "exceptional" wine list. / SW1X 7RJ; www.harveynichols.com; 10.45 pm; closed Sun D; SRA-63%.

La Figa E14 £40 ❸②④
45 Narrow St 7790 0077 11–1B
"Family-friendly and often packed", this long-established Limehouse
Italian has a big name for "generous portions" and "great value" –
"worth a detour!" / E14 8DN; www.lafigarestaurant.co.uk; 11 pm,
Sun 10.30 pm.

Fino W1 £49 ❸❸❸
33 Charlotte St 7813 8010 2–1C
"A modern take on classic tapas" has helped win major popularity for
the Hart brothers' "hidden-away" and "classy" Fitzrovia basement;
is it "stuck in a bit of a rut", though? – there's a feeling "it's not
as good as it was", and "bills are quite high". / W1T 1RR;
www.finorestaurant.com; 10.30 pm; closed Sat L & Sun; booking: max 12.

Fire & Stone £41 ④④④
31-32 Maiden Ln, WC2 08443 712550 4–3D
Westfield, Ariel Way, W12 0844 371 2551 7–1C
4 Horner Sq, E1 0844 371 2554 12–2B
A "different spin on pizzas" ("some quite inspiring") – and at
"reasonable prices" too – wins fans for these large and "hectic" chain
outlets; "if you have to eat at Westfield, this may be one of the better
choices". / www.fireandstone.com; WC2 11 pm; W12 11.15 pm; E1 11pm,
Sun 8 pm.

First Floor W11 £46 ❸④❶
186 Portobello Rd 7243 0072 6–1A
As a "superb venue for a party", this high-ceilinged Portobello fixture,
with its sense of "faded grandeur", is ideal; it's a romantic spot too,
and the food is never less than "dependable". / W11 1LA;
www.firstfloorportobello.co.uk; 10.30 pm.

The Fish & Chip Shop N1 NEW £43 ❶②②
189 Upper St 3227 0979 8–2D
"A new stand-out in an area spoilt for choice!"; this "lovely"
newcomer – run by the ex-supremo of the Caprice group –
is "everything you want from a fish 'n' chip shop", and its "brilliant"
food includes some "nostalgic" puds. / N1 1RQ;
www.thefishandchipshop.uk.com; 11 pm, Sun 10 pm.

Fish Central EC1 £29 ❸②④
149-155 Central St 7253 4970 12–1A
"Unbeatable value and flavour" draw many fish 'n' chip fans to this
"busy" but "welcoming" spot, 'twixt Old Street and Islington.
/ EC1V 8AP; www.fishcentral.co.uk; 10.30 pm, Fri & Sat 11 pm; closed Sun.

Fish Club £38 ②②④
189 St John's Hill, SW11 7978 7115 10–2C
57 Clapham High St, SW4 7720 5853 10–2D
"Fish 'n' chips as they should be", served battered or grilled –
plus oysters, fish pie, sweet potato wedges and so on – win all-round
praise for these "upmarket" south London chippies.
/ www.thefishclub.com; 10 pm; closed Mon L; no bookings.

Fish in a Tie SW11 £36 ④②②
105 Falcon Rd 7924 1913 10–1C
"Always reliable and budget-friendly", this super-inexpensive bistro,
tucked away behind Clapham Junction, offers "really good food";
it's invariably "full and lively". / SW11 2PF; www.fishinatie.co.uk; midnight,
Sun 11 pm; no Amex; set always available £20 (FP).

Fish Market EC2 £53 ❸❷❸
16 New St 3503 0790 9–2D
A "businessy" D&D group yearling, near Liverpool Street; it's been instantly hailed as a handy set-up offering "simple" but "expertly-cooked" fish. / EC2M 4TR.

fish! SE1 £54 ④④❸
Cathedral St 7407 3803 9–4C
This striking all-glass brasserie, by Borough Market, can seem "a victim of its own success" – the fish can be "excellent", but the overall experience often seems "a bit pricey for what it is", especially when it's so "crammed-in". / SE1 9AL; www.fishkitchen.com; @fishborough; 10.45 pm, Sun 10.30 pm.

Fishworks £50 ❸④④
7-9 Swallow St, W1 7734 5813 3–3D
89 Marylebone High St, W1 7935 9796 2–1A
"It's a little formulaic, but for all that you get good fish" – and a "wonderful selection" too – at these low-key fishmongers-cum-restaurants, in Mayfair and Marylebone (and also Richmond). / www.fishworks.co.uk; 10.30 pm.

Fitou's Thai Restaurant W10 £26 ❷❸④
1 Dalgarno Gdns 8968 0558 6–1A
"A hidden neighbourhood gem"; this "great-value" BYO café, by Little Wormwood Scrubs, serves Thai scoff of "very good quality". / W10 5LL; www.fitourestaurant.co.uk; 10.30 pm; closed Sun L.

The Five Fields SW3 NEW £70 ❷❶❷
8-9 Blacklands Ter 7838 1082 5–2D
"The most assured new opening" of recent times, say fans – this Chelsea newcomer (on the site of El Blason, RIP) is "a great addition to the London scene" is "a beautiful" (if quite tightly-packed) and service "attentive"; ex-NYC chef Taylor Bonnyman's "very interesting" dishes deliver some "mind-blowing" flavours too. / SW3 2SP; www.fivefieldsrestaurant.com; @The5Fields; 10.30 pm.

Five Guys WC2 NEW £13
1-3 Long Acre 0833 005 4–3C
This major US burger chain recently established its first European bridgehead in Covent Garden; it caused much excitement on opening, but we'll look forward to next year's survey to see what people really think of it. / WC2E 9LH; www.fiveguys.co.uk.

500 N19 £44 ❸❸④
782 Holloway Rd 7272 3406 8–1C
An Archway phenomenon, this "fabulous family-run place" has made a big name for its "genuine" Sicilian cooking; it still attracts much praise, not least for its "sensible prices", but quite a few reporters this year found it "failed to deliver". / N19 3JH; www.500restaurant.co.uk; 10.30 pm, Sunday 9.30 pm; Mon-Thu D only, Fri-Sun open L & D.

The Flask N6 £43 ④④❷
77 Highgate West Hill 8348 7346 1–1C
A "lovely" (and extensive) ancient inn, in Highgate, most recommended as "a cracking place for Sunday lunch". / N6 6BU; www.theflaskhighgate.com; @flaskn6; 10 pm, Sun 9 pm.

Flat Iron W1 NEW £22 ❸❷❷
17 Beak St   no tel   3–2D
"Simple" and "straightforward", this steak-for-a-tenner newcomer offers "serious value, by the standards of Soho's often overpriced no-bookings eateries"; "squeezing onto benches" at communal tables doesn't seem to be a problem. / W1F 9RW; www.flatironsteak.co.uk; @flatironsteak.

Flat White W1 £11 ❷❷❷
17 Berwick St   7734 0370   3–2D
"The granddaddy of Antipodean coffee shops"; this Soho fixture "still packs the smoothest, creamiest coffee punch", and "the breakfasts are delicious too". / W1F 0PT; www.flat-white.co.uk; L only; no credit cards; no booking.

Fleet River Bakery WC2 £20 ❷❹❸
71 Lincolns Inn Fields   7691 1457   2–1D
"In a side alley near Holborn tube", an "original" and "delightful" café, where the menu offers not just delectable cakes, but other "interesting" dishes, as well as "expert" coffee; beware queuing at peak times, though, and service which can be "very slow". / WC2A 3JF; www.fleetriverbakery.com; 5 pm, Sat 3 pm; L only, closed Sun.

Flesh and Buns WC2 NEW £50
41 Earlham St   7632 9500   4–2C
A new izakaya (informal Japanese) restaurant, in a Covent Garden basement, from the team behind Soho's trendy Bone Daddies; early press reviews have been very positive. / WC2H 9LX; www.fleshandbuns.com.

Florence SE24 £41 ❹❹❷
131-133 Dulwich Rd   7326 4987   10–2D
"If you don't have kids, you may wish to stay away", but if you do, this "very child-friendly" Brockwell Park boozer may seem like a gift from the gods, "standard pub fare" notwithstanding. / SE24 0NG; www.florencehernehill.com; @theflorencepub; 10 pm, Sun 9.30 pm.

Food for Thought WC2 £23 ❸❸❹
31 Neal St   7836 0239   4–2C
A dear old basement veggie in Covent Garden which, for its many loyal fans, remains "a unique and amazing centrally-located gem"… "basic" presentation, "harassed" staff and "overcrowding" are all just part of the formula; BYO. / WC2H 9PR; www.foodforthought-london.co.uk; 8 pm, Sun 5 pm; closed Sun D; no credit cards; no booking; set always available £15 (FP).

Forman's E3 £54 ❷❸❹
Stour Rd, Fish Island   8525 2365   1–1D
The "light and airy" canalside dining room of London's sole salmon-smokery – with its "amazing views" of the Olympic Stadium – makes "a good spot... once you find it", and the "best-of-British" cuisine can be "surprisingly imaginative" too. / E3 2NH; www.formans.co.uk; 9 pm; Closed Mon-Wed, Thu & Fri D only, Sat open L & D, closed Sun D.

**Formosa Dining Room
The Prince Alfred W9** £49 ❹❹❸
5a Formosa St   7286 3287   6–1C
"Handily attached to a great pub" (one of London's most imposing), this Maida Vale dining room is a "solid" sort of destination, that's often "busy"; "the specials tend to be good". / W9 1EE; www.theprincealfred.com; @theprincealfred; 10 pm, Fri & Sat 11 pm; Sun 9 pm; no Amex; set weekday L £33 (FP).

(1707)
Fortnum & Mason W1 £45 ❸❷❸
181 Piccadilly 7734 8040 3–3D
"Browse the whole of the Fortnum's list, at cost plus £10 corkage" –
that's the unbeatable (for the West End) proposition that makes this
basement wine bar especially worth seeking out; "tapas-style snacks
and platters" too. / W1A 1ER; www.fortnumandmason.co.uk;
@fortnumandmason; 8 pm, Sun 6 pm; closed Sun D.

(The Diamond Jubilee Tea Salon)
Fortnum & Mason W1 £50 ❸❶❶
181 Piccadilly 7734 8040 3–3D
"A splendid venue for a sumptuous afternoon tea" – this "light, airy,
spacious and very comfortable dining room" is proving a tremendous
addition to the store…"fresher and more serene" than the nearby
Ritz! / W1A 1ER; www.fortnumandmason.com.

(The Fountain)
Fortnum & Mason W1 £62 ❹❸❸
181 Piccadilly 7734 8040 3–3D
"Definitely a place to take your favourite aunt" – the buttery of the
Queen's grocer remains "a beautiful oasis of calm and manners"
(if one with "prices to match the location"); the menu offers "choice
in abundance" too, with the top option being the "spectacular Full
English breakfast". / W1A 1ER; www.fortnumandmason.com;
@fortnumandmason; 7.45 pm; closed Sun D.

Fortune Cookie W2 £28 ❷❹❺
1 Queensway 7727 7260 6–2C
Right by Queensway tube, a "good old-reliable", where an "authentic
Cantonese fix" can be had at "reasonable prices". / W2 4QJ; 11 pm.

40 Maltby Street SE1 £40 ❷❸❸
40 Maltby St 7237 9247 9–4D
"Basic, but totally cool", this wine bar – located "under the arches"
of "the 'new' Borough Market" – offers "excellent" tapas-style dishes,
complemented by "adventurous" natural wines that are "always
interesting". / SE1 3PA; www.40maltbystreet.com; 9.30 pm; closed Mon,
Tue, Wed L, Thu L, Sat D & Sun; no Amex; no bookings.

Four Regions TW9 £43 ❸❷❹
102-104 Kew Rd 8940 9044 1–4A
"The local Chinese everyone dreams of!" – a Richmond mainstay,
which owes its enduring popularity to its "enjoyable" cooking, and the
often "excellent" service. / TW9 2PQ; 11.30 pm, Sun 11 pm.

The Four Seasons £31 ❷❺❺
12 Gerrard St, W1 7494 0870 4–3A
23 Wardour St, W1 7287 9995 4–3A
84 Queensway, W2 7229 4320 6–2C
"The best roast duck this side of Beijing" is the headline attraction
at this "ridiculously inexpensive" Bayswater fixture; the Chinatown
outpost is equally "great, rough and ready". / www.fs-restaurants.co.uk;
Queensway 11 pm, Sun 10h45 pm; Gerrard St 1 am; Wardour St 1am, Fri-Sat
3.30 am.

Fox & Grapes SW19   £55   ④④❸
9 Camp Rd   8619 1300   10–2A
*Claude Bosi's pub certainly has a "good location", right
by Wimbledon Common, and fans say its "imaginative" cooking has
made it "a great additional" locally; it takes a lot of flak too, however,
for a menu that's "dull" and "vastly overpriced". / SW19 4UN;
foxandgrapeswimbledon.co.uk; 9.30 pm, Sun 8.15 pm; no Amex.*

The Fox & Hounds SW11   £47   ❷❷❷
66 Latchmere Rd   7924 5483   10–1C
*A "really friendly" Battersea gastroboozer, where most reporters find
the food – with its "definite Mediterranean theme" – "never fails
to deliver". / SW11 2JU; www.thefoxandhoundspub.co.uk; @thefoxbattersea;
10 pm; Mon-Thu D only, Fri-Sun open L & D.*

The Fox and Anchor EC1   £49   ❷❷❶
115 Charterhouse St   7250 1300   9–1B
*A marvellously "cosy" and "historic" inn, "tucked away"
in Clerkenwell, where British dishes are executed with a "creativity
and lightness of touch rarely found"; breakfast is a famous highlight –
"a full cholesterol fry-up washed down with a pint of Guinness".
/ EC1M 6AA; www.foxandanchor.com; @MeetMeAtTheFox; 9.30 pm.*

Foxlow EC1 NEW   £48
St John St   awaiting tel   9–2A
*On the former Clerkenwell site of North Road (RIP),
the latest outpost of the – now venture-capitalist-backed –
Hawksmoor steakhouse empire opens in late 2013. / EC1;
www.foxlow.co.uk.*

Foxtrot Oscar SW3   £55   ④④⑤
79 Royal Hospital Rd   7352 4448   5–3D
*Perhaps the most eloquent commentary on the Chelsea bistro, just a
few doors from Ramsay HQ and nowadays owned by him, is the
scant survey feedback it inspires – such as there is suggests a visit
is a "very flat" experience. / SW3 4HN;
www.gordonramsay.com/foxtrotoscar/; 10 pm, Sun 9 pm.*

Franco Manca   £22   ❷❸❸
144 Chiswick High Rd, W4   8747 4822   7–2A
76 Northcote Rd, SW11   7924 3110   10–2D
Unit 4 Market Row, SW9   7738 3021   10–2D
Westfield Stratford, E20   8522 6669   1–1D
*Thanks to their "awesome" sourdough crusts, and their "beautiful
toppings", these "really Neapolitan" pizza stops (SW9 in particular)
are hailed as "the best in the country"; as the venture-capital-backed
roll-out gathers pace, however, ratings are beginning to go just a little
bit soggy. / www.francomanca.co.uk; SW9 10.30, Mon 5 pm; W4 11 pm;
E20 9 pm, Thu-Sat 10 pm, Sun 6 pm; SW9 no bookings.*

Franco's SW1   £74   ❸❸❸
61 Jermyn St   7499 2211   3–3C
*A "lush" St James's Italian, under the same ownership as nearby
Wilton's, which has been inspiring impressively consistent reports
of late; its "well-spaced" tables make it a handy business destination,
if not a bargain one. / SW1Y 6LX; www.francoslondon.com; 10.30 pm;
closed Sun; set weekday L £38 (FP).*

Franklins SE22 £49 ❸④❸
157 Lordship Ln 8299 9598 1–4D
"A local institution", down East Dulwich way – this "comfortable" pub-conversion wins praise for an "interesting" menu (especially for carnivores); it does have the odd critic, though, who says "it's never quite as good as it thinks it is". / SE22 8HX; www.franklinsrestaurant.com; @frankinsse22; 10.30 pm; no Amex; set weekday L £30 (FP).

Frantoio SW10 £57 ④❷❷
397 King's Rd 7352 4146 5–3B
"More like a club", this very "local"-feeling World's End Italian is a "welcoming" sort of place offering "genuine" food at "reasonable" prices; "more menu variety", however, might not go amiss. / SW10 0LR; www.frantoio.com; 11.15 pm, Sun 10.15 pm.

Frederick's N1 £62 ❸❷❷
106 Islington High St 7359 2888 8–3D
Critics may still find the food "more reliable than exciting", and prices "somewhat inflated", but this (surprisingly) grand and "charming" Islington veteran is "as popular as ever"; the conservatory is undoubtedly a "special venue". / N1 8EG; www.fredericks.co.uk; 11 pm; closed Sun; set weekday L & pre-theatre £37 (FP).

Freemasons Arms NW3 £41 ⑤⑤④
32 Downshire Hill 7433 6811 8–2A
This Hampstead Heath-side boozer looks "promising", but it "relies too much on its location" – too often the food's "nondescript" and "overpriced", and service can be "abominable". / NW3 1NT; www.freemasonsarms.co.uk; @Freemasons_Arms; 11 pm, Sat 10.30 pm, Sun 10.30 pm.

Frizzante at City Farm
Hackney City Farm E2 £31 ❷④④
1a Goldsmiths Row 7729 6381 12–1D
"Restaurant-standard food in a ramshackle school classroom, or at least that's what it feels like!" – this family-friendly spot, between Columbia Road and Broadway Market, remains particularly popular as a breakfast destination. / E2 8QA; www.frizzanteltd.co.uk; @frizzanteltd; D only, closed Mon; no Amex.

Frizzante Cafe
Surrey Docks Farm SE16 £34 ❸❷❸
South Whf, Rotherhithe St 7231 1010 11–2B
The "very friendly" café of this Thames-side farm, in deepest Rotherhithe, has a "tolerance for kids" which makes it a natural weekend destination... most particularly for a brunch using "tasty organic produce". / SE16 5ET; www.frizzanteltd.co.uk; 4.30 pm; closed Mon, Tue-Sun D; no Amex.

La Fromagerie Café W1 £38 ❷④❷
2-6 Moxon St 7935 0341 3–1A
"Much improved, now it's bigger"; the café of the famous Marylebone cheese shop offers "interesting" light bites – "everything tastes deliciously fresh, and of itself!" / W1U 4EW; www.lafromagerie.co.uk; @lafromagerieuk; 6.30 pm, Sat 6 pm, Sun 5 pm; L only; no booking.

The Frontline Club W2 £54 ❸④❸
13 Norfolk Pl 7479 8960 6–1D
"Eclectic dishes, cooked well" and an "unusual, great-value wine list" win consistent praise for this professional dining room "on Paddington's doorstep"; it's part of a club for war-reporters, and the photography on display is often "very striking". / W2 1QJ; www.frontlineclub.com; 10.30 pm; closed Sat L & Sun; set weekday L £34 (FP).

Fryer's Delight WC1 £13 ❸④⑤
19 Theobald's Rd   7405 4114   2–1D
This "greasy-spoon-type" Bloomsbury chippy may be "scrappy-looking", but it certainly inspires loyalty – "I have a visitor from NYC, in his 70s, who always insists we go: it's his corner of England, serving fish 'n' chips as he remembers it from 50 years ago!"; BYO.
/ WC1X 8SL; 10.30 pm; closed Sun; no credit cards.

Fujiyama SW9 £28 ❸④④
5-7 Vining St   7737 2369   10–2D
"Better than Wagamama!"; though it's "overshadowed by the trendy new places" down Brixton way, this cheap 'n' cheerful Japanese canteen remains a "very solid option". / SW9 8QA; www.newfujiyama.com; 11 pm.

Fulham Wine Rooms SW6 £52 ❸❸❸
871-873 Fulham Rd   7042 9440   10–1B
It's sometimes "too busy", but this contemporary-style wine bar pleases most reporters with its interesting vintages from "atmosphere-controlled cabinets"; the food's not bad, and there's a pleasant terrace too. / SW6 5HP; www.greatwinesbytheglass.com; 11 pm.

Fuzzy's Grub £14 ❸④④
6 Crown Pas, SW1   7925 2791   3–4D
10 Well Ct, EC4   7236 8400   9–2B
62 Fleet St, EC4   7583 6060   9–2A
Curious that these British-themed diners haven't caught on more; they offer "a good deal" – especially for a "top breakfast" – and their generous sandwiches (packed with quality, traditional roast meats) are in a style that's currently rather à la mode. / www.fuzzysgrub.co.uk; most branches between 3 pm and 5 pm; closed Sat & Sun; no Amex; no booking.

Gaby's WC2 £34 ❸❸④
30 Charing Cross Rd   7836 4233   4–3B
"Holding out against the chains and redevelopers of the West End!" – this grungy deli, by Leicester Square tube, has won a stay of execution from its landlords; still time, then, to enjoy "the best falafel and salt beef"! / WC2H 0DE; midnight, Sun 10 pm; no Amex.

Gail's Bread £27 ④④❸
138 Portobello Rd, W11   7460 0766   6–1B
282 Chiswick High Rd, W4   8995 2266   7–2A
64 Hampstead High St, NW3   7794 5700   8–1A
5 Circus Rd, NW8   7722 0983   8–3A
64 Northcote Rd, SW11   7924 6330   10–2C
33-35 Exmouth Mkt, EC1   7713 6550   9–1A
"You can't fault Gail's for its great bread, coffee, cakes and take-out salads" – it may be "noisy" and a bit "chaotic", but a visit to this upmarket café/bakery chain rarely disappoints. / www.gailsbread.co.uk; W11 & WC1 7 pm; NW3 & NW6 8 pm, W1 10 pm, SW7 9 pm, Sun 8 pm; no booking.

Galicia W10 £39 ❸❸❷
323 Portobello Rd   8969 3539   6–1A
Surprisingly little survey comment on this age-old North Kensington tapas bar – all tends to confirm, though, that it remains a "great local". / W10 5SY; 11.15 pm; closed Mon.

Gallery Mess
Saatchi Gallery SW3   £51   ④④④
Duke of Yorks HQ, Kings Rd   7730 8135   5–2D
Near Sloane Square, and with many tables al fresco, this large café
attached to the gallery certainly has a "great" location; no huge
surprise, then, that the food can be "uninspired", and service "slow"
– "a decent bet, but it could aim a bit higher". / SW3 4RY;
www.saatchigallery.com/gallerymess; @gallerymess; 9.30 pm, Sun 6.30 pm;
closed Sun D.

Gallipoli   £35   ④❷❸
102 Upper St, N1   7359 0630   8–3D
107 Upper St, N1   7226 5333   8–3D
120 Upper St, N1   7226 8099   8–3D
"For a buzzy cheap eat", it's hard to beat these "basic" but brilliant
Turkish bistros, in the heart of Islington. / www.cafegallipoli.com; 11 pm,
Fri & Sat midnight.

Galvin at Windows
Park Lane London Hilton Hotel W1   £93   ④❸❶
22 Park Ln   7208 4021   3–4A
"Talk about a room with a view!" – the Galvins' 28th-floor Mayfair
eyrie boasts the most "amazing panorama"; away from the windows,
though, the ambience can fall flat, making the prices of the "good but
unremarkable" cuisine hard to stomach. / W1K 1BE;
www.galvinatwindows.com; 10.30 pm, Thu-Sat 11 pm; closed Sat L & Sun D;
no shorts; set weekday L £49 (FP).

GALVIN BISTROT DE LUXE W1   £63   ❷❷❷
66 Baker St   7935 4007   2–1A
"A very slick and dependable operation"; the original Marylebone
Galvin "has all the virtues of a good Parisian bistro, with a few British
ones thrown in" – "excellent-value" cuisine, "unobtrusive" service and
a "convivial" (if slightly "formal") setting. / W1U 7DJ;
www.galvinrestaurants.com; @galvin_brothers; Mon-Wed 10.30 pm, Thu-Sat
10.45 pm, Sun 9.30 pm; set weekday L £37 (FP), set pre-theatre £39 (FP), set
Sun L £48 (FP).

GALVIN LA CHAPELLE E1   £74   ❷❷❶
35 Spital Sq   7299 0400   12–2B
"Stunning food in a stunning location" makes for a "superb
experience" at the Galvin brothers' cathedral-like dining hall,
by Spitalfields Market – a "courteous" operation, with cuisine that's
"modern enough to be interesting, but classic enough to be
uncontentious". / E1 6DY; www.galvinrestaurants.com; 10.30 pm,
Sun 9.30 pm; set weekday L & pre-theatre £49 (FP).

Ganapati SE15   £43   ❶❶❷
38 Holly Grove   7277 2928   1–4C
"Consistently superior to flashy Indians you find in the West End!" –
with its "divine" Keralan cooking, this "unassuming" diner is held out
as "Peckham's claim to being a dining destination"; it's a "fun" and
"chilled" experience too. / SE15 5DF; www.ganapatirestaurant.com;
10.30 pm, Sun 10 pm; closed Mon; no Amex.

Gandhi's SE11   £28   ❸④❸
347 Kennington Rd   7735 9015   1–3C
"Popular with the locals, so book ahead" – this old-school Kennington
Indian may offer an "unchanging" menu, but it's realised to an
"above-average" standard. / SE11 4QE; www.gandhis.co.uk; 11.30 pm.

Garnier SW5 £55 ❸❷④
314 Earl's Court Rd   7370 4536   5–2A
"A most welcome addition to Earl's Court" – the Garnier brothers'
local restaurant serves "the sort of simple, classic French food you
can't get in France any more", and with aplomb; it does, however,
"lack the ambience" of its sibling, Le Colombier. / SW5 9BQ; Mon-Sat
10.30 pm, Sun 10 pm; set Sun L £43 (FP).

Le Garrick WC2 £41 ④④❸
10-12 Garrick St   7240 7649   4–3C
A "pleasant" Covent Garden fixture with a decidedly "quaint" lay-out;
its "classic" French staples are on the "predictable" side of "solid".
/ WC2E 9BH; www.garrickrestaurantbar.co.uk; @le_garrick; 10.30 pm;
closed Sun.

Garrison SE1 £48 ❸❸❷
99-101 Bermondsey St   7089 9355   9–4D
A "very busy" Bermondsey gastroboozer, with a "lovely interior" and
a "great vibe"; the food in general is "very decent", with the
"dependable" brunch a particular highlight. / SE1 3XB;
www.thegarrison.co.uk; 10 pm, Fri-Sat 10.30 pm, Sun 9.30 pm.

Garufa N5 £48 ❷④❸
104 Highbury Pk   7226 0070   8–1D
"Marvellous for meat-lovers!" – "terrific" steaks and "the best" chips
are what this Argentinian grill, near the Emirates Stadium, is all
about. / N5 2XE; www.garufa.co.uk; @GarufaLondon; 10.30 pm; no Amex.

Garufin WC1 NEW £48 ❸❷❸
8b, Lamb's Conduit Pas   7430 9073   2–1D
Just south (NB) of Holborn, a "scruffy" but "very friendly" new
basement operation, offering "Argentinian comfort food" and
a "cracking" wine list to go with it; we enjoyed our visit, but reports
are a bit up-and-down. / WC1R 4RH; 10.30 pm; closed Sun.

Gastro SW4 £42 ④④❷
67 Venn St   7627 0222   10–2D
"Toujours français!"; for authenticity alone, this "stalwart" café/bistro,
by the Clapham Picture House, is hard to beat; service this year,
though, has seemed less stereotypically Gallic. / SW4 0BD; midnight;
no Amex.

The Gate £43 ❸④④
51 Queen Caroline St, W6   8748 6932   7–2C
370 St John St, EC1   7278 5483   8–3D
"A welcome addition to Islington" – the new N1 branch of this veggie
duo wins praise for its "calm" style and "fresh and interesting"
cooking; it's not yet as highly rated as the stellar Hammersmith
original, however (reopening, after a major refurb, in late-2013).
/ www.thegaterestaurants.com; @gaterestaurant; EC1 10.30 pm, W6 10.30,
Sat 11 pm.

Gaucho £70 ❸④④

25 Swallow St, W1   7734 4040   3–3D
60a, Charlotte St, W1   7580 6252   2–1C
125 Chancery Ln, WC2   7242 7727   2–2D
89 Sloane Ave, SW3   7584 9901   5–2C
64 Heath St, NW3   7431 8222   8–1A
02 Centre, Peninsular Sq, SE10   8858 7711   11–2D
Tooley St, SE1   7407 5222   9–4D
Tow Path, TW10   8948 4030   1–4A
29 Westferry Circus, E14   7987 9494   11–1B
93a Charterhouse St, EC1   7490 1676   9–1B
5 Finsbury Ave, Broadgate, EC2   7256 6877   12–2B
1 Bell Inn Yd, EC3   7626 5180   9–2C

"Good, but at a price…"; this "slick" and "funky" chain is still a "winner" for a business rendezvous (and has "the best Argentinian wine list in London" too); in an ever more competitive steakhouse world however, it risks seeming "overpriced", especially as standards seem "increasingly patchy". / www.gauchorestaurants.co.uk; 11 pm, Fri & Sat 11.30 pm, SE10, Piccadilly midnight, Sun 11 pm; EC3 & EC1 closed Sat & Sun; WC2 & EC2 closed Sat L & Sun.

Gauthier Soho W1 £63 ❶❶❷

21 Romilly St   7494 3111   4–3A

Alexis Gauthier's "inspired" modern French cuisine goes from strength to strength, at his "quirky" and "faultlessly charming" Soho townhouse (where "ringing the door to get in adds novelty"); "I can't understand why they lost their Michelin star!" / W1D 5AF; www.gauthiersoho.co.uk; 10.30 pm; closed Mon L & Sun; set weekday L £46 (FP); SRA-52%.

LE GAVROCHE W1 £131 ❶❶❷

43 Upper Brook St   7408 0881   3–2A

"As relevant today as it ever was!" – M Roux Jr's "timeless classic", in Mayfair, won this year's vote as "London's finest gastronomic experience"; "the bill's stratospheric, but so's the performance!", with "sublime" Gallic cuisine and magisterial "old school" service; "unbelievably good" set lunch (book months ahead). / W1K 7QR; www.le-gavroche.co.uk; 11 pm; closed Sat L & Sun; jacket required; set weekday L £59 (FP).

Gay Hussar W1 £47 ④❸❷

2 Greek St   7437 0973   4–2A

The "snug" and "unchanging" charms of this "iconic" (socialist) haunt make it, for diehard fans, "Soho's best restaurant" – the "old-fashioned" Hungarian fodder is "not wonderful, but who cares?" / W1D 4NB; www.gayhussar.co.uk; 10.45 pm; closed Sun.

Gaylord W1 £50 ❸❸④

79-81 Mortimer St   7580 3615   2–1B

A grand old Indian, just north of Oxford Street – the food is "delicious", but critics can find prices "startling". / W1W 7SJ; www.gaylordlondon.com; 10.45 pm, Sun 10.30 pm; no Amex.

Gazette £38 ④④❷

79 Sherwood Ct, Chatfield Rd, SW11   7223 0999   10–1C
100 Balham High St, SW12   8772 1232   10–2C

"Very good food" plus "typically Gallic service" – that's the formula that's made quite a hit of these "good-value" Balham and Battersea brasseries. / www.gazettebrasserie.co.uk; 11 pm.

Geales £47 ④④④
1 Cale St, SW3   7965 0555   5–2C
2 Farmer St, W8   7727 7528   6–2B
A tale of two (upmarket) chippies – reports from the heart-of-Chelsea branch suggest a "chaotic" performance of late, while the original, off Notting Hill Gate, continues on its usual dependable course.
/ www.geales.com; @geales1; 10.30 pm, Sun 9.30 pm; Mon L.

Gelupo W1 £10 ❶❷❸
7 Archer St   7287 5555   3–2D
"Exquisite" ices – "from far-out flavours to classics" – are on offer at this "simply fabulous" gelateria, tucked-away in Soho, opposite Bocca di Lupo (same owners). / W1D 7AU; www.gelupo.com; 11 pm, Fri & Sat 12.30 am; no Amex; no booking.

Gem N1 £30 ❸❷❸
265 Upper St   7359 0405   8–2D
"Mezze are particularly good" (and there are some "excellent" Kurdish grill dishes on offer too), at this "low-key" bolthole – an "always-reliable" Islington "staple". / N1 2UQ; www.gemrestaurant.org.uk; 11 pm, Fri-Sat midnight, Sun 10.30 pm; no Amex.

La Genova W1 £59 ④④④
32 North Audley St   7629 5916   3–2A
This "shamelessly retro" Mayfair Italian is one of a dying breed; it doesn't please everyone, but fans praise its "comfortable" virtues. / W1K 6ZG; www.lagenovarestaurant.com; 11 pm; closed Sun.

George & Vulture EC3 £48 ④❸❷
3 Castle Ct   7626 9710   9–3C
An "old-style City place" – yes, it really is in Dickens – which sells itself "on not having been updated"; "go for the experience, not the food!" / EC3V 9DL; 2.45 pm; L only, closed Sat & Sun.

The Giaconda Dining Rooms WC2 £51 ❸❷④
9 Denmark St   7240 3334   4–1A
The relaunch of this "friendly" bistro, in the shadow of Centre Point, has proved a mixed blessing; fans say its looks are "improved", and that it offers "adventurous" cooking that's "as good as ever" – others feel that it's "lost its way". / WC2H 8LS; www.giacondadining.com; @giacondadining; 9.15 pm; closed Sat L & Sun.

Gifto's Lahore Karahi UB1 £18 ❷❸④
162-164 The Broadway   8813 8669   1–3A
A "buzzy, Formica-top delight" – this popular Southall diner draws in the weekend crowds with its "excellent range" of "delicious" dishes, particularly meat, at "very good prices". / UB1 1NN; www.gifto.com; 11.30 pm, Sat-Sun midnight.

Gilak N19 £35 ❸❷④
663 Holloway Rd   7272 1692   8–1C
"Huge and incredibly fresh salads", followed by "interesting stews and kebabs, loaded with herbs" – that's the sort of meal you might enjoy at this "courteous and efficient" Archway gem, specialising in the cuisine of Northern Iran. / N19 5SE; www.gilakrestaurant.co.uk; @Gilakrestaurant; 11 pm; no Amex.

Gilbert Scott
St Pancras Renaissance NW1 £61 ④④❷

Euston Rd   7278 3888   8–3C

A "glorious" neo-Gothic setting is the backdrop to Marcus Wareing's airy (but tightly-packed) St Pancras dining room; fans applaud its "superb" British cuisine too, but service is "mixed", and for a large minority of sceptics the food is "underwhelming" or "poor value". / NW1 2AR; www.thegilbertscott.co.uk; @Thegilbertscott; 10.45 pm.

Gilgamesh NW1 £70 ❸❸❷

The Stables, Camden Mkt, Chalk Farm Rd   7428 4922   8–3B

"A bit like visiting an Asian leisure park attraction in Blackpool"; this gigantic Camden Town venue, with ultra-lavish wood-carved decor, doesn't attract a huge amount of feedback, but its pan-Asian cuisine is surprisingly well-rated – worth a go "for a special occasion". / NW1 8AH; www.gilgameshbar.com; 11 pm, Fri-Sat 11.30 pm.

Gin Joint EC2 NEW £50

Barbican Centre, Silk St   7588 3008   12–2A

Opening as this guide was going to press, Searcy's have rebranded their former Brasserie (RIP) within the Barbican, with this hipper concept, where the food comes on small plates, and the drinks list is themed around mother's ruin. / EC2Y 8DS; www.searcys.co.uk/venues/gin-joint.

Ginger & White £17 ❸❷❷

2 England's Ln, NW3   7722 9944   8–2A
4a-5a, Perrins Ct, NW3   7431 9098   8–2A

A brunch-friendly duo of cafés in Hampstead and Belsize Park; they offer "tempting cakes and great coffee" too. / www.gingerandwhite.com; 5.30 pm, W1 6 pm; W1 closed Sun.

Giraffe £41 ⑤⑤⑤

120 Wilton Rd, SW1   7233 8303   2–4B
6-8 Blandford St, W1   7935 2333   2–1A
19-21 The Brunswick Centre, WC1   7812 1336   8–4C
120 Holland Park Ave, W11   7229 8567   6–2A
270 Chiswick High Rd, W4   8995 2100   7–2A
7 Kensington High St, W8   7938 1221   5–1A
29-31 Essex Rd, N1   7359 5999   8–3D
196-198 Haverstock Hill, NW3   7431 3812   8–2A
46 Rosslyn Hill, NW3   7435 0343   8–2A
Royal Festival Hall, Riverside, SE1   7928 2004   2–3D
1 Crispin Pl, E1   3116 2000   12–2B

Recently acquired by Tesco, this "easy-going" world food chain is "built for families", and "brilliant for breakfast" too – perhaps that's another way of saying it's "ideal for people who don't care about food that much"! / www.giraffe.net; 10.45 pm, Sun 10.30 pm; no booking, Sat & Sun 9 am-5 pm.

The Glasshouse TW9 £67 ❷❷❸

14 Station Pde   8940 6777   1–3A

This "light and airy" (if "noisy") Kew sibling of the fabled Chez Bruce still wins acclaim for its "first-class" food, "superb" wine and "enormously professional" service; ratings, though, slipped this year from their traditional peaks – let's hope it's just a blip. / TW9 3PZ; www.glasshouserestaurant.co.uk; @The_Glasshouse; 10.30 pm, Sun 10 pm.

Gold Mine W2 £33 ❸④⑤

102 Queensway   7792 8331   6–2C

"Roast duck to die for" – top of the bill at this "inexpensive" Bayswater Chinese. / W2 3RR; 11 pm.

Golden Dragon W1 £33 ❸④❸
28-29 Gerrard St   7734 1073   4–3A
*For "a reliable-quality Chinese in the heart of Chinatown",
this (relatively) smart but "brusque" fixture is just the job; it serves
up "all the standard dishes, and plenty of unusual ones",
plus "excellent" dim sum. / W1 6JW; 11 pm, Fri & Sat 11.30 pm,
Sun 10.20 pm.*

Golden Hind W1 £26 ❸❶❸
73 Marylebone Ln   7486 3644   2–1A
*"A winner on every visit"; this "welcoming" Marylebone chippy
is "brilliant at what it does" – "BYO, and enjoy!" / W1U 2PN; 10 pm;
closed Sat L & Sun.*

Good Earth £56 ❷❸❸
233 Brompton Rd, SW3   7584 3658   5–2C
143-145 The Broadway, NW7   8959 7011   1–1B
*"The food is exceptionally good, but it's a shame the prices are
so high" – the story from these "upmarket" Chinese veterans,
in Knightsbridge and Mill Hill, never really changes.
/ www.goodearthgroup.co.uk; 11 pm, Sun 10.30 pm.*

Goode & Wright W11 £54 ❸④④
271 Portobello Rd   7727 5552   6–1A
*An Anglo-French Notting Hill spot that "doesn't look like a pub or bar,
but has that sort of feel about it" – breakfasts are "excellent",
but standards at other times can be a touch "variable". / W11 1LR;
www.goodeandwright.co.uk; 10 pm; closed Mon & Sun L.*

Goodman £63 ❷❷❸
24-26 Maddox St, W1   7499 3776   3–2C
3 South Quay, E14   7531 0300   11–1C
11 Old Jewry, EC2   7600 8220   9–2C
*"Just getting the edge over Hawksmoor"; these "high-powered" and
"male-dominated" Mayfair, City and Canary Wharf locations are
"probably the closest London has to a proper US steakhouse" –
"incredibly consistent" standards, plus that "genuine NYC/London
feel"! / www.goodmanrestaurants.com; 10.30 pm; W1 & E14 closed Sun;
EC2 closed Sat & Sun.*

Gopal's of Soho W1 £30 ❸❸④
12 Bateman St   7434 1621   4–2A
*An "authentic" Indian, in the traditional sense of the word, hidden-
away in Soho – still probably the West End's top old-style
subcontinental. / W1D 4AH; www.gopalsofsoho.co.uk; 11.30 pm, Sun 11 pm.*

Gordon Ramsay SW3 £126 ④④④
68-69 Royal Hospital Rd   7352 4441   5–3D
*Clare Smyth's "classic" cuisine is, say fans, "outstanding", and helps
to make the Sweary One's rather "stuffy" Chelsea HQ a "peerless"
destination; too many critics, though complain of "mundane" cooking
served in a "sterile" ambience… and all at "piss-take" prices!
/ SW3 4HP; www.gordonramsay.com; 10.15 pm; closed Sat & Sun; no jeans
or trainers; booking: max 8; set weekday L £82 (FP).*

Gordon's Wine Bar WC2 £32 ❺④❶
47 Villiers St   7930 1408   4–4D
*"Mad busy", for a reason!; this cellar wine bar, by Embankment tube,
has a wonderfully "idiosyncratic" style, plus an "impressive" list that's
"a must for wine lovers" (and, in summer, one of central London's
largest terraces); the food is incidental. / WC2N 6NE;
www.gordonswinebar.com; 10 pm, Sun 9 pm; no booking.*

The Goring Hotel SW1 £78 ❸⓿⓿
15 Beeston Pl   7396 9000   2–4B
"Englishness at its best"; the "well spaced" dining room of this family-owned hotel, near Victoria, is a "supremely civilised" bastion where the food – "generous" and "old school" – is exactly as you would hope; it makes a great venue for breakfast or for business (or for the two combined). / SW1W 0JW; www.thegoring.com; 10 pm; closed Sat L; no jeans or trainers; table of 8 max.

Gourmet Burger Kitchen £29 ④④④
Branches throughout London
Although the formula is "no longer novel", many fans love the "super-juicy" burgers and toppings on offer at this "WYSIWYG" chain; it was rated only a hair's breadth behind Byron's this year. / www.gbkinfo.com; most branches close 10.30 pm; no booking.

Gourmet Pizza Company
Gabriels Wharf SE1 £30 ④④❸
56 Upper Ground   7928 3188   9–3A
This Thames-side pizzeria (with great views from the outside tables) is the only survivor of the former chain which has not been re-branded by its owner, PizzaExpress; it's generally held out as a "reliable" option (and "crowded at weekends"), but there were a couple of "below par" reports this year too. / SE1 9PP; www.gourmetpizzacompany.co.uk; 11.30 pm.

Gourmet San E2 £25 ❷⑤⑤
261 Bethnal Green Rd   7729 8388   12–1D
"Don't be put off by the décor" – this "unassuming" Bethnal Green spot offers "some of the best Sichuanese food in London", with "plenty of spice" and "a fiery kick". / E2 6AH; www.oldplace.co.uk; 11 pm; D only.

Gow's EC2 £57 ❸❸④
81 Old Broad St   7920 9645   9–2C
"Staid" it may be, but this long-established cellar operation, near Liverpool Street is, "still a good City option if you like fish". / EC2M 1PR; www.ballsbrothers.co.uk; 9 pm; closed Sat & Sun.

The Gowlett SE15 £31 ❷❸❷
62 Gowlett Rd   7635 7048   1–4C
This "good honest local" is not prized only for its "interesting and regularly-changing selection of draught beers"; it's also world-famous in Peckham as the claimed supplier of "London's best pizza". / SE15 4HY; www.thegowlett.com; @theGowlettArms; 10.30 pm, Sun 9 pm; no credit cards.

Goya SW1 £44 ④❸④
34 Lupus St   7976 5309   2–4C
The food "may not scale the heights", but this long-established tapas bar is nonetheless a "friendly" sort of place, prized by locals as "one of those few Pimlico establishments that's not a tourist trap!" / SW1V 3EB; www.goyarestaurant.co.uk; 11.30 pm.

Grain Store N1 🆕 £50 ❷❷⓿
1-3 Stable St, Granary Sq   7324 4466   8–3C
"An exciting new venture for Bruno Loubet and his team"; this King's Cross newcomer – "a fantastic warehouse space with open-plan kitchen" – promotes an "innovative" brand of vegetable-centric cuisine, which early-days reports rate as approaching the "sublime". / N1C 4AB; www.grainstore.com; @GrainStoreKX; 10.30 pm; closed Sun D; SRA-89%.

Gran Paradiso SW1 £46 ④❸④
52 Wilton Rd 7828 5818 2–4B
"An excellent old-fashioned Italian" – this *"comfortable"* Pimlico
fixture is the epitome of a *"reliable"* warhorse; younger bloods,
though, feel a *"make-over"* would do no harm. / SW1V 1DE; 10.45 pm;
closed Sat L & Sun.

The Grand Imperial
Guoman Grosvenor Hotel SW1 £52 ❸❷❷
101 Buckingham Palace Rd 7821 8898 2–4B
"Outstanding for dim sum, when it's a bargain too!"; at any time,
though, this *"very grand"* dining room – almost part of Victoria
Station – makes a *"reliable"* destination, and some reporters describe
it as a surprise *"gem"*! / SW1W OSJ; www.grandimperiallondon.com;
10.30 pm.

Granger & Co W11 £48 ④❺❸
175 Westbourne Grove 7229 9111 6–1B
Bill Granger's *"buzzy and cool"* Notting Hill outpost is *"a decent
effort at re-creating the Sydney original"*, and can make a good
destination for a *"delicious brunch"*; queues can be *"ludicrous"*
though, and the service *"really bad"*. / W11 2SB; www.grangerandco.com;
@grangerandco; 10.30 pm.

The Grapes E14 £42 ④④❷
76 Narrow St 7987 4396 11–1B
This *"Limehouse treasure"* is perhaps the *"smallest, oldest,
and quaintest Docklands pub"*; it has quite a name for its fish cooking
too, but ratings have slipped significantly in recent times – *"go for the
history and the river setting"*. / E14 8BP; www.thegrapes.co.uk;
@TheGrapesLondon; 9.30 pm; closed Sat L & Sun D; no Amex.

Grazing Goat W1 £53 ❸④❸
6 New Quebec St 7724 7243 2–2A
Near Marble Arch, a notably *"decent"* gastroboozer, hailed in some
reports for the *"best pub food locally"* – although it's not really
a 'destination' to match its Belgravia cousins, the Thos Cubitt and
so on, its survey ratings are actually rather higher! / W1H 7RQ;
www.thegrazinggoat.co.uk; @TheGrazingGoat; 10 pm, Sun 9.30 pm;
; SRA-75%.

Great Nepalese NW1 £33 ❸❷⑤
48 Eversholt St 7388 6737 8–3C
"A long-enduring and welcoming retreat" from the Euston streetscape
– this *"friendly"* stalwart serves a *"somewhat exotic"* menu, offering
not just your standard curries, but also some *"interesting Nepalese
specialities"*. / NW1 1DA; www.great-nepalese.co.uk; 11.30 pm, Sun 10 pm.

Great Queen Street WC2 £45 ❷❸❸
32 Great Queen St 7242 0622 4–1D
"Eclectic" British seasonal cooking that's *"full of flavour and finesse"*
has made a runaway hit of this *"pub-like"*, *"cramped"* and *"incredibly
noisy"* Covent Garden operation; *"the only real problem is getting
a table!"* / WC2B 5AA; @greatqueenstreet; 10.30 pm; closed Sun D;
no Amex.

The Greedy Buddha SW6 £32 ❸④④
144 Wandsworth Bridge Rd 7751 3311 10–1B
"Excellent" Nepalese dishes are a highlight of the menu at this
"good local Indian", in Fulham; brace yourself, though, for sometimes
"chaotic" service. / SW6 2UH; www.thegreedybuddha.com; 10.30 pm,
Fri-Sat 11.30 pm; no Amex.

Green Cottage NW3   £40   ❸④⑤
9 New College Pde   7722 5305   8–2A
*"Still very much as it was 30 years ago", this "unpretentious" Swiss
Cottage Cantonese continues to impress the locals with its "freshly-
cooked" cuisine. / NW3 5EP; 10.30 pm, Sun 9.30 pm; no Amex.*

Green Man & French Horn WC2   £44   ❸❷❸
54 St Martin's Ln   7836 2645   4–4C
*"The Terroirs empire goes from strength to strength", and this
latest "cosy" offshoot in a converted Theatreland pub is, say fans,
a "thrilling" West End début, where "superlative" biodynamic (Loire)
wines are complemented by a "short" but slightly "different" menu.
/ WC2N 4EA; www.greenmanfrenchhorn.co.*

Green Papaya E8   £31   ❷❸④
191 Mare St   8985 5486   1–1D
*A "cheap 'n' cheerful" but "courteous", Hackney spot, offering
"crunchy" Vietnamese scoff with some "amazing" flavours. / E8 3QT;
www.green-papaya.com; @goGreenPapaya; 10.30 pm; Closed
L, Mon; no Amex.*

Green's SW1   £61   ❸❸④
36 Duke St   7930 4566   3–3D
*For "classic British nursery fare in the heart of clubland", it's hard
to match Simon Parker Bowles's "marvellously old-fashioned" stalwart;
some change is afoot however – it may move in 2014 to the old
Wheeler's premises, by St James's Palace; the EC3 branch is no more.
/ SW1Y 6DF; www.greens.org.uk; 10.30 pm; closed Sun; no jeans or trainers.*

Greenberry Cafe NW1 NEW   £44   ❸❸④
101 Regent's Park Rd   7483 3765   8–2B
*"A great addition to Primrose Hill"; the proprietor of Islington's former
Lola's restaurant has set up a "wonderful new café" on the site that
was Troika (RIP) – a "helpful" sort of all-day establishment, offering
"tasty food" at "reasonable prices", and already very popular.
/ NW1 8UR; www.greenberrycafe.co.uk.*

The Greenhouse W1   £107   ❷❶❷
27a Hays Mews   7499 3331   3–3B
*"An unparalleled wine list for sheer quality" is the stand-out attraction
at this "beautiful", "well-spaced" and "very professional" Mayfair
stalwart, where Arnaud Bignon's "exquisite" cuisine is the centrepiece
of "a superb all-round gastronomic experience". / W1J 5NX;
www.greenhouserestaurant.co.uk; 10.30 pm; closed Sat L & Sun; booking:
max 12.*

Grillshack W1 NEW   £21   ❸❷④
61-63 Beak St   no tel   3–2D
*On the former Alphabet site, Richard Caring's latest venture is a
Lower East Side-feeling parlour, offering very simple American-style
dishes; on our early-days visit, we didn't find it very atmospheric,
but prices are impressively low. / W1R 3LF; Rated on Editors' visit;
www.grillshack.com; @grillshackuk; 10.30 pm, Sun 10 pm.*

Grumbles SW1   £42   ④❸❸
35 Churton St   7834 0149   2–4B
*Some say it's "past its sell-by date", but this "cosy" Pimlico fixture
mostly gets the thumbs-up as a "great local bistro"; it must be doing
something right – it can be "hard to get a table". / SW1V 2LT;
www.grumblesrestaurant.co.uk; 10.45 pm; set weekday L £26 (FP), set
pre-theatre £27 (FP), set Sun L £28 (FP).*

Guglee £32 ❸❸④
7 New College Pde, NW3   7317 8555   8–2A
279 West End Ln, NW6   7317 8555   1–1B
*"Very good for a local Indian, with more authentic food than you'd
normally find" – these "accommodating" West Hampstead and Swiss
Cottage establishments continue to inspire only positive reports;
they're "always busy". / www.guglee.co.uk; 11 pm.*

The Guinea Grill W1 £67 ❸❷❷
30 Bruton Pl   7499 1210   3–3B
*It's the quaint (if perhaps "male-dominated") atmosphere which
makes this "smart" Mayfair dining room – attached to a "classic, old-
fashioned pub" – so popular, but the steaks and pies can
be "excellent" too, if decidedly "not cheap". / W1J 6NL;
www.theguinea.co.uk; @guineagrill; 10.30 pm; closed Sat L & Sun; booking:
max 8.*

The Gun E14 £52 ❸❸❷
27 Coldharbour   7515 5222   11–1C
*"A perfect antidote to Canary Wharf!" – this "classy" waterside pub
has "lots of character" and "a stunning panoramic view" (over the
Thames to the O2); the food is of "high quality" too. / E14 9NS;
www.thegundocklands.com; 10.30 pm, Sun 9.30 pm; set weekday L £33 (FP).*

Gung-Ho NW6 £39 ❸❷❸
328-332 West End Ln   7794 1444   1–1B
*A change of management has unsettled reports on this
West Hampstead stalwart; most, however, are upbeat – it's "still one
of the best local Chineses". / NW6 1LN; www.stir-fry.co.uk; 11.30 pm;
no Amex.*

The Gunmakers EC1 £40 ❷❷❸
13 Eyre Street Hill   7278 1022   9–1A
*Hidden away in Farringdon, a boozer which "looks pretty ordinary",
but which invariably "hits the spot" with its "classic" pub cuisine,
realised to a "surprisingly good" standard. / EC1R 5ET;
www.thegunmakers.co.uk; @thegunmakers; 10 pm; closed Sat & Sun D;
no booking Fri D.*

Gustoso Ristorante & Enoteca SW1 £43 ❸❶❸
33 Willow Pl   7834 5778   2–4B
*"Tucked away" in a side street, just off Vauxhall Bridge Road,
this "friendly" Italian yearling has been "a welcome addition" to a
"thinly-provided" area; "it has already gathered a good local
following". / SW1P 1JH; 10.30 pm, Fri & Sat 11 pm, Sun 9.30 pm.*

Gymkhana W1 NEW £65
42 Albemarle St   3011 5900   3–3C
*From the people who brought you Trishna, this smart new Indian
restaurant, not far from the Ritz, opened shortly before this guide
went to press; the media have raved, including a very rare 5* award
from the doyenne of critics, Fay Maschler. / W1S 3FE;
www.gymkhanalondon.com.*

Haché £36 ❸❸❷

329-331 Fulham Rd, SW10   7823 3515   5–3B
24 Inverness St, NW1   7485 9100   8–3B
153 Clapham High St, SW4   7738 8760   10–2D **NEW**
147-149 Curtain Rd, EC2   7739 8396   12–1B

*"Greasy-fingered heaven!"; this "excellent" and "appealing" little
chain outscores its bigger rivals with its "wonderful" burgers –
not only do "they really taste of meat", but they can be ordered rare
too! / www.hacheburgers.com; 10.30 pm, Fri-Sat 11 pm, Sun 10 pm.*

Hakkasan £86 ❸❺❷

17 Bruton St, W1   7907 1888   3–2C
8 Hanway Pl, W1   7927 7000   4–1A

*"Oligarchs and their leggy girlfriends" party at the newer Mayfair
branch of these dimly-lit "beautiful-people" haunts; regular folk,
though, appear to be finding them ever less attractive – even if the
Chinese cooking is "decent", prices seem ever-more "ferocious",
and service is sometimes "spectacularly bad". / www.hakkasan.com;
midnight, Sun 11 pm.*

Halepi W2 £43 ❸❶❸

18 Leinster Ter   7262 1070   6–2C

*Critics find it a little "tired", but this long-established Greek taverna,
just north of Hyde Park, still delights its loyal band of devotees.
/ W2 3ET; www.halepi.co.uk; midnight.*

The Hampshire Hog W6 £49 ④❸❸

227 King St   8748 3391   7–2B

*With its "bright and pretty" styling, and huge garden, this large
gastropub brings no end of cheer to the drab environs
of Hammersmith Town Hall – perhaps why it's "always busy", even if
the "simple" cooking can seem "expensive" for what it is. / W6 9JT;
www.thehampshirehog.com; @TheHampshireHog; 11 pm; closed Sun D;
SRA-68%.*

Haozhan W1 £51 ❷④⑤

8 Gerrard St   7434 3838   4–3A

*"Bistro-style" in operation, this "now slightly shabby" spot serves
"interesting" cuisine that's "a step up from the rest of Chinatown";
it's "speedily served" too… not always a good thing. / W1D 5PJ;
www.haozhan.co.uk; @haozhan; 11.15 pm, Fri & Sat 11.45 pm,
Sun 10.45 pm.*

Harbour City W1 £39 ❸④⑤

46 Gerrard St   7439 7859   4–3B

*"Terrific dim sum, very cheap" – the headline attraction at this
otherwise "OK-ish" Chinatown "stalwart". / W1D 5QH; 11.30 pm,
Fri-Sat midnight, Sun 10 pm.*

Hard Rock Café W1 £48 ❸❸❷

150 Old Park Ln   7629 0382   3–4B

*The world's original Hard Rock continues to please children of all
ages, and surprisingly consistently too – "you can't beat their burgers,
ribs or even steaks… provided you are willing to put up with the
music", and the "depressing" queue. / W1K 1QZ;
www.hardrock.com/london; @HardRockLondon; midnight; need 20+ to book.*

Hardy's Brasserie W1 £48 ❸④❸

53 Dorset St   7935 5929   2–1A

*"A pleasant regular haunt for a quick lunch or a lengthy dinner" –
this Marylebone fixture always impresses, thanks not least to its
"comprehensive" wine list and its "reasonable" prices. / W1U 7NH;
www.hardysbrasserie.com; @hardys_W1; 10 pm; closed Sat & Sun.*

Hare & Tortoise £29 ❸❸❸
11-13 The Brunswick, WC1 7278 9799 2–1D
373 Kensington High St, W14 7603 8887 7–1D
38 Haven Grn, W5 8810 7066 1–2A
296-298 Upper Richmond Rd, SW15 8394 7666 10–2B
90 New Bridge St, EC4 7651 0266 9–2A
"Choice and efficiency"; these "bustling" pan-Asian canteens offer
an "always-enjoyable" combination of "cheap, cheerful and healthy"
dishes (sushi, noodles, curries), and at a "speedy" pace too.
/ www.hareandtortoise-restaurants.co.uk; 10.45 pm, Fri & Sat 11.15 pm;
EC4 10 pm; EC4 closed Sun; W14 no bookings.

Harrison's SW12 £46 ④④❸
15-19 Bedford Hill 8675 6900 10–2C
"The Balham Set" (there is such a thing, apparently) is the core
clientele at this laid-back brasserie; it's "always buzzing", even if both
food and service are a bit up-and-down. / SW12 9EX;
www.harrisonsbalham.co.uk; @harrisonsbalham; 10.30 pm, Sun 10 pm;
set pre theatre £30 (FP); SRA-71%.

Harry Morgan's NW8 £39 ❸❸④
31 St John's Wood High St 7722 1869 8–3A
"There isn't a great Jewish deli in Britain, but this is the nearest",
say fans of this St John's Wood institution; it offers "all the classics",
not least a "very good salt beef sandwich". / NW8 7NH;
www.harryms.co.uk; 10.30 pm.

Harwood Arms SW6 £54 ❶❷❸
Walham Grove 7386 1847 5–3A
"Consistently faultless seasonal British cooking" (with "terrific" game
a highlight) has made this Fulham backstreet hostelry
an "outstanding" destination; you can still get a pint and Scotch egg
at the bar, but "you need to book weeks ahead for a full meal".
/ SW6 1QP; www.harwoodarms.com; 9.15 pm, Sun 9 pm; closed Mon L.

Hashi SW20 £35 ❷❷❸
54 Durham Rd 8944 1888 10–2A
"Just as good as the most expensive places in the West End!" –
this "brilliant" (and "friendly") Raynes Park Japanese impresses all
who report on it. / SW20 0TW; 10.30 pm; closed Mon; no Amex.

The Havelock Tavern W14 £43 ❷④❷
57 Masbro Rd 7603 5374 7–1C
"Consistently great, despite the changes of ownership and staff" –
the main problem with this "laid-back" gastroboozer, in the
backstreets of Olympia, is that it's often "hard to find a seat".
/ W14 0LS; www.havelocktavern.com; 10 pm, Sun 9.30 pm; no booking.

The Haven N20 £49 ④④⑤
1363 High Rd 8445 7419 1–1B
For most reporters, this "noisy" Whetstone fixture is an "always
reliable" local favourite; there are also quite a few critics, though,
who find the place "over-rated" and "overpriced". / N20 9LN;
www.haven-bistro.co.uk; 11 pm.

Hawksmoor £62 ❷❷❸
5a, Air St, W1   7406 3980   3–3D
11 Langley St, WC2   7420 9390   4–2C
157 Commercial St, E1   7426 4850   12–2B
10-12 Basinghall St, EC2   7397 8120   9–2C
"The group that can do no wrong" (well for the blogosphere anyway)
– Huw Gott and Will Beckett's "failsafe", "meat-paradises" mix
"superlative" steaks with "tantalising" cocktails; prices can seem
"hideous" however and – by a smidgeon – its overall rating is pipped
by rival Goodman. / www.thehawksmoor.com; all branches between
10 pm & 11 pm; EC2 closed Sat-Sun.

Haz £36 ❹❹❸
9 Cutler St, E1   7929 7923   9–2D
34 Foster Ln, EC2   7600 4172   9–2B
112 Hounsditch, EC3   7623 8180   9–2D
6 Mincing Ln, EC3   7929 3173   9–3D
"Not bad for a quick bite"; no denying, though, that this "crammed-
in" Turkish chain, in the City, is attracting increasing flak for
"uninspiring" food and "brusque" service. / www.hazrestaurant.co.uk;
11.30 pm; EC3 closed Sun.

Hazev E14 £34 ❹❸❸
2 South Quay Sq, Discovery Dock West   7515 9467   11–1C
Worth knowing about in the E14 chain-hell, a "striking" Turkish
restaurant (including an "affordable" cafeteria), near Surrey Quays
DLR; it's usually "busy", thanks not least to its "tasty" cuisine.
/ E14 9RT; www.hazev.com; 11.30 pm, Sun 10.30 pm, Mon 11 pm.

Hazuki WC2 £40 ❸❹❹
43 Chandos Pl   7240 2530   4–4C
"Like stepping into Tokyo, a genuine little Japanese restaurant,
informal, good value, and friendly" – a handy place to know about,
by the Trafalgar Square post office. / WC2M 4HS;
www.hazukilondon.co.uk; 10.30 pm, Sun 9.30 pm.

Hedone W4 £78 ❷❸❸
301 Chiswick High Rd   8747 0377   7–2A
Mikael Jonsson's "incredibly original" two-year-old ("at the wrong end
of Chiswick") is "like nothing else in London", particularly in its
"unsurpassed sourcing" of ingredients; "given the hype in foodie
circles", however, it can strike the uninitiated as "underwhelming",
especially at the price. / W4 4HH; www.hedonerestaurant.com; 9.30 pm;
closed Mon, Tue L, Wed L, Thu L & Sun.

Hélène Darroze
The Connaught Hotel W1 £127 ❸❸❷
Carlos Pl   3147 7200   3–3B
For "old world elegance", few hotel dining rooms can match the
"classic" allure of this Mayfair legend; its star Parisian chef's reign
remains an inconsistent one – many "simply outstanding" meals are
reported, but even fans of the "refined" cuisine can declare bills
"ridiculous". / W1K 2AL; www.the-connaught.co.uk; 10 pm; closed
Mon & Sun; jacket & tie; set weekday L £70 (FP).

Hellenic W1 £45
45 Crawford St   7935 1257   6–1D
The premises may be "new" and "smart", but this "old gentleman"
of a Marylebone restaurant remains true to the "friendly" values
which so long sustained it in Thayer St; its "classic" Greek menu
seems as good as ever too, but there's too little feedback as yet
to make a rating appropriate. / W1H 1JT; 10.45 pm; closed Sun; no Amex.

The Henry Root SW10 £52 ④④❸
9 Park Walk 7352 7040 5–3B
This "casual" Chelsea hang-out is "a useful combination of bar and restaurant" – "not a fine food destination", but a "very flexible format". / SW10 0AJ; www.thehenryroot.com; @thehenryroot; 10.45 pm, Sun 8.45 pm.

Hereford Road W2 £47 ❷❸❸
3 Hereford Rd 7727 1144 6–1B
Tom Pemberton's open-kitchen Bayswater bistro "rarely disappoints" with its "regularly-changing" and "good-value" seasonal fare, which spotlights "great ingredients, simply cooked"; if you can, though, get a booth at the front – the rear dining room can seem "clinical". / W2 4AB; www.herefordroad.org; 10.30 pm, Sun 10 pm.

Hibiscus W1 £120 ④④④
29 Maddox St 7629 2999 3–2C
Despite its "sterile" ambience, Claude Bosi's Mayfair HQ is, say fans, a "showcase" for his "ground-breaking and challenging" cuisine; ratings are undercut, however, by the criticisms of "unreal" pricing and "hit 'n' miss" results – perhaps, now he's bought out his business partner, the place will finally truly shine? / W1S 2PA; www.hibiscusrestaurant.co.uk; 11 pm; closed Sun; set weekday L £61 (FP).

High Road Brasserie W4 £49 ④④❸
162-166 Chiswick High Rd 8742 7474 7–2A
"A great spot for brunch and people-watching"; this Chiswick brasserie is certainly a "buzzing" destination, with some nice tables al fresco, and can certainly deliver a "great burger"; critics, however, feel it "trades on its name". / W4 1PR; www.brasserie.highroadhouse.co.uk; @sohohouse; 10.45 pm, Fri & Sat 11.45 pm, Sun 9.45 pm.

High Timber EC4 £58 ④❸❸
8 High Timber 7248 1777 9–3B
"Lovely views" of the Thames and Tate Modern, plus "amazing" wines (mostly South African), score points for this business-friendly spot; not everyone's impressed, though – "nothing was outrageously wrong, it's just that there's no wow-factor". / EC4V 3PA; www.hightimber.com; @HTimber; 10 pm; closed Sat & Sun; set weekday L £38 (FP).

Hilliard EC4 £28 ❷❷❸
26a Tudor St 7353 8150 9–3A
"Packed out with barristers from the nearby Temple" – a cramped all-day canteen serving "fresh, simple dishes from high-quality ingredients" (not least "the best sarnies in the City", plus "a couple of hot options" at lunchtime); "great coffee" too. / EC4Y 0AY; www.hilliardfood.co.uk; 6 pm; L only, closed Sat & Sun; no booking.

Hix W1 £66 ④④⑤
66-70 Brewer St 7292 3518 3–2D
"His weekly column is better than his food!"; Mark Hix may have the blogosphere eating out of his hand, but his "self-consciously chic" Soho diner strikes reporters as ever-more "overpriced and over-hyped" – the cooking can be "surprisingly bland", service is disinterested, and there is "no atmosphere to speak of". / W1F 9UP; www.hixsoho.co.uk; @HixRestaurants; 11.30 pm, Sun 10.30 pm; set weekday L & pre-theatre £44 (FP).

Hix Oyster & Chop House EC1 £58 ④❸❸
36-37 Greenhill Rents, Cowcross St 7017 1930 9–1A
Fans of Mark Hix's "lively" eatery, near Smithfield Market, say it's a "carnivore's heaven", offering "interesting cuts of meat" alongside some "excellent" fish; overall, however, the food is "below the standard his name would lead you to expect". / EC1M 6BN; www.restaurantsetcltd.com; 11 pm, Sun 9 pm.

HKK EC2 £127 ❷❷④
Broadgate West, 88 Worship St 3535 1888 12–2B
"As good as anything in Hong Kong"; this "exceptional" City-fringe newcomer, from the Hakkasan group, may have a "sterile" ("monastic") ambience, but its "refined" cuisine and "slick" service have made it an immediate smash hit… even if it is "very pricey". / EC2A 2BE; www.hkklondon.com; 9.45 pm; closed Sat L & Sun; set weekday L £52 (FP).

Hoi Polloi
Ace Hotel E1 NEW £59
100 Shoreditch High St 8880 6100 12–1B
The dining room of the new ACE hotel in Shoreditch opens as this guide goes to press; if it turns out anything like the NYC ACE, it will quickly become in-crowd central. / E1 6JQ.

Hole in the Wall W4 £40 ④❸❸
12 Sutton Lane North 8742 7185 7–2A
A spacious garden is the stand-out feature of this cute Gunnersbury gastropub; it's just the place "for those evenings when no one fancies cooking". / W4 4LD; 9.45 pm, Sun 9.15 pm; closed Mon L & Tue L.

Holy Cow SW11 £25 ❷④❸
166 Battersea Pk Rd 7498 2000 10–1C
"First-rate Indian take-away food"; we don't normally list delivery services, but we've made an exception for this "reliable" Battersea operation, where the dishes always tastes "freshly prepared". / SW11 4ND; www.holycowfineindianfood.com; 11 pm, Sun 10.30 pm; D only.

Homage
Waldorf Hilton WC2 £73 ④④❸
22 Aldwych 7836 2400 2–2D
"Fairly unmemorable" but still "always bustling", this grandly-housed Gallic brasserie, on the fringe of Covent Garden, is relatively "reasonably priced", and makes a "great stand-by" for lunch or pre-theatre. / WC2B 4DD; www3.hilton.com/en/hotels/united-kingdom/the-waldorf-hilton-london-LONWAHI/dining/index.html; Mon-Wed 10 pm, Thu-Sat 10.30 pm, Sun 9.30 pm; D only; set pre theatre £46 (FP).

Honest Burgers £37 ❶❷❸
4 Meard St, W1 3609 9524 4–2A
159 Portobello Rd, W11 awaiting tel 6–1B NEW
54-56 Camden Lock Pl, NW1 8617 3949 8–2B NEW
Brixton Village, Coldharbour Ln, SW9 7733 7963 10–2D
"AMAZING" burgers and fries "to which the word 'chip' does not do justice" – the original Brixton branch of this growing small chain serves London's No 1. burger; the queue, though, is "a total pain". / www.honestburgers.co.uk; @honestburgers; 10 pm - 11 pm; SW9 closed Mon D.

Honey & Co W1 NEW £31 ❷❷④
25a, Warren St 7388 6175 2–1B
*"What a thrill to find a place like this!" – a "tiny" instant smash hit,
near Warren Street tube, where "lovely people" serve "simple" but
"high impact" Middle Eastern-inspired dishes; it's a "cramped" spot,
though, which some reporters feel risks getting "overhyped".
/ W1T 5JZ; www.honeyandco.co.uk.*

The Horseshoe NW3 £47 ❸❸❸
28 Heath St 7431 7206 8–2A
*"Great ales" are a highpoint at this "friendly" microbrewery
in "the very heart of Hampstead" – the origin of what's now Camden
Town Brewery; to accompany them – "well-presented comfort food".
/ NW3 6TE; www.thehorseshoehampstead.com; @getluckyatthehorseshoe;
10pm, Fri-Sat 11pm.*

Hot Stuff SW8 £20 ❷❷❸
23 Wilcox Rd 7720 1480 10–1D
*"Cheap 'n' cheerful, but so tasty and different!"; this BYO Vauxhall
Indian feels like a "very genuine" sort of place and it offers
"generous" dishes with "a glorious Asian/African fusion". / SW8 2XA;
www.eathotstuff.com; 9.30 pm; closed Mon; no Amex.*

The Hoxton Grill EC2 £51 ④④❷
81 Great Eastern St 7739 9111 12–1B
*"Trendy", by the standards of dining areas off hotel lobbies –
a "buzzy and comfortable" Shoreditch venue, offering
"straightforward American-style diner food". / EC2A 3HU;
www.hoxtongrill.co.uk; @hoxtongrill; 11.45 pm; set weekday L £33 (FP).*

Hudsons SW15 £41 ④④❸
113 Lower Richmond Rd 8785 4522 10–1A
*A "fantastic neighbourhood bistro"; this Putney fixture has quite
a name locally as a "fun" hang out; "great brunch" a highlight.
/ SW15 1EX; www.hudsonsrestaurant.co.uk; @hudsonsw15; 10 pm,
Sun 9.30 pm; closed Tue L.*

Hummus Bros £17 ❸❸④
88 Wardour St, W1 7734 1311 3–2D
37-63 Southampton Row, WC1 7404 7079 2–1D
62 Exmouth Mkt, EC1 7812 1177 9–1A NEW
128 Cheapside, EC2 7726 8011 9–2B
*"A great and very reasonable cheap eat"; "whatever it is they put
in the hummus, I suspect it's addictive", says one fan of these
cafeteria-style pit stops, which offer "a range of delicious toppings
and wholesome pitta" to complement the main event.
/ www.hbros.co.uk; W1 10 pm, Thu-Sat 11 pm; WC1 9 pm, EC1 10 pm,
Thu-Sat 11 pm, Sun 4 pm; WC1, EC2 closed Sat & Sun; no booking.*

Hunan SW1 £65 ❶❸④
51 Pimlico Rd 7730 5712 5–2D
*"Let Mr Peng feed you, and you won't go wrong!" – that's the way
to go at this "unique" Pimlico veteran, regarded by many as "hands
down, London's best Chinese"; the setting is "undistinguished",
though, and service of late has been more "hit 'n' miss" than usual.
/ SW1W 8NE; www.hunanlondon.com; 11 pm; closed Sun.*

Huong-Viet
An Viet House N1 £34 ③④④
12-14 Englefield Rd 7249 0877 1–1C
In De Beauvoir, a "community-centre-turned-restaurant" – it offers
"something different, even in an area with a lot of Vietnamese
variety", and the food can be "superb"; BYO. / N1 4LS; 11 pm; closed
Sun; no Amex.

Hush £57 ④⑤④
8 Lancashire Ct, W1 7659 1500 3–2B
95-97 High Holborn, WC1 7242 4580 2–1D
"Nice to sit outside on a balmy summer evening... but that's about
it" – this Mayfair restaurant, with its extensive terrace, is mainly
"popular" because of its cute, tucked-away location; well, it can't
be the "so-so" cooking and sometimes "pushy" service.
/ www.hush.co.uk; @Hush_Restaurant; W1 10.45 pm; WC1 10.30 pm,
Sun 9.30 pm; WC1 closed Sun.

Hutong
The Shard SE1 NEW £75 ③④❶
31 St Thomas St 7478 0540 9–4C
"Stunning" hardly does justice to the views from the 33rd floor
of London's newest landmark; the grandest of the eateries opening
in 2013 – this dark and dimly-lit Chinese dining room, serves food
that's "surprisingly good". / SE1 9RY; www.hutong.co.uk; @HutongShard;
11 pm.

Ibérica £45 ❸❸❸
195 Great Portland St, W1 7636 8650 2–1B
12 Cabot Sq, E14 7636 8650 11–1C
With their "easy-going" style and their true "Spanish hospitality",
these "relaxing" tapas bars "feel like the real deal"; the E14 branch
is something of "a safe haven in Canary Wharf", but the Great
Portland St original is more highly rated. / 11 pm; W1 closed Sun D.

Ikeda W1 £65 ❷❷⑤
30 Brook St 7629 2730 3–2B
"Purist" and "expensive", this Mayfair veteran is known
by aficionados for its very accomplished sushi; "like many long-lived
Japanese operations, it feels very stiff", and it's interior – "stuck
somewhere round 1988" – is a "let-down". / W1K 5DJ; 10.20 pm;
closed Sat L & Sun.

Imli Street W1 £37 ❸❷❷
167-169 Wardour St 7287 4243 3–1D
Formerly called plain Imli, this "busy" street food operation in Soho
is praised in all reports for its "delicious" and "authentic" Indian small
plates, and at "reasonable prices" too. / W1F 8WR; www.imlistreet.com;
11 pm, Sun 10 pm.

Imperial China WC2 £44 ④④④
25a Lisle St 7734 3388 4–3B
"Dependable, and more spacious than most", this large and "busy"
Chinatown fixture attracts particular praise for "the freshest dim
sum". / WC2H 7BA; www.imperialchina-london.co.uk; 11 pm, Sun 9.30 pm.

Imperial City EC3 £48 ④④④
Royal Exchange, Cornhill 7626 3437 9–2C
"Decent, but not remarkable"; this once-celebrated Chinese – in the
"spacious" and (potentially) "atmospheric" vaults of the Royal
Exchange – is nowadays merely "a safe place for a working City
lunch or dinner". / EC3V 3LL; www.orientalrestaurantgroup.co.uk; 10.15 pm;
closed Sat & Sun.

Inaho W2 £39 ❶⑤⑤
4 Hereford Rd 7221 8495 6–1B
A "little slice of Tokyo", oddly located in a tiny Bayswater shack,
where – despite "variable service and basic decor" – you "always
need to book"; why? – the food (especially sushi) is "top-grade".
/ W2 4AA; 10.30 pm; closed Sat L & Sun; no Amex or Maestro.

Inamo £44 ④④④
4-12 Regent St, SW1 7484 0500 3–3D
134-136 Wardour St, W1 7851 7051 3–1D
These "wacky" West End Japanese outfits – where "you order
by tapping images projected onto your table" – can be "fun",
especially with children; with their "average" food and "poor" service,
though, critics dismiss them as "a gimmick, and not one to be
repeated". / www.inamo-restaurant.com; @InamoRestaurant; 11 pm,
SW1 12 am.

Indali Lounge W1 £43 ❷❷④
50 Baker St 7224 2232 2–1A
"Very good for a low-fat Indian meal!"; this singularly healthy
Marylebone subcontinental "looks more like a nightclub when you
go in", but its "interesting" cuisine pleases all who comment on it.
/ W1U 7BT; www.indalilounge.com; 11.30, Sun 11 pm; closed Sat L.

India Club
Strand Continental Hotel WC2 £25 ❸⑤⑤
143 Strand 7836 0650 2–2D
"Visit at least once, just for the experience!" – this canteen near the
Indian High Commission offers a return to "a world of red-lino post-
war austerity"; it's a "dependable" place, though, where the food
is "surprisingly good", and "cheap" too; BYO. / WC2R 1JA;
www.strand-continental.co.uk; 10.50 pm; no credit cards; booking: max 6.

Indian Moment SW11 £34 ❸④④
44 Northcote Rd 7223 6575 10–2C
"A real breath of fresh air in the curry house world" – this "ghee-
free" Battersea Indian has quite a local following for its "delicious"
and "healthy" cuisine; its "cramped" premises, however, sometimes
seem a mite "crowded". / SW11 1NZ; 11.30 pm, Fri & Sat midnight;
no Amex.

Indian Ocean SW17 £29 ❷❷❸
214 Trinity Rd 8672 7740 10–2C
"The best Indian, no argument!" – this "lively" Wandsworth
institution may have moved sites in recent times, but it retains
a devoted local following for its "really delicious" cuisine. / SW17 7HP;
www.indianoceanrestaurant.com; 11.30 pm.

Indian Rasoi N2 £37 ❷❷❸
7 Denmark Ter 8883 9093 1–1B
"Unusually good for this part of town"; this "buzzy" Muswell Hill
Indian offers "refreshingly different" cuisine – the "delicate" and
"nuanced" dishes can be "extraordinarily good". / N2 9HG;
www.indian-rasoi.co.uk; 10.30 pm; no Amex.

Indian Zilla SW13 £45 ❶❶❸
2-3 Rocks Ln 8878 3989 10–1A
The Barnes offshoot of Indian Zing is, similarly, "not your average
curry house", and Manoj Vasaikar's "original" and "distinctly
flavoured" dishes are "first-class". / SW13 0DB; www.indianzilla.co.uk;
11 pm, Sun 10.30 pm; closed Mon L, Tue L & Wed L.

Indian Zing W6 £46 ❶❷❸
236 King St 8748 5959 7–2B
"They must be missing Michael Winner", at what used to be his favourite curry house, near Ravenscourt Park; Manoj Vasaikar's "delicate" and "original" cuisine is as "outstanding" as ever, but the "well-appointed" dining room can get rather "noisy". / W6 0RS; www.indianzing.co.uk; 11 pm, Sun 10 pm; set weekday L £28 (FP).

Indigo
One Aldwych WC2 £66 ❹❸❹
I Aldwych 7300 0400 2–2D
"Good for a pre-theatre dinner", "great for breakfast", "lovely for brunch" – these are the occasions for which reporters seek out this Aldwych hotel mezzanine; "for most buzz, get a table overlooking the bar". / WC2B 4BZ; www.onealdwych.com; 10.15 pm; set pre theatre £46 (FP).

Inn the Park SW1 £49 ❹❸❷
St James's Pk 7451 9999 2–3C
This architecturally striking venue certainly has a stellar location, within St James's Park, and some "wonderful al fresco tables"; standards, traditionally lacklustre, have improved of late, and breakfast here is always "an uplifting way to start the day". / SW1A 2BJ; www.peytonandbyrne.co.uk; @PeytonandByrne; 8.30 pm; closed Sun D; no Amex.

Inside SE10 £42 ❷❷⑤
19 Greenwich South St 8265 5060 1–3D
"Still the best bet in Greenwich"; in a sea of mediocrity, this is a "reliable neighbourhood restaurant" which "aims high, and delivers", even if it does have an interior that's "plain" and rather "cramped". / SE10 8NW; www.insiderestaurant.co.uk; @insideandgreenwich; 10.30 pm, Fri-Sat 11 pm; closed Mon & Sun D.

Isarn N1 £57 ❷❷❹
119 Upper St 7424 5153 8–3D
"Streets ahead of most Thai restaurants", this rather corridor-like Islington spot is hailed in pretty much all reports for its "original" and "delicious" cuisine. / N1 1QP; www.isarn.co.uk; 11 pm, Sun 10.30 pm; no Amex.

Ishbilia SW1 £52 ❸❷⑤
9 William St 7235 7788 5–1D
Handy for Knightsbridge, a Lebanese café typically packed with customers from the Arab world, drawn by the "wide and authentic" menu; critics, though, do feel "it could do with a bit of a facelift". / SW1X 9HL; www.ishbilia.com; @Ishbilia; 11.30 pm.

Ishtar W1 £44 ❸❷❸
10-12 Crawford St 7224 2446 2–1A
Not far from Baker Street, a "fabulous" Turkish all-rounder, hailed by many reporters for its "unbeatable-value" set lunch menu. / W1U 6AZ; www.ishtarrestaurant.com; 11 pm, Sun 10.30 pm; set weekday L £26 (FP).

Isola del Sole SW15 £48 ❹❹❹
16 Lacy Rd 8785 9962 10–2B
For some locals, an "unfavourable upgrade" knocked the gloss off this Putney Sicilian a couple of years ago; it has its fans, though, who praise its "home-made" fare, "sweet" service and "lovely" ambience. / SW15 1NL; www.isoladelsole.co.uk; @isoladelsoleuk; 10.30 pm; closed Sun.

Itsu £32 ④❸④

118 Draycott Ave, SW3 7590 2400 5–2C
100 Notting Hill Gate, W11 7229 4016 6–2B
Level 2, Cabot Place East, E14 7512 5790 11–1C
From "healthy" take-away options to conveyor-sushi (some branches only), this 21st-century chain wins praise for its "decent" grub and "fun" style; not everyone, though is taken – "it's got the health", says one critic, "but not the happiness". / www.itsu.co.uk; 11 pm; E14 10 pm; some are closed Sat & Sun; no booking.

The Ivy WC2 £72 ④❸❷

1-5 West St 7836 4751 4–3B
"Forget the celeb label and enjoy!"; this "iconic" panelled dining room, at the heart of Theatreland, is still – for its huge fan club – a "vibrant" metropolitan lynchpin; critics, though, say it has "had its day", and offers "rather underwhelming" British dishes at "silly" prices. / WC2H 9NQ; www.the-ivy.co.uk; 11.30 pm, Sun 10.30 pm; no shorts; booking: max 6; set pre theatre £50 (FP).

Izgara N3 £33 ❸④⑤

11 Hendon Lane 8371 8282 1–1B
"Decent kebabs and stews" are the headline attraction at this "busy" Turkish establishment, in North Finchley; service is "efficient, but not especially friendly". / N3 1RT; www.izgararestaurant.net; 11.30 pm; no Amex.

Jackson & Whyte W1 NEW

56 Wardour St awaiting tel 3–2D
How many more 'American' restaurants can we bear/cope with? – the Grillshack team is to open this all-day restaurant, specialising in the food of the East Coast, in late-2013 on the former Soho site of Satsuma (RIP). / W1D 4JG.

Jai Krishna N4 £19 ❷④④

161 Stroud Green Rd 7272 1680 8–1D
A "friendly and cheap" South Indian BYO, in Stroud Green, hailed by locals for its "astonishing value". / N4 3PZ; 10.30 pm; closed Sun; no credit cards.

The Jam Tree £47 ❸❸❷

541 King's Rd, SW6 3397 3739 5–4B
13-19 Old Town, SW4 3397 4422 10–2D NEW
Surprisingly little survey commentary on these Olympia and Fulham gastropubs, but they are almost invariably noted for their "generous" cuisine and their "friendly" service. / SW4 12 am, Sun-Wed 11 pm; SW6 11 pm, Fri-Sat 2 am.

Jamie's Italian £43 ⑤⑤④

11 Upper St Martin's Ln, WC2 3326 6390 4–3B
Westfield, Ariel Way, W12 8090 9070 7–1C
2 Churchill Pl, E14 3002 5252 11–1C
Jamie O's "basic and noisy" Italian chain undeniably pleases many fans with its "easy and fun" style; it has far too many detractors, however, who say "just don't go", on account of "very slack" service, and food that can be "really appalling". / www.jamiesitalian.com; @JamiesItalianUK; 11.30 pm, Sun 10.30 pm; over 6.

Jenny Lo's Tea House SW1 £34 ❸❷④
14 Eccleston St 7259 0399 2–4B
"A great, quick-bite option"; this "simple noodle house", by Victoria
Coach Station, offers "better-than-average" chow, canteen-style,
and at "amazingly reasonable prices". / SW1W 9LT; www.jennylo.co.uk;
9.55 pm; closed Sat & Sun; no credit cards; no booking.

Jin Kichi NW3 £41 ❶❷④
73 Heath St 7794 6158 8–1A
The ambience "may not be the best", but this "tiny and cramped"
(and ultra-"authentic") Hampstead Japanese stalwart has offered
"quality and consistency for over 20 years"; the speciality
is "the best yakitori", but all the food (sushi included) is "fantastic" .
/ NW3 6UG; www.jinkichi.com; 11 pm, Sun 10 pm; closed Mon L.

Joanna's SE19 £44 ❸❷❷
56 Westow Hill 8670 4052 1–4D
"A really good neighbourhood restaurant"; thanks to its "lovely"
ambience, "attentive" service and "great" views of Canary Wharf,
this Crystal Palace fixture is a destination that's always "buzzing".
/ SE19 1RX; www.joannas.uk.com; @JoannasRest; 10.45 pm, Sun 10.15 pm.

Joe Allen WC2 £53 ⑤④❷
13 Exeter St 7836 0651 4–3D
It's still as "thespy" as ever, and the late-night atmosphere is as
"fabulous" as ever, but this Theatreland basement changed hands
this year (after 35 years); the food? – the straightforward American
dishes (including an off-menu burger) "have never been the point",
but too often of late they have been plain "awful". / WC2E 7DT;
www.joeallen.co.uk; Sun-Thu 11.45 pm, Fri & Sat 12.45 am; set weekday L &
pre-theatre £24 (FP).

Joe's Brasserie SW6 £42 ❸❷❸
130 Wandsworth Bridge Rd 7731 7835 10–1B
"Standard but very reliable" staples, "strongly supported by a very
reasonable wine list" – still a winning formula for John Brinkley's
deepest-Fulham veteran; it has a "super terrace" too, that's "great for
people-watching". / SW6 2UL; www.brinkleys.com; 11 pm.

John Salt N1 NEW £35 ④④❸
131 Upper St 7359 7501 8–3D
The blogosphere has been well impressed by this "loud and echoey"
new Islington hang-out, and many reporters acclaim Neil Rankin's
"brilliant", BBQ-heavy menu as "taking pub food up a level"; there's
also a school of thought, though, that it is "so over-rated". / N1 1QP;
www.john-salt.com; 10 pm; no Amex.

José SE1 £40 ❶❷❶
104 Bermondsey St 7403 4902 9–4D
"The only serious competition for Barrafina"; with its "divine" tapas,
"wonderfully diverse" wines and sherries, "super-efficient" service,
and brilliant style, José Pizarro's tiny Bermondsey corner-bar is "worth
the hype, the squeeze, and the inevitable wait". / SE1 3UB;
@Jose_Pizarro; 10.30 pm, Sun 5.30; closed Fri D, Sat D & Sun D.

Joy King Lau WC2 £34 ❸④④
3 Leicester St 7437 1132 4–3A
Just off Leicester Square, this "always-packed", three-floor operation
offers a classic Chinatown experience... in a good way; "authentic
dim sum" (expect a queue) is the highlight of the "reliable"
Cantonese menu. / WC2H 7BL; www.joykinglau.com; 11.30 pm,
Sun 10.30 pm.

Jubo EC2 NEW £18
68 Rivington St   7033 0198   12–1B
A large new Korean canteen in Shoreditch, which opened in mid-2013; early published reviews suggests it will be a useful standby (no bookings) for the local hipsters, rather than a destination in itself. / EC2A 3AY; www.jubolondon.com.

The Jugged Hare EC1Y £50   ④④❸
49 Chiswell St   7614 0134   12–2A
Near the Barbican, this former pub (now "themed along hunting lodge lines") makes a "pleasant, down-to-earth environment" for an "unfussy" meal; many reporters are impressed by the "big-flavoured and hearty" British fare, but sceptics can find it "a bit pricey" for what it is. / EC1Y 4SA; www.juggedhare.com; @juggedhare; 11 pm, Thu-Sat midnight, Sun 10.30 pm.

Julie's W11 £62   ④④❶
135 Portland Rd   7229 8331   6–2A
"The home of countless romances" – this "very lovely" semi-subterranean Holland Park labyrinth is a time capsule of sexy '70s London; as always, though, it's a "shame about the food". / W11 4LW; www.juliesrestaurant.com; 11 pm.

The Junction Tavern NW5 £43   ❸⓿❷
101 Fortess Rd   7485 9400   8–2B
"Trying hard, and doing a good job at a reasonable price" – this Kentish Town fixture continues to please with its "very welcoming and friendly" style, and its "surprisingly good" pub grub. / NW5 1AG; www.junctiontavern.co.uk; 10.30 pm, Sun 9.30 pm; Mon-Thu D only, Fri-Sun open L & D; no Amex.

Juniper Dining N5 £46   ❷❸❸
100 Highbury Pk   7288 8716   8–1D
"A gem of a local restaurant", whose "uncomplicated but imaginative" dishes delight Highbury reporters; fish is a highlight. / N5 2XE; www.juniperdining.co.uk; 9.30 pm; closed Mon & Sun D.

JW Steakhouse
Grosvenor House Hotel W1 £75   ④④❸
86 Park Ln   7399 8460   3–3A
For "superb" USDA and British steaks, this cavernous but "comfortable" Park Lane spot is – say fans – "surprisingly good" for a hotel operation; top tip? – the cheesecake is "easily the best this side of the Atlantic!" / W1K 7TN; www.jwsteakhouse.co.uk; 10.30 pm, Fri & Sat 11 pm.

K10 £36   ❷❷④
20 Copthall Ave, EC2   7562 8510   9–2C
3 Appold St, EC2   7539 9209   12–2B NEW
"It still rocks!"; this City conveyor-Japanese serves an "unusually wide variety of dishes", and "you could eat everything that whooshes by"; the new one on Appold/Sun St is "quick and really good" too. / www.k10.com; Appold 9 pm, Wed-Fri 9.30 pm; both branches Sat & Sun, Copthall closed Mon-Fri D.

Kaffeine W1 £12   ❸❷❶
66 Great Titchfield St   7580 6755   3–1C
"A real stand-out amongst London's thousands of coffee shops" – this "compact" Soho café combines "multi-award-winning" coffee with "exemplary" service, as well as superior sandwiches, cakes and salads. / W1W 7QJ; www.kaffeine.co.uk; L only; no Amex; no bookings.

Kai Mayfair W1 £97 ④④④
65 South Audley St   7493 8988   3–3A
The cuisine at this swanky Mayfair Chinese really is "truly
exceptional"; prices more than measure up, though, and its following
among reporters is relatively modest. / W1K 2QU; www.kaimayfair.co.uk;
10.45 pm, Sun 10.15 pm.

Kaifeng NW4 £59 ❷❷❸
51 Church Rd   8203 7888   1–1B
"There is no better kosher Chinese in London" than this "consistently
busy" Hendon stalwart (which is also coeliac- and allergy-friendly);
even fans concede it's "very expensive", but they do say it's "worth
every penny". / NW4 4DU; www.kaifeng.co.uk; 10 pm; closed Fri & Sat.

Kaosarn £26 ❷❷❷
110 St Johns Hill, SW11   7223 7888   10–2C
Brixton Village, Coldharbour Ln, SW9   7095 8922   10–2D
These "always-buzzing" cafés, in Brixton Village and Battersea, offer
"snappy" service of "superb, home-cooked Thai food"; "be prepared
to queue if you haven't booked"; BYO. / SW9 10 pm, Sun 9 pm;
sw11 closed Mon L.

Karma W14 £39 ❷❶④
44 Blythe Rd   7602 9333   7–1D
An "overlooked" Indian, "off the beaten track in Olympia", which
is well worth seeking out for its "exciting" cooking and "brilliant"
service – even those who are "not so sure about the decor" say they
"keep returning". / W14 0HA; www.k-a-r-m-a.co.uk; 11 pm; no Amex.

Karpo NW1 £48 ❸④④
23 Euston Rd   7843 2221   8–3C
An "excellent" and "quirky" King's Cross find – "a little oasis of calm"
with a "very airy" interior (complete with living wall), serving
"surprisingly sophisticated" food. / NW1 2SD; www.karpo.co.uk;
10.30 pm.

Kaspar's Seafood and Grill
The Savoy Hotel WC2 NEW £74 ❸❷❸
91 The Strand   7836 4343   4–3D
"Better than the reviews have generally suggested", this seafood-led
relaunch of the former River Restaurant has pleased most early-days
reporters, even if the décor is "a bit TOWIE" for some tastes.
/ WC2R 0EU; www.kaspars.co.uk; 11 pm.

Kateh W9 £42 ❷❷❷
5 Warwick Pl   7289 3393   8–4A
"Small but perfectly formed"; this Little Venice outfit offers a "modern
and elegant twist" on Persian cuisine "of a very high standard";
"shame it's so cramped", though. / W9 2PX; www.katehrestaurant.co.uk;
11 pm, Sun 9.30 pm; closed weekday L.

Kazan £45 ❸❸④
77 Wilton Rd, SW1   7233 8298   2–4B
93-94 Wilton Rd, SW1   7233 7100   2–4B
"Don't be fooled by the plain exteriors!"; this duo of Turkish
operations, in Pimlico, serve "quality" meze and other "reliable" fare
– just the job for "a good light meal at a very reasonable price".
/ www.kazan-restaurant.com; 10 pm.

The Keeper's House W1 NEW £65
Royal Academy Of Arts, Burlington Hs, Piccadilly   7300 5881
3–3D
*A garden is, implausibly, among the attractions of the RA's major new
bar/restaurant development, opening as this guide goes to press; let's
hope it offers a step up from the standards at the RA's existing
restaurant! / W1J 0BD; www.keepershouse.org.uk.*

Ken Lo's Memories SW1 £62 ❸❸④
65-69 Ebury St   7730 7734   2–4B
*Fans insist this "high-end" (but rather "clinical") Belgravia
"old faithful" is "still London's best Chinese"; it's difficult, though,
to avoid the conclusion that many ambitious recent openings have left
it "outclassed". / SW1W 0NZ; www.memoriesofchina.co.uk; 10.45 pm,
Sun 10 pm.*

Ken Lo's Memories of China W8 £57 ❸④④
353 Kensington High St   7603 6951   7–1D
*Fans say this upscale (and once-pre-eminent) establishment, on the
Olympia/Kensington border, can still be "very good"; for an
"expensive" place, though, it's sometimes seemed "nothing special"
of late. / W8 6NW; www.memoriesofchina.co.uk; 10.45 pm.*

Kennington Tandoori SE11 £48 ❷❷❷
313 Kennington Rd   7735 9247   1–3C
*"A cracking local Indian", offering "modern dishes and old classics
with a twist"; thanks not least to its "very welcoming" service, it has
an impressive local following (including many politicos). / SE11 4QE;
www.kenningtontandoori.com; 11.30 pm; no Amex.*

Kensington Place W8 £54 ❸❸④
201-209 Kensington Church St   7727 3184   6–2B
*"Reincarnated as a fish restaurant", the seminal '90s British brasserie
seems to be slowly "rediscovering its mojo"; some things don't
change, though – this goldfish bowl of a place gets "very noisy" when
it's full. / W8 7LX; www.kensingtonplace-restaurant.co.uk; @kprestaurantW8;
10.30 pm; closed Mon L & Sun D; SRA-63%.*

Kensington Square Kitchen W8 £32 ❸0❷
9 Kensington Sq   7938 2598   5–1A
*Offering a warm welcome to "Kensington ladies who lunch", a cute,
if "slightly cramped", café on this pretty square, providing
an "amazingly good" breakfast, and coffee and light meals all day.
/ W8 5EP; www.kensingtonsquarekitchen.co.uk; @KSKRestaurant; 3.30 pm;
L only; no Amex.*

The Kensington Wine Rooms W8 £50 ④❸❸
127-129 Kensington Church St   7727 8142   6–2B
*"Stunning, esoteric, and wine-ranging", the wine list (all available
by the glass) at this pub-conversion, near Notting Hill Gate, is ideal
"for a liquid dinner"; indeed, "you probably wouldn't go there for the
food…" / W8 7LP; www.greatwinesbytheglass.com; 10.45 pm.*

Kentish Canteen NW5 £44 ④❸❸
300 Kentish Town Rd   7485 7331   8–2C
*A "reliable and enjoyable" two-year-old; perhaps one might "expect
more flair", but overall it's "a lovely local", most tipped for its
"good family brunch". / NW5 2TG; www.kentishcanteen.co.uk; 10.30 pm.*

(Brew House)
Kenwood House NW3 £32 ④❸❶
Hampstead Heath 8341 5384 8–1A
*"Nothing beats sitting outside on the terrace", and a Full English
at this smart self-service café, at the top of Hampstead Heath,
makes a great way to start the day; later on, you can "eat delicious
sandwiches, while sipping expensive coffee". / NW3 7JR;
www.companyofcooks.com; 6 pm (summer), 4 pm (winter); L only.*

Kenza EC2 £58 ④④❸
10 Devonshire Sq 7929 5533 9–2D
*Surprisingly little feedback on this large basement Lebanese,
near Liverpool Street; it can be handy, though, for a "good set lunch",
and fans say the raucous evening ambience – complete with belly
dancing – is "superb" too. / EC2 4YP; www.kenza-restaurant.com; 10 pm;
closed Sat L & Sun.*

Kerbisher & Malt £19 ❸❸④
53 New Broadway, W5 8840 4418 1–3A NEW
164 Shepherd's Bush Rd, W6 3556 0228 7–1C
*"Spankingly fresh, traditional fish 'n' chips" (plus "homemade
sauces") have made quite a hit of these Shepherd's Bush and
(now) Ealing chippies; the décor, though, strikes critics as on the
"chilly" side. / www.kerbisher.co.uk; 10 pm - 10.30pm, Sun 9 pm - 9.30 pm;
W6 Closed Mon.*

Kettners W1 £56 ④❸❸
29 Romilly St 7734 6112 4–2A
*"The room remains beautiful", the food "promises more than
it delivers", and the service is a bit "hit 'n' miss" – in fact, plus ça
change at this Soho fixture, with its "excellent position in the heart
of Theatreland"; the top tip, as ever, is the swish Champagne bar.
/ W1D 5HP; www.kettners.com; 11 pm, Fri & Sat 11.30 pm, Sun 9.30 pm.*

Kew Grill TW9 £58 ❸❷❸
10b Kew Grn 8948 4433 1–3A
*Antony Worrall Thompson's "warm" and "friendly" home base seem
to have benefited from his more concentrated personal attention
in recent times – its "simple grills" are pricey, but can be "very good".
/ TW9 3BH; www.awtrestaurants.com; 10.30 pm, Fri-Sat 11 pm, Sun 10 pm;
closed Mon L.*

Khan's W2 £23 ❸④❸
13-15 Westbourne Grove 7727 5420 6–1C
*A "legendary" Indian veteran, in Bayswater, offering a selection
of dishes at rock-bottom prices in a "no-frills" setting, with an
ambience sometimes likened to a railway station; no booze. / W2 4UA;
www.khansrestaurant.com; 11.30 pm, Sat-Sun midnight.*

Khan's of Kensington SW7 £43 ❸❸④
3 Harrington Rd 7584 4114 5–2B
*The name says it all – this is a very standard Indian restaurant,
but it's very handily located, by South Kensington tube, and was
consistently well-rated by reporters this year. / SW7 3ES;
www.khansofkensington.co.uk; 11pm, Fri & Sat 11.30 pm, Sun 10.30 pm.*

Kiku W1 £55 ❷❷⑤
17 Half Moon St 7499 4208 3–4B
*"Authentic, all the way down to the quality of the sushi... and the
neon lighting!" – this "boring"-looking Mayfair fixture makes "a great
lunch/work place", and the food is "very reliable". / W1J 7BE;
www.kikurestaurant.co.uk; 10.15 pm, Sun 9.45 pm; closed Sun L.*

Kikuchi W1 £49 ❶④⑤
14 Hanway St 7637 7720 4–1A
Food that's just "out of this world" makes it well worth seeking out
this "tucked-away" Japanese, off Tottenham Court Road, which fans
hail for some of the best sushi in town; unless you're a native,
however, it's "not the friendliest place". / W1T 1UD; 10.30 pm;
closed Sun.

Kimchee WC1 £38 ④④❸
71 High Holborn 7430 0956 2–1D
"A worthy competitor to Wagamama"; fans say this "always
humming" Holborn two-year-old offers a "vast menu" of "enticing"
Korean dishes, and "great value" too; others, however are less
impressed, finding the food "uninspiring" and service "haphazard".
/ WC1V 6EA; www.kimchee.uk.com; @kimcheerest; 10.30 pm.

Kings Road Steakhouse & Grill SW3 £51 ④④⑤
386 King's Rd 7351 9997 5–3B
"Quite swanky-looking, but uninspiring" – this MPW-branded Chelsea
steakhouse strikes too many reporters for comfort as "very average"
(or worse); "be on the lookout for discounts!" / SW3 5UZ;
www.kingsroadsteakhouseandgrill.com; 10.30 pm, Sun 10 pm.

Kipferl N1 £43 ❸④❸
20 Camden Pas 77041 555 8–3D
A "busy" Islington deli/restaurant, where "authentic" (and "slightly
unusual") Austrian treats – including top cakes and pancakes –
are served with "fabulous" coffee. / N1 8ED; www.kipferl.co.uk; 9 pm;
closed Mon.

Kiraku W5 £34 ❶❷❸
8 Station Pde 8992 2848 1–3A
"Local Japanese residents flock" to this "laid-back" café near Ealing
Common tube; given the superb standard of the "wide and varied
menu" (which incorporates, but is far from limited to, "fantastic
sushi"), prices are notably "competitive". / W5 3LD; www.kiraku.co.uk;
@kirakulondon; 10 pm; closed Mon; no Amex.

Kirazu W1 NEW £35
47 Rupert St 7494 2248 3–2D
A trendy Soho newcomer, offering Kyoto-style home cooking
at modest cost; it opened just too late to attract survey commentary,
but press reports have been very encouraging. / W1D 7PD;
www.kirazu.co.uk.

Kitchen W8 W8 £65 ❶❷❸
11-13 Abingdon Road 7937 0120 5–1A
The part-backing of Phil Howard (of The Square) helps explain the
"surprisingly gourmet" cuisine, "charmingly" served, at this
"unheralded" local on a Kensington side street; "its open-plan series
of small rooms", however, never seems to spark on the atmosphere
front. / W8 6AH; www.kitchenw8.com; @KitchenW8; 10.15 pm,
Sun 9.15 pm; set weekday L £40 (FP), set pre-theatre £42 (FP).

Koba W1 £43 ❸❸④
11 Rathbone St 7580 8825 2–1C
"The excellent BBQ" is a "reliable" attraction of this friendly Fitzrovia
Korean; its ratings have slipped a notch of late, though, as even fans
note the "prices are a little high". / W1T 1NA; 10.30 pm; closed Sun L.

Koffmann's
The Berkeley SW1   £80   ❷⓿❸
The Berkeley, Wilton Pl   7107 8844   5–1D
*"A chance to savour the cooking of a culinary legend!"; Pierre K ran
'90s-London's best restaurant (La Tante Claire) and the "rich" and
"old-fashioned" Gallic dishes on offer at this "cosy", if "low-ceilinged",
Knightsbridge basement are "sublime", with wine and service
to match.* / SW1X 7RL; www.the-berkeley.co.uk/top_restaurants.aspx;
10.30 pm; set weekday L £48 (FP), set Sun L £49 (FP), set pre-theatre
£51 (FP).

Kolossi Grill EC1   £32   ❹❷❷
56-60 Rosebery Ave   7278 5758   9–1A
"Unpretentious, reasonably-priced, pleasantly located…" – this old-
time Farringdon taverna invariably pleases: *"I've been eating meze
here for 40 years, and they are still great value!"* / EC1R 4RR;
www.kolossigrill.com; 11 pm; closed Sat L & Sun.

Konditor & Cook   £27   ❸❹❹
Curzon Soho, 99 Shaftesbury Ave, W1   854 9367   4–3A
46 Gray's Inn Rd, WC1   854 9365   9–1A
10 Stoney St, SE1   854 9363   9–4C
22 Cornwall Road, SE1   854 9361   9–4A
30 St Mary Axe, EC3   854 9369   9–2D
"Wonderful" coffee and cakes, and "first-rate savouries" too –
reporters find little to fault at the *"bustling"* branches of this
consistent small chain. / www.konditorandcook.com; 6 pm; W1 11 pm;
WC1 & EC3 closed Sat & Sun; SE1 closed Sun; no booking.

Kopapa WC2   £56   ❸❹❹
32-34 Monmouth St   7240 6076   4–2B
"Peter Gordon does it again", says one of the many fans of his
"cramped" Theatreland dining room, where *"delicious and quirky
small plates"* are the menu staple (and breakfasts are *"fantastic"*
too); service, though is sometimes *"nowhere to be seen"*.
/ WC2H 9HA; www.kopapa.co.uk; @Kopapacafe; 10.45 pm, Sun 9.45 pm.

Koya W1   £34   ❷❸❸
49 Frith St   7434 4463   4–2A
"Queues, even in the depth of winter" advertise the charms of this
"basic" but *"brilliant"* Soho Japanese, where the menu features not
just *"the best udon noodles in London"*, but also some notably
"creative" specials. / W1D 4SG; www.koya.co.uk; @KoyaUdon; 10.30 pm;
no booking.

Koya-Ko W1 NEW   £33
50 Frith St   awaiting tel   4–2A
*Next to the mega-popular Soho udon restaurant, a fast-service all-day
newcomer; special attractions?* – such cross-cultural delights as an
English breakfast soup! / W1D 4SQ.

Kulu Kulu   £31   ❹❺❹
76 Brewer St, W1   7734 7316   3–2D
51-53 Shelton St, WC2   7240 5687   4–2C
39 Thurloe Pl, SW7   7589 2225   5–2C
"They don't look much" (*"like a hole in the wall"*), the service
is *"basic"*, and the food quality *"mixed"*, but this grungy conveyor-café
chain is still hailed by fans as a *"great place to satisfy a sushi-craving
on the cheap"*. / 10 pm; SW7 10.30 pm; closed Sun; no Amex; no booking.

Kurumaya EC4 £41 ❸❸④
76-77 Watling St 7236 0236 9–2B
"Consistently good" food makes this "friendly" and "efficient"
Japanese a handy City stand-by... not least the ground-floor kaiten
(conveyor) operation, which serves "fantastic fresh sushi". / EC4M 9BJ;
www.kurumaya.co.uk; @Kurumaya76; 9.30 pm; closed Sat & Sun.

The Ladbroke Arms W11 £49 ❷❸❷
54 Ladbroke Rd 7727 6648 6–2B
"Well-cooked dishes, pretty people and dogs" – this smart Notting
Hill boozer really leaves nothing to be desired; in fact, the only
problem is that, "whether it's a sunny day, or a grey one", it can
sometimes be "a bit too popular". / W11 3NW;
www.capitalpubcompany.com; 9.30 pm; no booking after 8 pm.

Ladudu NW6 £35 ❸❸④
152 West End Ln 7372 3217 1–1B
"Great spicing" peps up the Vietnamese scoff on offer at this
"busy but always accommodating" West Hampstead café.
/ NW6 1SD; www.ladudu.com; @ladudufood; 10.30 pm.

Ladurée £60 ❷④❸
Harrods, 87-135 Brompton Rd, SW1 3155 0111 5–1D
71-72 Burlington Arc, Piccadilly, W1 7491 9155 3–3C
1 Covent Garden Mkt, WC2 7240 0706 4–3D
14 Cornhill, EC3 7283 5727 9–2C
"The best macarons in a very plush setting" – the essential features
of these bijoux outposts of the famed Parisian pâtisserie, but they
do also offer other "beautifully made" cakes plus superior coffee,
omelettes and sandwiches (availability varies by branch).
/ www.laduree.com; SW1 8.45 pm, Sun 5.45 pm; W1 6.30 pm, Sun 5 pm,
EC3 8 pm; EC3 closed Sat-Sun; W1 no booking, SW1 no booking 3 pm-6 pm.

The Lady Ottoline WC1 £46 ④④❸
11a, Northington St 7831 0008 2–1D
This year-old relaunch of a characterful Victorian boozer is "a great
addition to Bloomsbury", say fans; others, though, can go no further
than finding it "decent enough". / WC1N 2JF; www.theladyottoline.com;
@theladyottoline; 10 pm, Sun 8 pm.

Lahore Karahi SW17 £23 ❷④④
1 Tooting High Street, London 8767 2477 10–2C
"Still the best subcontinental café around!" – this "busy", "canteen-
style" Tooting "favourite" has a big name for its "genuine Pakistani
food at bargain prices"; BYO. / SW17 0SN; www.lahorekarahi.co.uk;
midnight; no Amex.

Lahore Kebab House £26 ❶④④
668 Streatham High Rd, SW16 8765 0771 10–2D
2-10 Umberston St, E1 7488 2551 11–1A
"The best kebabs west of Lahore!"; with its "fantastic flavours
at great prices", this "plain" Pakistani canteen in Whitechapel
is nothing short of a "phenomenon" – even those who find the setting
"depressing" concede the food is "spectacular"; SW16 is good too;
BYO. / midnight.

Lamberts SW12   £47   ❶❶❷
2 Station Pde   8675 2233   10–2C
*"What an outstanding restaurant in an unlikely place!" –
this "unfailing" gem, near Balham station, is "excellent across the
board"; indeed, locals claim it's a rival to nearby Chez Bruce, but it's
no criticism to say it's not trying to play in quite the same league.*
/ SW12 9AZ; www.lambertsrestaurant.com; @lamberts_balham; 10. pm,
Sun 5 pm; closed Mon & Sun D; no Amex; set weekday L £33 (FP); SRA-60%.

(Winter Garden) The Landmark NW1   £82   ❸❷❶
222 Marylebone Rd   7631 8000   8–4A
*It's the "fabulous" Sunday jazz brunch – "not gourmet, but excellent
for a buffet", and with "unlimited" champagne – which is the
particular draw to this "relaxed" venue, in the soaring atrium of a
Marylebone hotel; lunch and afternoon tea also have their fans.*
/ NW1 6JQ; www.landmarklondon.co.uk; 10.30 pm; no trainers; booking:
max 12.

Langan's Brasserie W1   £64   ④❷❷
Stratton St   7491 8822   3–3C
*This "legendary" grand brasserie, near the Ritz, may seem a little
"dated", but its upbeat style has proved amazingly enduring over the
years (especially for business); it's given a more "professional"
impression of late since recent management changes – might this
be the start of a comeback?* / W1J 8LB; www.langansrestaurants.co.uk;
11 pm, Fri & Sat 11.30 pm, Sun 10 pm.

Lantana Cafe W1   £34   ❸❸❷
13-14 Charlotte Pl   7323 6601   2–1C
*"Laid-back", it may be, but this Oz café in Fitzrovia – with its
"amazing" cakes, its "top-notch" coffee and its "interesting" other
dishes – is becoming quite a beacon; "shame they don't take
reservations!"* / W1T 1SN; www.lantanacafe.co.uk; 3 pm; L only; no Amex;
no booking.

Lardo E8   £38   ❸④❸
Richmond Rd   8533 8229   1–2D
*A "hip crowd" Hackney yearling, offering a menu of pizza, pasta and
cured meats for which "you won't have to re-mortgage"; what it
arguably "lacks in ambition", it makes up for with "fantastic
sourcing".* / E8 3NJ; www.lardo.co.uk; 10.30 pm, Sun 9.30 pm.

Latium W1   £49   ❷❶❸
21 Berners St   7323 9123   3–1D
*"Reminiscent of a top Rome restaurant" – Maurizio Morelli's
"civilised" venture, just north of Oxford Street, is a "totally
professional but genuinely warm" operation, serving up an
"elaborate" menu of "fine" dishes (ravioli is the house speciality),
plus a "fabulous selection of wines".* / W1T 3LP;
www.latiumrestaurant.com; 10.30 pm, Sat 11 pm; closed Sat L & Sun;
set weekday L & pre-theatre £34 (FP).

Launceston Place W8   £74   ❷❷❷
1a Launceston Pl   7937 6912   5–1B
*With its "off-the-beaten track" location "in the backstreets
of Kensington", and its "elegant" townhouse interior, this "intimate"
and "professional" D&D group all-rounder is a natural romantic
"oasis"; under chef Tim Allen, the cuisine is returning to "superb"
form too.* / W8 5RL; www.launcestonplace-restaurant.co.uk; 10 pm; closed
Mon L; set weekday L £48 (FP); SRA-63%.

The Lawn Bistro SW19 £57 ④❷④
67 High St   8947 8278   10–2B
"A necessary addition to the Wimbledon Village scene, but overpriced
for what it is" – a good example of the somewhat ambivalent
reception to this "fancy" yearling; it is however "the best lunch option
in the village" (which is "not saying much!"). / SW19 5EE;
www.thelawnbistro.co.uk; 9.30 pm, Sat 10 pm; closed Sun D.

THE LEDBURY W11 £113 ❶❶❷
127 Ledbury Rd   7792 9090   6–1B
"Brett Graham is a genius, whose French/Australasian fusion still
dazzles", and his "impeccable" Notting Hill fixture was again rated
London's foodie No. 1, thanks to its "enchanting" food and "silky
smooth" service; can he push on for the dreaded third Michelin star,
though, without succumbing to stuffiness and overpricing? / W11 2AQ;
www.theledbury.com; 10.15 pm, Sun 10 pm; closed Mon L; set weekday L
£62 (FP).

Lemonia NW1 £46 ④❷⓿
89 Regent's Park Rd   7586 7454   8–3B
"Amazingly reliable through the decades", this "unique" Primrose Hill
mega-taverna is still "always packed to the gills"; it can't be the food,
so it must be that this is an "always-fun" destination that's become
a "home from home" for many locals. / NW1 8UY; www.lemonia.co.uk;
11 pm; closed Sun D; no Amex.

Leon £26 ④❸❸
275 Regent St, W1   7495 1514   3–1C
35-36 Gt Marlborough St, W1   7437 5280   3–2C
73-76 The Strand, WC2   7240 3070   4–4D
7 Canvey St, SE1   7620 0035   9–3B
Cabot Place West, E14   7719 6200   11–1C
3 Crispin Pl, E1   7247 4369   12–2B
12 Ludgate Circus, EC4   7489 1580   9–2A
86 Cannon St, EC4   7623 9699   9–3C
"A saviour from boring lunches" – with their "lovely", "clean-tasting"
wraps, salads and juices, these wholesome diners are still,
for most reporters, "a great alternative to typical fast food";
as expansion continues, though, ratings are heading south.
/ www.leonrestaurants.co.uk; 10 pm; W1 8.45 pm; E14 8 pm; EC4 closed Sun;
W1 closed Sat & Sun; no booking L.

Leong's Legends W1 £36 ❸④❸
3 Macclesfield St   7287 0288   4–3A
"A slightly more unusual Taiwanese take on the typical Chinatown
offering" – this budget diner specialises in Xiao Long Bao
(soup dumplings), and offers "authentic" and "tasty" scoff at a
"knock-down price". / W1D 6AX; www.leongslegend.com; 11 pm,
Sat 11.30 pm; no booking.

Levant W1 £54 ④❸❷
Jason Ct, 76 Wigmore St   7224 1111   3–1A
"You are no longer really in London", if you pay a visit to this party-
Lebanese, in a basement near Selfridges; it has only attracted
modest survey feedback of late, but all positive. / W1U 2SJ;
www.levant.co.uk; 9.45pm, Fri-Sat midnight.

The Lido Cafe
Brockwell Lido SE24 £44 ❸❸❷
Dulwich Rd 7737 8183 10–2D
*"Brilliant" breakfasts are a highlight of the dining experience at this
"spectacular" south London lido, but its "good honest grub"
is enjoyable at any time; "book a table by the window, so you can
watch the swimmers".* / SE24 0PA; www.thelidocafe.co.uk; @thelidocafe;
9.30 pm; closed Mon D & Sun D; no Amex.

The Light House SW19 £49 ❹❸❸
75-77 Ridgway 8944 6338 10–2B
*Mixed reports on this "bustling" Wimbledon spot; fans insist that
it "punches above its weight", with "greatly improved" post-refurb
décor, and a menu that's "always interesting"; execution, though,
can be "variable".* / SW19 4ST; www.lighthousewimbledon.com; 10.30 pm;
closed Sun D.

Lima W1 £56 ❸❹❹
31 Rathbone Pl 3002 2640 2–1C
*"Ceviche to die for" is the highlight of the "colourful" cuisine at the
Fitzrovia yearling sometimes acclaimed as "London's top Peruvian";
acoustics are "poor", though, and some reporters just "can't see what
everyone goes on about".* / W1T 1JH; www.limalondon.com;
www.twitter.com/lima_london; 10.30 pm; closed Sun; SRA-51%.

Lisboa Pâtisserie W10 £8 ❸❸❹
57 Golborne Rd 8968 5242 6–1A
*"The best pasteis de nata (custard tarts) in the world" – well, nearly
– are served at this "stalwart" North Kensington café.* / W10 5NR;
7 pm; L & early evening only; no booking.

Little Bay £31 ❹❷❶
228 Belsize Rd, NW6 7372 4699 1–2B
171 Farringdon Rd, EC1 7278 1234 9–1A
*"Is there a better-value meal in London?", say fans of these
"gorgeous", "fun" and "romantic" budget bistros, where the scoff
"isn't fancy" but it is "unbelievably reasonably priced"; live opera is a
"bonus" too.* / www.little-bay.co.uk; @TheLittleBay; 11.30 pm, Sun 11 pm;
no Amex, NW6 no credit cards.

Little Georgia Café £38 ❸❹❸
14 Barnsbury Rd, N1 7278 6100 8–3D
87 Goldsmiths Row, E2 7739 8154 1–2D
*"A hidden gem, and you can BYO too!" – this "cosy" café, in Bethnal
Green, offers an interesting Georgian menu; praise too for its year-old
Islington offshoot, though it takes some flak on the service front.*
/ www.littlegeorgia.co.uk.

Little Social W1 NEW £60 ❷❷❷
5 Pollen St 7870 3730 3–2C
*"The very amicable new sibling of Pollen Street Social" (over the road)
"recreates the feel of a French bistro", and fans find
it "more relaxed", "more personal" and "more atmospheric" than big
brother; the cooking is "lovely" too.* / W1S 1NE; www.littlesocial.co.uk.

LMNT E8 £36 ❹❸❶
316 Queensbridge Rd 7249 6727 1–2D
*"Crazy" OTT classical decor (Sphinx, Greek urns, hieroglyphics)
makes it "always fun" to visit this pharaoh-kitsch Dalston pub-
conversion; it matters not that the food is "a bit variable".* / E8 3NH;
www.lmnt.co.uk; 10.30 pm; Mon-Thu D only, Fri-Sun open L & D; no Amex.

Lobster Pot SE11 £61 ❷❸④
3 Kennington Ln 7582 5556 1–3C
"A quirky little place that's stood the test of time" – this family-run stalwart may have an "odd" location, in deepest Kennington, plus surreal 'sunken schooner' decor (complete with taped gulls), but "it excels at what it does – traditionally-prepared Gallic seafood". / SE11 4RG; www.lobsterpotrestaurant.co.uk; 10.30 pm; closed Mon & Sun; booking: max 8.

Locanda Locatelli
Hyatt Regency W1 £75 ❸❸④
8 Seymour St 7935 9088 2–2A
Fans still extol Giorgio Locatelli's "elegant and understated" Marylebone dining room for "perfect" Italian cuisine "that both respects and pushes tradition"; it can also seem "absurdly expensive" though, and service occasionally "lets the place down". / W1H 7JZ; www.locandalocatelli.com; 11 pm, Thu-Sat 11.30 pm, Sun 10.15 pm; booking: max 8.

Locanda Ottomezzo W8 £66 ④④④
2-4 Thackeray St 7937 2200 5–1B
"Tucked-away", "Intimate" and "idiosyncratic", this "upmarket neighbourhood Italian" has a devoted Kensington following; "if the prices were lower, it would be amazing…" / W8 5ET; www.locandaottoemezzo.co.uk; 10.30 pm, Fri & Sat 10.45 pm; closed Mon L & Sun.

Loch Fyne £44 ④❸④
2-4 Catherine St, WC2 7240 4999 2–2D
77-78 Gracechurch St, EC3 7929 8380 9–3C
Whether this comfy, if slightly sedate national seafood chain is "highly dependable", or merely "formulaic", has long been a matter of dispute; this year, however, a number of reporters suggested it's "trying hard to raise its game". / www.lochfyne-restaurants.com; 10 pm; WC2 10.30 pm.

The Lockhart W1 NEW £50
24 Seymour Pl 3011 5400 2–2A
Not far from Marble Arch, a summer 2013 newcomer specialising in the cuisine of the American Southwest; we sadly didn't have the opportunity to visit before this guide went to press. / W1H 7NL; www.lockhartlondon.com; @LockhartLondon; 10.30 pm; set weekday L £33 (FP).

Lola & Simón W6 £48 ❸❷❸
278 King St 8563 0300 7–2B
This "quirky" Argentinian/Kiwi café – run with "energy and commitment" – is a "cosy" feature of Hammersmith's main drag; it's open all day, but particularly known locally as the "perfect morning pit stop". / W6 0SP; www.lolaandsimon.co.uk; @lola_simon; 10 pm; no Amex.

Lola Rojo SW11 £42 ❸④④
78 Northcote Rd 7350 2262 10–2C
Offering "a modern twist on tapas", this "lively" and "friendly" Battersea spot is an almost invariable crowd-pleaser. / SW11 6QL; www.lolarojo.net; 10.30 pm, Sat & Sun 11 pm; no Amex.

Look Mum No Hands! EC1 £29 ❸❸❷
49 Old St 7253 1025 9–1B
"Where else can you have a snack and get your bike repaired at the same time?" – this "hip" café-cum-cycle-shop dishes up "delicious healthy food", plus plenty of "super-friendly attitude too". / EC1V 9HX; www.lookmumnohands.co.uk; @lookmumnohands; 10 pm.

The Lord Northbrook SE12 £35 ❸❷❷
116 Burnt Ash Rd 8318 1127 1–4D
This Lea Green boozer – "beautifully done up" two years ago – hasn't entirely gone 'gastro', but its "friendly" staff serve up "surprisingly good" grub from a "short and sensible menu". / SE12 8PU; www.thelordnorthbrook.co.uk; 9 pm, Fri-Sat 10 pm.

Lorenzo SE19 £41 ❹❷❸
73 Westow Hill 8761 7485 1–4D
A "cosy" fixture of Upper Norwood – a dependable Italian that's "always full", thanks to its "simple" but "great-value" pizza and pasta menu. / SE19 1TX; www.lorenzo.uk.com; 10.30 pm.

Lotus Chinese Floating Restaurant E14 £42 ❹❹❸
9 Oakland Quay 7515 6445 11–2C
Permanently-moored, near Canary Wharf, a boat offering "really good dim sum" at lunchtime; as an evening destination, though, it can feel pretty "soulless". / E14 9EA; www.lotusfloating.co.uk; 10.30 pm; closed Mon.

Lucio SW3 £64 ❸❹❹
257 Fulham Rd 7823 3007 5–3B
"In the end, everyone in Chelsea will be seated next to you!" – this "old-money" Italian certainly doesn't lack local custom, but even fans may note that it's "pricey", and a "distinct feeling of priority for the regulars" irks some. / SW3 6HY; 10.45 pm; set weekday L £42 (FP).

Lucky Seven W2 £39 ❸❸❷
127 Westbourne Park Rd 7727 6771 6–1B
Brace yourself to share a booth at Tom Conran's funky, tightly-packed slice of Americana, on the fringe of Notting Hill; it does a mean burger, and some "pretty amazing chocolate malts" too. / W2 5QL; www.tomconranrestaurants.com; 10.15 pm, Sun 10 pm; no Amex; no booking.

Lupita WC2 £38 ❹❹❸
13-15 Villiers St 7930 5355 4–4D
"So much better than your average Tex-Mex", this "refreshing" corner Mexican, right by Charing Cross, offers "proper food, like you find in Mexico". / WC2N 6ND; www.lupita.co.uk; @LupitaUK; 11 pm, Fri-Sat 11.30 pm, Sun 10 pm.

Lutyens EC4 £72 ❹❹❹
85 Fleet St 7583 8385 9–2A
Sir Terence Conran's large Fleet Street outpost is a "noisy" and "impersonal" affair, where the food is "rarely exciting" – no doubt why many reports confirm it's "fine for a business lunch"! / EC4Y 1AE; www.lutyens-restaurant.com; 10 pm; closed Sat & Sun; set weekday L £50 (FP).

Ma Cuisine TW9 £41 ❸❸❸
9 Station Approach 8332 1923 1–3A
"The best middle-of-the-road restaurant in Kew!"; this slightly "middle-aged" Gallic venture, near the tube, is currently in an "up-phase"; it serves classic bistro fare at affordable prices. / TW9 3QB; www.macuisinekew.co.uk; 10 pm, Fri & Sat 10.30 pm; no Amex.

Ma Goa SW15 £39 ❷❶❷

242-244 Upper Richmond Rd   8780 1767   10–2B

"Utterly reliable, and fantastic value"; this "consistently warm and friendly" family-fun Putney local is well worth seeking out for its Goan cuisine – "a revelation". / SW15 6TG; www.ma-goa.com; @magoarestaurant; 11 pm, Sun 10 pm; closed Mon L & Sat L.

Made In Camden
Roundhouse NW1 £38 ❸❸❸

Chalk Farm Rd   7424 8495   8–2B

It may be attached to Camden Town's Roundhouse, but this "inventive" café is a destination in its own right; it serves an "enterprising and cosmopolitan" small plates menu that's "especially great for brunch". / NW1 8EH; www.madeincamden.com; 10.15 pm.

Made in Italy £41 ❸④❸

14a, Old Compton St, W1   0011 1214   4–2B
50 James St, W1   7224 0182   3–1A NEW
249 King's Rd, SW3   7352 1880   5–3C

"I love the metre-long pizzas!" – this "fun" Chelsea outfit serves up stone-baked pizzas that consistently satisfy, and it even has a terrace for sunny days; good (if limited) feedback on Soho too. / www.madeinitalygroup.co.uk; 11 pm, Sun 10 pm; SW3 closed Mon L.

Madhu's UB1 £34 ❸❸❸

39 South Rd   8574 1897   1–3A

A pilgrimage to this landmark of Southall's curry strip is the stuff of foodie legend; some devotees do declare it "the best in town", but "enjoyable" is the better mark of overall survey approval. / UB1 1SW; www.madhus.co.uk; 11.30 pm; closed Tue, Sat L & Sun L.

Madsen SW7 £48 ❸④⑤

20 Old Brompton Rd   7225 2772   5–2B

A "simple" South Kensington Scandinavian, recommended for a "slightly different but reasonably-priced" meal of Smørrebrød (open sarnies) and other "Danish staples"; on the downside, however, it can all seem "rather bland". / SW7 3DL; www.madsenrestaurant.com; @madsenlondon; 10 pm, Fri-Sat 10.45 pm; closed Sun D; no Amex.

The Magazine Restaurant
Serpentine Gallery W2 NEW

Kensington Gdns   7402 6075   6–2D

Zaha Hadid, no less, is the architect of the restaurant of this new gallery in the heart of Hyde Park, opening as this guide goes to press; the chef, Berlin-born Oliver Lange, apparently cooks in British style. / W2 3XA.

Magdalen SE1 £55 ❷❸❸

152 Tooley St   7403 1342   9–4D

"Thoughtful" and "gutsy" seasonal British cuisine at "sensible" prices, with a "wonderful wine list" too, have helped win a large, loyal following for this "hidden gem" – well "worth a detour" in the thin area round City Hall. / SE1 2TU; www.magdalenrestaurant.co.uk; 10 pm; closed Sat L & Sun; set weekday L £35 (FP).

Maggie Jones's W8 £55 ④④❶
6 Old Court Pl   7937 6462   5–1A
"A blast from the past" – this "'70s throwback" (named after
a former fan, Princess Margaret, who used to book in that name) is a
"very atmospheric" Kensington destination, serving English cooking
of a rather "solid" type; service can be "patchy", but it is "with a
smile". / W8 4PL; www.maggie-jones.co.uk; 11 pm, Sun 10.30 pm; set Sun L
£39 (FP).

Maguro W9 £37 ❶❷❸
5 Lanark Pl   7289 4353   8–4A
With its growing reputation for "awesome" sushi (in particular),
this "consistently brilliant" Maida Vale "hidden gem" isn't really
so hidden any more – its "tiny" premises are "always packed".
/ W9 1BT; www.maguro-restaurant.com; 10.30 pm; no Amex.

Maison Bertaux W1 £16 ❷❸❶
28 Greek St   7437 6007   4–2A
"Delightfully unchanging" and "eccentric", this Soho café (est 1871)
may seem like a "bizarre throw-back", but the cakes it offers are still
"always delicious". / W1D 5DQ; www.maisonbertaux.com; 10.15 pm,
Sun 8 pm.

Malabar W8 £44 ❷❷❸
27 Uxbridge St   7727 8800   6–2B
"An old classic, still keeping the punters happy after more than
25 years" – this "accommodating" Indian, off Notting Hill Gate,
is still a definite "cut above", and offers some "thoughtfully-spiced"
dishes. / W8 7TQ; www.malabar-restaurant.co.uk; 11.30 pm, Sun 10.30 pm;
set Sun L £29 (FP).

Malabar Junction WC1 £40 ❸④❸
107 Gt Russell St   7580 5230   2–1C
"Behind an unprepossessing entrance, near the British Museum",
lurks this "surprisingly spacious, light and airy" spot, in which to enjoy
"classic" Keralan cuisine; service here has long been of note,
but recently it has been rather up-and-down. / WC1B 3NA;
www.malabarjunction.com; 11 pm.

The Mall Tavern W8 £48 ❸❸❸
71-73 Palace Gardens Ter   7229 3374   6–2B
The "famous Cow Pie" – twinned with other "modern British classics"
– has carved out quite a name for this Kensington gastropub
(particularly the "fantastic chef's table"); the cooking, though,
is perhaps a touch "less exciting than it used to be". / W8 4RU;
www.themalltavern.com; 10 pm.

The Malt House SW6 NEW £53 ❷❸❸
17 Vanston Pl   7084 6888   5–3A
"This is not pub food, it is serious food!" – with its "interesting"
menu, this "friendly" Fulham newcomer offers "a perfect combination
of delicious food and easy-going surroundings". / SW6 1AY;
www.malthousefulham.co.uk; @MalthouseFulham; 10 pm, Sun 9 pm;
set weekday L £35 (FP).

Mandalay W2 £27 ❸❷⑤
444 Edgware Rd   7258 3696   8–4A
This family-run Burmese (Indian/Chinese) stalwart, near Edgware
Road tube "has had its ups and downs", but it's "incredibly cheap",
and generally worth a try; "the interior is a bit rough-round-the-edges,
but the welcome is warm and attentive". / W2 1EG;
www.mandalayway.com; 10.30 pm; closed Sun.

Mandarin Kitchen W2 £40 ❷④⑤
14-16 Queensway   7727 9012   6–2C
"Undoubtedly the best lobster noodles" – highlight of the "fantastic"
Chinese seafood dishes on offer at this Bayswater veteran;
the "very '70s" décor, though, "desperately needs work". / W2 3RX;
11.15 pm.

Mangal I E8 £30 ❶④④
10 Arcola St   7275 8981   1–1C
"Still the best Turkish grill in London despite the increasing number
of imitators" – this Dalston marvel offers a "wonderful meat-fest"
and "beautiful salads" too… all at "unbelievably low prices"; BYO.
/ E8 2DJ; www.mangal1.com; midnight, Sat-Sun 1 am; no credit cards.

Mangal II N16 £36 ❸❸④
4 Stoke Newington Rd   7254 7888   1–1C
"Notorious as Gilbert & George's go-to supper destination",
this "cheap and cheerful" Dalston Ocakbasi "never fails to satisfy
your cravings for grilled meat". / N16 8BH; www.mangal2.com; 1 am.

Mango & Silk SW14 £34 ❷❷❸
199 Upper Richmond Rd   8876 6220   1–4A
"So much better than a lot of the 'standard' Indians… a bit more
expensive, but you get what you pay for" – this East Sheen spot
serves a "good selection of gourmet" dishes. / SW14 8QT;
www.mangoandsilk.co.uk; @Mangoandsilk; 9.30 pm, Fri & Sat 10 pm; D only,
closed Sun.

Mango Food of India SE1 £50 ❸❸④
5-6 Cromwell Buildings, Redcross Way   7407 0333   9–4C
"Busy, and with plenty of buzz", a tucked-away modern Indian,
near Borough Market, offering "good-quality" cooking, and a "a few
'different' dishes". / SE1 9HR; 11 pm.

Mango Room NW1 £44 ❸❸❸
10-12 Kentish Town Rd   7482 5065   8–3B
"Unchanged in two decades", this buzzy haunt remains a well-rated
Camden Town hang-out, serving "sophisticated" Caribbean grub with
easy-going style. / NW1 8NH; www.mangoroom.co.uk; 11 pm.

Mango Tree £53 ❸④④
46 Grosvenor Pl, SW1   7823 1888   2–4B
Harrods, 87-135 Brompton Rd, SW1   7730 1234   5–1D
Fans of these "busy" Thai outfits (part of an international chain) laud
their "authentic" fare; critics, however, dismiss their regularly price-
promoted cooking as "pretty uninteresting" – "even at 50% off it was
too expensive!" / www.mangotree.org.uk; @MangoTreeLondon; Brompton
Rd Mon-Sat 8.30 pm, Sun 7.30 pm; Grosvenor Pl Mon-Wed 11 pm, Thu-Sat
11.30 pm, Sun 10.30 pm.

Manicomio £59 ❸④❸
85 Duke of York Sq, SW3   7730 3366   5–2D
6 Gutter Ln, EC2   7726 5010   9–2B
"Competent food with a light touch" helps make these "female-
friendly" Italians popular with most Chelsea and City reporters; lots of
outside tables make for "good people-watching" too.
/ www.manicomio.co.uk; SW3 10.30 pm, Sun 10 pm; EC2 10 pm; EC2 closed
Sat & Sun.

Manna NW3 £52 ④④④
4 Erskine Rd 7722 8028 8–3B
The UK's longest-established veggie (1968) has put in an up-and-down performance in recent years; fans say it's "back on form", but sceptics say its Primrose Hill setting is too "Spartan", and that it "trades on its longevity". / NW3 3AJ; www.mannav.com; @mannacuisine; 10.30 pm; closed Mon, Tue-Fri D only, Sat & Sun open L & D.

The Manor Arms SW16 £37 ❷❸④
13 Mitcham Ln 3195 6888 10–2C
A huge success, down Streatham way; this "family-friendly" boozer is acclaimed in many reviews for its "high quality", with "superb" seafood and "brilliant Sunday lunches" among the highlights. / SW16 6LQ; www.themanorarms.com.

Mao Tai SW6 £63 ❷❷❷
58 New King's Rd 7731 2520 10–1B
A pricey pan-Asian veteran, in Fulham, offering "a good mixture of old favourites and more contemporary dishes"; "it's always been good, but it's got even better in recent times!" / SW6 4LS; www.maotai.co.uk; 11.30 pm, Sun 10.30 pm; D only, ex Sun open L & D.

Mar I Terra SE1 £31 ❸❸❷
14 Gambia St 7928 7628 9–4A
A long-established bar that's "slightly out of the way, but worth tracking down" as a "useful pre-theatre" (South Bank) destination, thanks not least to its "authentic" and "tasty" cuisine. / SE1 0XH; www.mariterra.co.uk; 10.30 pm; closed Sat L & Sun.

MARCUS WAREING THE BERKELEY SW1 £116 ❸❷❷
Wilton Pl 7235 1200 5–1D
For "precision and perfection", fans still hail the "unbelievable experience" offered by Marcus Wareing's "elegantly relaxed" Knightsbridge dining room, vaunting "superlative" cuisine and "top drawer" service; prices are "eye-watering", however, and ratings support those who feel it's "not as tip-top as it used to be". / SW1X 7RL; www.marcus-wareing.com; 10.45 pm; closed Sun; no jeans or trainers; booking: max 8; set weekday L £63 (FP), set pre-theatre £82 (FP).

Mari Vanna SW1 £68 ④⑤❷
116 Knightsbridge 7225 3122 5–1D
A visit to this rustic-chic Russian yearling, by Knightsbridge tube, is just like "entering Chekhov's world" – the food is "average", but the atmosphere is "fantastic", and the people-watching is "fabulous"! / SW1X 7PJ; www.marivanna.co.uk; @marivannalondon; 11.30 pm; set weekday L £46 (FP).

Marianne W2 NEW £82
104 Chepstow Rd 3675 7750 6–1B
A Bayswater newcomer of note for its sheer (lack of) size; Marianne Lumb has an impressive cv behind her, and just 14 seats in her restaurant; early press reaction has been very positive. / W2 5QS; www.mariannerestaurant.com; @marianne_w2.

Marine Ices NW3 £39
8 Haverstock Hill 7482 9003 8–2B
"Glorious Italian gelati" have served generations of kids at this Camden Town "perennial", and the pizzas are traditionally "pretty good too"; the founding family sold out this year, though, so we don't think a rating is yet appropriate. / NW3 2BL; www.marineices.co.uk; 11 pm, Sun 10 pm; closed Mon; no Amex.

Market NW1 £49 ❸④④
43 Parkway 7267 9700 8–3B
"A noughties update of the 1970s bistro format"; this "bare-brick" Camden Town haunt offers a "short but intriguing" menu of "well-produced" dishes, and a "relaxed" experience overall. / NW1 7PN; www.marketrestaurant.co.uk; @MarketCamden; 10.30 pm, Sun 3 pm; closed Sun D; set weekday L £31 (FP).

Maroush £47 ❷❸④
I) 21 Edgware Rd, W2 7723 0773 6–1D
II) 38 Beauchamp Pl, SW3 7581 5434 5–1C
V) 3-4 Vere St, W1 7493 5050 3–1B
VI) 68 Edgware Rd, W2 7224 9339 6–1D
'Garden') 1 Connaught St, W2 7262 0222 6–1D
"Fresh, aromatic and tasty" dishes have long made this Lebanese chain a London fixture; as well as the grander dining rooms, the "busy, hustling and bustling" café/take-aways at some branches (I, II and IV) are "great for a light meal"; top tip – ask for the 'wraps' menu. / www.maroush.com; most branches close between 12.30 am-5 am.

Masala Zone £32 ❸❷❷
9 Marshall St, W1 7287 9966 3–2D
48 Floral St, WC2 7379 0101 4–2D
147 Earl's Court Rd, SW5 7373 0220 5–2A
583 Fulham Rd, SW6 7386 5500 5–4A
75 Bishop's Bridge Rd, W2 7221 0055 6–1C
80 Upper St, N1 7359 3399 8–3D
25 Parkway, NW1 7267 4422 8–3B
"It's hard to be disappointed", at this "buzzy and efficient" Indian street-food chain; "it may not be the most adventurous cuisine-wise", but it's "reliable" and very "sensibly priced" – for best value, grab a Thali. / www.realindianfood.com; 11 pm, Sun 10.30 pm; no Amex; booking: min 10.

MASH Steakhouse W1 £75 ❸❸❸
77 Brewer St 7734 2608 3–2D
Occupying a subterranean "Art Deco masterpiece", near Piccadilly Circus, this new (from Denmark) steakhouse concept has struck most, if not quite all, early-days reporters as "pricey, but worth it", and it makes a notably "well-spaced" destination for a business rendezvous; BYO, no corkage on Sundays. / W1F 9ZN; www.mashsteak.dk/restaurants/london; 11.30 pm, Sun 11 pm; closed Sun L; set Sun L £43 (FP).

Massimo
Corinthia Hotel SW1 £81 ⑤⑤④
10 Northumberland Ave 7998 0555 2–3D
Since Massimo left in mid-2012, this unbelievably opulent chamber, near Embankment, has given the impression of "needing to be kicked into action" – offering cooking of no more than "trattoria" standard, is this perhaps the Most-Expensive-Least-Exploited dining room in town? / SW1A 2BD; www.massimo-restaurant.co.uk; 10.45 pm; closed Sun; SRA-50%.

Masters Super Fish SE1 £29 ❷④⑤
191 Waterloo Rd 7928 6924 9–4A
"All those cabbies can't be wrong!" – you "consistently get the best fish 'n' chips", at this "seriously unpromising-looking" chippy, near the Old Vic. / SE1 8UX; 10.30 pm; closed Sun, Mon L; no Amex; no booking Fri D.

Matsuba TW9 £43 ❷④④
10 Red Lion St 8605 3513 1–4A
This stalwart family-run Japanese is one of Richmond's foodie stand-outs – "gorgeous sashimi" a particular highlight. / TW9 1RW;
10.30 pm; closed Sun.

Matsuri SW1 £80 ❸❷⑤
15 Bury St 7839 1101 3–3D
"Very good teppanyaki" is the prime draw to this long-established St James's basement, where there is also a high-quality sushi bar – both inspire pretty solid feedback, but little in the way of excitement. / SW1Y 6AL; www.matsuri-restaurant.com; 10.30 pm, Sun 10 pm.

Maxela SW7 NEW £45 ❶❸④
84 Old Brompton Rd 7589 5834 5–2B
"An Italian addition to the steakhouses in London" – a South Kensington newcomer that's "a butcher's shop with kitchen attached" where "magical" imported meat is used to "divine" effect. / SW7 3LQ; www.maxela.co.uk; @MaxelaUk; 11 pm.

Maxim W13 £38 ❸④❸
153-155 Northfield Ave 8567 1719 1–3A
Who cares if it looks "dated"?; this Chinese stalwart is prized by Ealing and Northfields locals for its "consistently reliability". / W13 9QT; 11.30 pm, Sun 11 pm.

maze W1 £80 ④④④
10-13 Grosvenor Sq 7107 0000 3–2A
Gordon Ramsay's large Mayfair tapas-operation inspires mixed feelings; fans find the "numerous courses, beautifully presented" to be "tirelessly exquisite" – critics say you pay "huge money" for a formula that's simply "tired". / W1K 6JP; www.gordonramsay.com/maze; 10.30 pm; set weekday L & pre-theatre £48 (FP).

maze Grill W1 £76 ④④④
10-13 Grosvenor Sq 7495 2211 3–2A
Somewhat steadied of late, Gordon Ramsay's Mayfair steakhouse can make a handy business lunch rendezvous (and for Saturday family lunching too); non-meat dishes, however, "can leave a lot to be desired", contributing to an experience that's often "underwhelming" overall. / W1K 6JP; www.gordonramsay.com; 11 pm; no shorts; set weekday L & pre-theatre £46 (FP).

Mazi W8 £55 ❸④④
12-14 Hillgate St 7229 3794 6–2B
"Exciting Greek food with a twist" inspires rave reviews from fans of this "very cramped" restaurant off Notting Hill Gate (on the site which, for many years, was Costa's Grill); the odd sceptic, though, does find the cooking rather "average". / W8 7SR; www.mazi.co.uk; closed Mon L & Tue L; set weekday L £31 (FP).

The Meat & Wine Co
Westfield W12 £54 ④❸④
Unit 1026 Ariel Way 8749 5914 7–1C
Prominently sited at the main entrance to Westfield, this large operation won better feedback this year "for great steaks and quality wines"; it's not inexpensive, so the "great £10 lunch special" is a particular bonus. / W12 7GA; www.themeatandwineco.com; 11.30 pm, Sun 10.30 pm.

Meat Mission N1 NEW £32 ❷④❸

14-15 Hoxton Mkt 7739 8212 12–1B
"The ability to book a table and avoid ridiculous queues" – a major
bonus at this latest "grungy and cool" 'meat' outlet, on the way in to
Hoxton Square, serving "ace monkey fingers" and "brilliant-value"
burgers. / N1 6HG; www.meatmission.com/; @MEATmission; midnight,
sun 10 pm.

MEATLiquor W1 £35 ❷④❸

74 Welbeck St 7224 4239 3–1B
"Finger-lickin' good!"; this "sinful" yearling, near Oxford Street, doles
out "greasy, unhealthy, and absolutely wonderful" burgers, in a
"stripped-back and grungy" setting; queues are a "nightmare",
however, and all that "striving to be edgy and urban" can be a "turn-
off" for some reporters. / W1G 0BA; www.meatliquor.com; @MEATliquor;
11 pm, Fri-Sat 1 am, Sun 9.30 pm; closed Sun; no booking.

MEATmarket WC2 NEW £30 ❸④④

Jubilee Market Hall, 1 Tavistock Ct 7836 2139 4–3D
Fans of the "dirty" burgers and "grungy" looks of this latest MEAT,
overlooking Covent Garden's Jubilee Market, proclaim it "an excellent
addition to the empire"; the group's "decidedly non-fancy style",
however, does not please everyone – "why can't the MEAT franchise
clean up a bit?" / WC2E 8BD; 11 pm, Sun 10 pm; no Amex.

Mediterraneo W11 £55 ❸❸❸

37 Kensington Park Rd 7792 3131 6–1A
"Always buzzy and welcoming", this corner Italian is a long-standing
feature of the heart of Notting Hill; "the food is good… but the
tiramisù is great!" / W11 2EU; www.mediterraneo-restaurant.co.uk;
11.30 pm, Sun 10.30 pm; booking: max 10; set weekday L £33 (FP).

MEDLAR SW10 £65 ❷❷④

438 King's Rd 7349 1900 5–3B
"Chez Bruce in Chelsea, marvellous!" – fans of this "clone" of the
Wandsworth icon (from a team who worked there) hail its
"superlative" food, and "knowledgeable" service; it's a "cramped"
site, however, and sceptics feel there's "still a way to go to eclipse the
south London favourite". / SW10 0LJ; @medlarchelsea; 10.30 pm.

Megan's Delicatessen SW6 £43 ❸❸❷

571 Kings Rd 7371 7837 5–4A
A "busy and bustling" Parson's Green spot, serving "simple and
satisfying" fare – in particular, an excellent brunch; "get a table in the
garden". / SW6 2EB; www.megansrestaurant.com; @meganscafe; 10 pm;
closed Sun D; no Amex.

Mela WC2 £41 ❸④④

152-156 Shaftesbury Avenue 7836 8635 4–2B
This "unprepossessing" Theatreland Indian, by Cambridge Circus,
is certainly "nothing special in terms of ambience", but it dishes
up some "tasty" scoff, and they "have some good offers" too.
/ WC2H 8HL; www.melarestaurant.co.uk; 11.30 pm, Sun 10.30 pm.

Mele e Pere W1 £49 ❸❸④

46 Brewer St 7096 2096 3–2D
"Loud" and "cavernous", this Soho Italian basement yearling inspires
up-and-down reports – supporters praise its "great bar area" and its
"interesting" and "authentic" cuisine, but there's also a school
of thought that standards are "adequate" at best. / W1F 9TF;
@meleepere; 11 pm; set pre theatre £32 (FP).

Mem & Laz N1 £29 ④❸❸
8 Theberton St 7704 9089 8–3D
A "loud" and "cosy" budget operation, in Islington, serving
an "eclectic menu, which ranges across the Mediterranean and
(especially for puds) the UK"; "it just keeps getting bigger, so the
formula must be working!" / N1 0QX; www.memlazuk.com; 11.30 pm,
Fri & Sat midnight; no Amex.

Menier Chocolate Factory SE1 £48 ⑤④❸
51-53 Southwark St 7234 9610 9–4B
This quirky adjunct to a Southwark theatre certainly has a "great
atmosphere" for a pre-performance meal; "sadly, the food doesn't
match up", but the "very cheap" show-'n'-dinner deal can still
be good value. / SE1 1RU; www.menierchocolatefactory.com; 10.45 pm;
closed Mon & Sun D.

The Mercer EC2 £56 ❸❸❸
34 Threadneedle St 7628 0001 9–2C
For a "reliably good-quality City lunch" – or "breakfast par
excellence" – this former banking hall is a safe all-round performer,
"conveniently located" in the heart of the Square Mile. / EC2R 8AY;
www.themercer.co.uk; 9.30 pm; closed Sat & Sun.

Le Mercury N1 £29 ④④❸
140a Upper St 7354 4088 8–2D
A "no-frills" Islingon bistro "institution", renowned for its "criminally
cheap" prices – it's "always buzzing, whenever you go", and the
grub's very "reasonable", considering; a recent nearby offshoot,
Deuxième, has made a "very good start" too. / N1 1QY;
www.lemercury.co.uk; 12.30 am, Sun 11 pm.

Meson don Felipe SE1 £39 ④④❸
53 The Cut 7928 3237 9–4A
A "fantastic buzz" evidences the ongoing appeal of this "noisy" and
"squashed" tapas veteran, near the Old Vic; it offers "an authentic
Spanish evening far cheaper than Ryanair", even if the food really
is "nothing special" nowadays; and as for the guitarist... / SE1 8LF;
www.mesondonfelipe.com; 11 pm; closed Sun; no Amex; no booking after
8 pm.

Mestizo NW1 £41 ④④❸
103 Hampstead Rd 7387 4064 8–4C
"A wide range of tequilas and cocktails" adds to the appeal of this
Mexican restaurant, near Warren Street Tube; some reporters
"remain a bit undecided" on the food, but almost everyone says it's
at least "reasonable". / NW1 3EL; www.mestizomx.com; @mestizomx;
11 pm, Fri-Sat 11.30 pm, Sun 10 pm.

Mews of Mayfair W1 £61 ④❸❷
10 Lancashire Ct, New Bond St 7518 9388 3–2B
"Well-crafted cocktails" add to the vibe of this trendified venue
"tucked-away" off Bond Street (and it's "great if you can sit outdoors
in the alley"); the food, though, is relatively "ordinary". / W1S 1EY;
www.mewsofmayfair.com; @mewsofmayfair; 10.45 pm; closed Sun D;
SRA-67%.

Meza SW17 £15 ❷❸❸
34 Trinity Rd 111299 10–2C
"Simple, spectacularly good, and almost obscenely cheap"; no wonder
this "tiny but perfectly formed" Wandsworth Lebanese is "always full"
– "you need to book quite a few weeks in advance". / SW17 7RE.

(Carom at Meza)
Meza W1 NEW £32 ❷❷❸
100 Wardour St 7314 4002 3–2D
"Light and Fresh" Indian street-food "bursting with flavour and colour" defies the dreary track record of this "cavernous" D&D venue in Soho, which was formerly just called 'Meza'. / W1F 0TN; www.meza-soho.co.uk; 11 pm; closed Sat L & Sun; set pre theatre £19 (FP); SRA-61%.

Mezzanine
Royal National Theatre SE1 £50 ❹❹❹
Royal National Theatre, Belvedere Rd 7452 3600 2–3D
"Convenient, willing service, dull food" – that's still the majority verdict on the RNT's "soulless" in-house dining facility; it does have its fans, though. / SE1 9PX; www.nationaltheatre.org.uk; @NationalTheatre; 11 pm; closed Mon, Tue L & Fri; SRA-55%.

Michael Nadra £53 ❶❸❹
6-8 Elliott Rd, W4 8742 0766 7–2A
42 Gloucester Ave, NW1 7722 2800 8–2B NEW
Michael Nadra is now in two places at once, having faithfully cloned his "memorably delicious" cuisine, as seen in Chiswick, to Camden Town; his new opening (on the site of Sardo Canale, RIP), is "a fantastic addition to NW1", even if – as in W4 – the ambience "needs work". / www.restaurant-michaelnadra.co.uk; W4 10 pm, Fri-Sat 10.30 pm, NW1 10.30 pm, Sun 9 pm; W4 closed Sun D.

Mien Tay £30 ❷❹❹
180 Lavender Hill, SW11 7350 0721 10–1C
122 Kingsland Rd, E2 7729 3074 12–1B
These family-run Vietnamese greasy spoons "do the obvious things very well", alongside "a long menu of more interesting stuff" (quail, goat, eel, frogs' legs…); the décor is "rather utilitarian", though, and service can be "haphazard"; BYO. / 11 pm, Fri & Sat 11.30 pm, Sun 10.30 pm; cash only.

Mildreds W1 £40 ❷❹❸
45 Lexington St 7494 1634 3–2D
This "unfailing favourite of many years' standing" is, for its many fans, the "best veggie around" – that must be why its cramped Soho premises are generally "incredibly noisy and busy". / W1F 9AN; www.mildreds.co.uk; 11 pm; closed Sun; no Amex; no booking.

Mill Lane Bistro NW6 £47 ❸❷❷
77 Mill Ln 7794 5577 1–1B
"Simple, suitably French and consistently good" – all reports agree that this "lovely" West Hampstead spot "does what it says, and does it well". / NW6 1NB; www.milllanebistro.com; @millanebistro; 10 pm, Fri-Sat 10.30 pm, Sun 9 pm; closed Mon & Sun D; no Amex.

Mimmo la Bufala NW3 £50 ❹❸❹
45a South End Rd 7435 7814 8–2B
"Mimmo brings a real sense of fun" to this Italian spot near Hampstead Heath BR, although it attracts some flak for its "Hampstead prices"; it changed its name last year from Fratelli la Bufala – a global chain, whose branches are popping up all over town. / NW3 2QB; www.mimmolabufala.co.uk; 11 pm; no credit cards.

Min Jiang
The Royal Garden Hotel W8 £73 ❷❷❶
2-24 Kensington High St 7361 1988 5–1A
Probably the best Chinese all-rounder in town; this 8th-floor dining room, with "beautiful" views over Kensington Gardens, has very few obvious flaws – highlights include "excellent" Peking duck (pre-order) and "superb" lunchtime dim sum too. / W8 4PT; www.minjiang.co.uk; 10 pm.

Mint Leaf £54 ❷❸❸
Suffolk Pl, Haymarket, SW1 7930 9020 2–2C
Angel Ct, Lothbury, EC2 7600 0992 9–2C
Surprisingly little commentary on this style-conscious duo of designer-Indians, in a large basement by Trafalgar Square, and near Bank... especially as almost all the feedback says their "different" dishes are "good" or better. / www.mintleafrestaurant.com; SW1 11 pm, Sun 10.30 pm; EC2 10.30 pm; SW1 closed Sat & Sun L; EC2 closed Sat & Sun; set weekday L £35 (FP).

Miran Masala W14 £23 ❶❷❸
3 Hammersmith Rd 7602 4555 7–1D
"The best Pakistani food ever" – that's fans claim as they truffle out this basic café, opposite Olympia; BYO – "you'll have trouble to spend as much as £30 for two". / W14 8XJ; www.miranmasala.com; 11.30 pm.

Mirch Masala £24 ❷④⑤
171-173 The Broadway, UB1 8867 9222 1–3A
1416 London Rd, SW16 8679 1828 10–2C
213 Upper Tooting Rd, SW17 8767 8638 10–2D
111-113 Commercial Rd, E1 7377 0155 12–2D
"Fantastically-flavoured" Pakistani curries at "amazingly low prices" make these "basic" and "busy" canteens well worth seeking out; unlicensed, but you can BYO. / www.mirchmasalarestaurant.co.uk; midnight.

Mishkin's WC2 £43 ⑤④❸
25 Catherine St 7240 2078 4–3D
Russell Norman's "cool" Covent Garden diner delights fans with its menu of "NYC-Jewish comfort food", and some "gorgeous" cocktails too; for critics, though, "it feels like an experience dreamt up by a branding consultant", and an "ultimately uninspiring" one at that. / WC2B 5JS; www.mishkins.co.uk; 11.30 pm, 10.30 pm Sun.

Miyama W1 £54 ❷❷⑤
38 Clarges St 7499 2443 3–4B
A stalwart Mayfair Japanese whose "sterile" dining room is sometimes "so quiet, you feel you have to whisper"... so the fact the place has lasted so long must be testament to the splendid quality of its sushi, and other fare! / W1J 7EN; www.miyama-restaurant.co.uk; 10.15 pm; closed Sat L & Sun.

The Modern Pantry EC1 £54 ④④④
47-48 St Johns Sq 7553 9210 9–1A
Anna Hansen's "inventive" fusion cuisine divides views on this "noisy" Clerkenwell venture; fans say it's "one of the best", offering food that's "never dull", but critics find it just "peculiar" – "seemingly interesting on paper, then failing to deliver"; perhaps try brunch first! / EC1V 4JJ; www.themodernpantry.co.uk; 10.30 pm, Sun 10 pm; SRA-82%.

Momo W1 £62 ④④❶
25 Heddon St 7434 4040 3–2C
"A great place for a lively night out" – Mourad Mazouz's *"lovely"*
Mayfair Moroccan is an energetically "characterful", if *"noisy"*
operation, offering *"quite authentic"* cuisine. / W1B 4BH;
www.momoresto.com; 11.30 pm, Sun 11 pm; closed Sun L; set weekday L
£38 (FP).

Mon Plaisir WC2 £59 ④❸❸
19-21 Monmouth St 7836 7243 4–2B
This *"old-fashioned bistro"* – a *"very French"* Theatreland stalwart for
over half a century – continues to dish up *"classic bourgeois cooking"*
in its *"bustling"* warren of dining rooms; *"some of the food falls a little
short"* nowadays, but the famous pre-theatre menu offers the same
great value as ever. / WC2H 9DD; www.monplaisir.co.uk; 11.15 pm; closed
Sun; set pre-theatre £29 (FP), set weekday L £33 (FP).

Mona Lisa SW10 £28 ❸❷❷
417 King's Rd 7376 5447 5–3B
"Like being transported back to the '70s" – this *"crowded and
buzzy"* Italian greasy spoon, at the far end of Chelsea, offers *"really
good value"*; *"everything is freshly cooked"*, including the top
"builders' breakfasts" (often enjoyed, with due irony of course, by the
local toffs). / SW10 0LR; 11 pm, Sun 5.30 pm; closed Sun D; no Amex.

Monmouth Coffee Company £12 ❶❶❷
27 Monmouth St, WC2 7379 3516 4–2B
Arches Northside, Dockley Rd, SE16 7232 3010 9–4D
2 Park St, SE1 7940 9960 9–4C
"Still the best coffee in town"; all of the many reports confirm that
these cult cafés are *"top quality"*, and that the bread 'n' jam
breakfasts at the Borough market branch are *"a London experience"*
(and, fortunately, one that's *"worth queuing for"* too).
/ www.monmouthcoffee.co.uk; 6 pm-6.30 pm; SE16 12 pm; closed Sun;
SE16 open Sat only; no Amex; no booking.

Monty's £32 ❸❸❸
692 Fulham Rd, SW6 7371 5971 10–1B
54 Northfield Ave, W13 8567 6281 1–2A
1 The Mall, W5 8567 8122 1–2A
"The go-to curry" for many an Ealing resident – these stalwart
subcontinentals (whose 'branches' are not in fact under common
ownership) are *"perennial"* favourites locally, thanks to their
"consistently fresh-flavoured dishes" (which include some Nepali
specials). / 11 pm.

The Morgan Arms E3 £46 ❸❸❷
43 Morgan St 8980 6389 1–2D
"What a delight of a neighbourhood pub"; this Bow boozer impresses
all who comment on it with its *"much better than average"* food,
its *"friendly"* service and its *"pleasant"* atmosphere. / E3 5AA;
www.morganarmsbo.com; @TheMorganArms; 10 pm, Sun 9 pm.

Morgan M EC1 £66 ❷❸⑤
50 Long Ln 3589 4521 9–2B
*"The transfer of Holloway's only top-class restaurant to Smithfield
does not seem to have gone well..."*; Morgan Meunier still produces
some *"creative and beautiful"* cuisine, but the wow factor has
decidedly gone AWOL; can't help that the interior is *"dreary"* beyond
all reason. / EC1A 9EJ; www.morganm.com; 10.30 pm; closed Sun;
set weekday L & pre-theatre £44 (FP).

Morito EC1 £35 ❷❷❸
32 Exmouth Mkt 7278 7007 9–1A
"The more Spanish, more bar-like little brother of the always excellent Moro"; it's "the hippest of places", offering "yummy and unusual" tapas... in a "really cramped" setting. / EC1R 4QE; www.morito.co.uk; 11 pm, Sun 4 pm; closed Sun D; no Amex; no booking for D.

Moro EC1 £52 ❶❷❷
34-36 Exmouth Mkt 7833 8336 9–1A
"There's nowhere quite like Moro!" – this *"joyous"* Exmouth Market perennial thrives on its *"exciting"* Moorish/Andalucian cuisine, *"massive and unusual wine list"*, and *"surprisingly good value"*; the acoustics, though, are *"challenging"*. / EC1R 4QE; www.moro.co.uk; 10.30 pm; closed Sun D.

Mosaica
The Chocolate Factory N22 £46 ④④❸
Unit C005, Clarendon Rd 8889 2400 1–1C
"Eclectic and visually interesting", the interior of this Wood Green venture (entered through a semi-abandoned factory) certainly creates quite a "surprise to newbies"; food reports have been a bit up-and-down of late, but fans insist it "just keeps getting better". / N22 6XJ; www.mosaicarestaurants.com; @MosaicaChocFac; 9.30 pm, Sat 10 pm; closed Sat L & Sun D.

Motcombs SW1 £60 ④❸❷
26 Motcomb St 7235 6382 5–1D
"A good local"; now occupying one of the glitziest corners in town, this long-established wine bar/restaurant seems an ever more "real" reminiscence of the very 'English' Belgravia of old – the slightly *"bland"* food is entirely in keeping. / SW1X 8JU; www.motcombs.co.uk; 11 pm; closed Sun D.

Moti Mahal WC2 £57 ❷❷④
45 Gt Queen St 7240 9329 4–2D
"Should be better known"; this "surprisingly good" Covent Garden outpost of a Delhi-based empire offers "refined and robust" North Indian cuisine with "big and imaginative flavours", albeit in a setting critics can find "a little unatmospheric". / WC2B 5AA; www.motimahal-uk.com; 10.45 pm; closed Sat L & Sun; set weekday L £38 (FP).

Moxon's Fish Bar SW12 🆕 £27 ❶❸⑤
7 Westbury Pde 8675 2468 10–2C
"Local fishmonger Robin Moxon really knows his cod from his pollock" – his *"tiny"* (8 seats) new Clapham chippy serves *"sensational", "Billingsgate-fresh"* fish, plus *"whale-size"* chips. / SW12 9DZ; www.moxonsfishbar.com; @moxonsfish; 10 pm; closed Mon, Tue L, Wed L, Thu L, Sat L & Sun.

Mr Chow SW1 £87 ④④④
151 Knightsbridge 7589 7347 5–1D
"The one and only!" – fans of this Knightsbridge Chinese veteran claim it's still *"going just as strong as back in the '70s... only they've replaced the Americans with Russians"*; survey feedback is limited, but the cooking generally gets the thumbs-up. / SW1X 7PA; www.mrchow.com; 11.45 pm; closed Mon L.

Mr Kong WC2 £31 ④❸④
21 Lisle St 7437 7341 4–3A
It looks "rather average", but this "bustling" Chinatown café – with its "good-humoured" service and "dependable" cooking – is the "go-to Chinese" for many reporters; that said, while "the specials deserve high marks", the standard fare is "just OK". / WC2H 7BA; www.mrkongrestaurant.com; 2.45 am, Sun 1.45 am.

Mr Wing SW5 £46 ④④❷
242-244 Old Brompton Rd 7370 4450 5–2A
Surprisingly few reports of late on the Earl's Court fixture once regarded as west London's premiere party/romantic Chinese; it's still "worth a trip just for the jazz brunch and the fish tank", explains one long-term fan, but "has lost some of its charm since the old manager retired". / SW5 0DE; www.mrwing.com; @MrWingLondon; 11.30 pm.

Mugen EC4 £47 ❸❸④
26 King William St 7929 7879 9–3C
This "efficient" outfit, by London Bridge, offers a wide variety of dishes, and is "very popular with the local Japanese community"; "arrive early if you want to eat at the bar, as the best options run out". / EC4R 9AW; 10.30 pm; closed Sat & Sun.

Murano W1 £95 ❸❷❸
20-22 Queen St 7495 1127 3–3B
"Still packing a punch", Angela Hartnett's "magnificent modern Italian", in Mayfair, is pleasing a growing proportion of reporters, not least with its "elegant" cuisine; critics, though, still find the performance rather "safe". / W1J 5PP; www.muranolondon.com; @muranolondon; 11 pm; closed Sun; set weekday L £55 (FP).

My Old Place E1 £38 ❷⑤④
88-90 Middlesex St 7247 2200 9–2D
"The real thing, just like Sichuan!"; this "authentic" and "busy" East End spot offers "mouth-watering" dishes ("pig's intestine, BBQ rabbit, frogs' legs"), in "massive" portions, and "with no frills and no pretentions". / E1 7EZ; www.oldplace.co.uk; 11 pm; no Amex.

Naamyaa Café EC1 £37 ④④❸
407 St John St 3122 0988 8–3D
Alan Yau's "very metropolitan and hip" Islington café has often seemed "rather overhyped" in its first year of operation – it has its fans, but too many reporters find the realisation of its Thai street food menu "terribly average". / EC1V 4AB; www.naamyaa.com; @Naamyacafe; 10.30 pm.

Nando's £30 ④④④
Branches throughout London
For "a quick, cheap eat", many reporters are "embarrassed to admit they like" this flame-roasted, peri-peri chicken chain – "easy", "reasonably healthy" and "reliable"… and if you "arrive with two hungry kids in tow, you'll be sat down and eating in 10 minutes flat". / www.nandos.co.uk; 11.30 pm, Sun 10.30 pm; no Amex; no booking.

Napulé SW6 £39 ❸❸❸
585 Fulham Rd 7381 1122 5–4A
"A relaxed" and "happy" outpost of the Made In Italy franchise, near Fulham Broadway – it inspires modest survey commentary, but all positive. / SW6 5UA; 11.30 pm, Sun 10.30 pm; closed weekday L; no Amex.

The Narrow E14 £48 ⑤④④
44 Narrow St 7592 7950 11–1B
Gordon Ramsay's Limehouse gastroboozer – with its "merely average" food, and its "higher than expected" prices – offers "nothing special, apart from a great river view". / E14 8DP; www.gordonramsay.com; @thenarrow; 10.30 pm, Sun 10 pm.

The National Dining Rooms
National Gallery WC2 £52 ⑤⑤④
Sainsbury Wing, Trafalgar Sq 7747 2525 2–2C
"A window table to enjoy the view" (if you can nab one) is the most certain attraction at this large first-floor dining room – sometimes "atrocious" service contributes to a performance critics otherwise brand a "disgrace". / WC2N 5DN; www.thenationaldiningrooms.co.uk; 7 pm; Sat-Thu closed D, Fri open L & D; no Amex.

National Gallery Café
National Gallery WC2 £45 ❸④❸
East Wing, Trafalgar Sq 7747 5942 4–4B
"An ideal location for exhausted tourists!" – this "haven of relative tranquility", right on Trafalgar Square, offers "classy" British snacks which "mainly succeed"; a "great-value" breakfast is the top tip. / WC2N 5DN; www.thenationaldiningrooms.co.uk; 11 pm, Sun 6 pm; closed Sun D; no Amex.

Natural Kitchen £36 ❸④❸
77-78 Marylebone High St, W1 3012 2123 2–1A
7 Pepys St, EC3 7702 4038 9–3D **NEW**
15-17 New Street Sq, Fetter Ln, EC4 7353 5787 9–2A
"Interesting, and decently priced" – the food at this "healthy" deli-diner duo usually satisfies; the setting, though, "can be a little noisy". / EC4 9 pm; EC3 4 pm; W1 8 pm, Sat & Sun 7 pm; EC4 & EC3 closed Sat & Sun.

Nautilus NW6 £42 ❶❷⑤
27-29 Fortune Green Rd 7435 2532 1–1B
"Yes, it is decked out in Formica", and "rather drab" too, but this West Hampstead chippy is "consistently superb" – "I first went 31 years ago, and it's still as good as ever!" / NW6 1DU; 10 pm; closed Sun; no Amex.

Navarro's W1 £42 ❸④❸
67 Charlotte St 7637 7713 2–1C
A "beautiful and very Spanish" tiled interior sets the scene at this Fitzrovia tapas veteran, where "high standards are maintained", and at "affordable prices" too. / W1T 4PH; www.navarros.co.uk; @SpanishEchelon; 10 pm; closed Mon L & Sun.

Nazmins SW18 £37 ❸❸❸
396-398 Garratt Ln 8944 1463 10–2B
In Earlsfield, an "excellent neighbourhood Indian" which, say local fans, "never fails to deliver on price, quality and service". / SW18 4HP; www.nazmins.com; @nazmins; 11.30 pm.

Needoo E1 £26 ❷④④
87 New Rd 7247 0648 12–2D
Don't be put off by the queue outside this East End Pakistani (or by the noise within) – this is an "outstanding" grill and curry house, where "you can eat like a king for £15 a head"; BYO. / E1 1HH; www.needoogrill.co.uk; 11.30 pm.

New China Boulevard SW18 £48 ❸④❸
1 The Boulevard, Smugglers Way   8871 3881   10–2B
*Surprisingly little feedback on this river-view Cantonese, in a
Wandsworth development; such as it is, however, confirms good
standards all-round, with "great Sunday dim sum" a highlight.*
/ SW18 1DE; www.chinaboulevard.com; 11 pm.

New Mayflower W1 £39 ❷❷④
68-70 Shaftesbury Ave   7734 9207   4–3A
*It may look "tired", but this stalwart Chinatown Cantonese delivers
some "quite authentic" flavours ("by London standards"), and the
service is "speedier and smilier than it use to be"; late, late opening
too.* / W1D 6LY; 4 am; D only; no Amex.

New Street Grill EC2 £60 ④❷❷
16 New St   3503 0785   9–2D
*Near Liverpool Street, a well-spaced D&D group yearling, created
from the conversion of a splendid old 18th-century warehouse;
it attracted surprisingly little feedback for such a business-friendly
venue, where "very good steaks" headline the "varied" menu.*
/ EC2M 4TR.

New World W1 £36 ④④❸
1 Gerrard Pl   7434 2508   4–3A
*"A real HK experience!"; children, especially, just "love the trolleys"
which whizz the lunchtime dim sum around this cavernous Chinatown
fixture; evenings? – "don't bother!"* / W1D 5PA;
www.newworldlondon.com; 11.30 pm, Sun 11 pm.

Newman Street Tavern W1 NEW £40 ④④❸
48 Newman St   3667 1445   3–1D
*"Deceptively plain", carefully sourced British dishes often realised to a
"really lovely" standard have won acclaim for this "light and bright"
Marylebone pub-conversion; ratings are undercut, however, by those
who (mystifyingly, in our view) say it's "massively over-hyped".*
/ W1T 1QQ; www.newmanstreettavern.co.uk; @NewmanStTavern; 10.30 pm;
closed Sun D; SRA-69%.

1901
Andaz Hotel EC2 £60 ④④❸
40 Liverpool St   7618 7000   12–2B
*It can seem a touch "cavernous" on entry, but this "spacious" and
"beautiful" hotel dining room, by Liverpool Street, makes "a reliable
place for a business breakfast, lunch or dinner", even if the food
is "forgettable".* / EC2M 7QN; www.andazdining.com; 10 pm; closed
Sat L & Sun; booking: max 20.

Nizuni W1 £46 ❷❷④
22 Charlotte St   7580 7447   2–1C
*"A quality Korean-hybrid spin on Japanese cuisine" is the stock-in-
trade of this "excellent-value" Fitzrovia two-year-old, whose styling
is akin to "a sort of upmarket Itsu".* / W1T 2NB; www.nizuni.com;
10.45 pm; closed Sun L.

No 11 Pimlico Road SW1 NEW £40 ④❺④
11 Pimlico Rd   7730 6784   5–2D
*Oh dear; only as a bar can reporters see any real reason to seek out
this "very noisy" new occupant of the attractive former Ebury
(RIP) site, on the fringe of Belgravia; rarely is the food rated better
than "undistinguished".* / SW1W 8NA; www.no11pimlicoroad.co.uk;
@no11pimlicoroad.

Nobu
Metropolitan Hotel W1 £87 ❷④④
19 Old Park Ln 7447 4747 3–4A
London's original Nobu still cranks out "wow" Japanese-fusion fare at "crazy-expensive" prices, still has "perfunctory" service, and still drags in a fair few "movers 'n' shakers"; "it's definitely past its glory days", though, and the atmosphere is "not what it was". / W1K 1LB; www.noburestaurants.com; 10.15 pm, Fri & Sat 11 pm, Sun 10 pm.

Nobu Berkeley W1 £87 ❸④④
15 Berkeley St 7290 9222 3–3C
The younger, showier (and nowadays better-known) of the two London outposts of the glamorous Japanese-fusion brand; it still offers "superlative" sushi and "great people-watching", but critics find it "extremely overpriced" for what it is. / W1J 8DY; www.noburestaurants.com; 11 pm, Sun 9.45 pm; closed Sat L & Sun L.

Noor Jahan £38 ❷❷❸
2a, Bina Gdns, SW5 7373 6522 5–2B
26 Sussex Pl, W2 7402 2332 6–1D
"A classic Indian in all respects"; these "consistently high-quality" curry houses – with their dingily comfortable decor and "obligatory gruff service" – are "as good as it gets for standard subcontinental fare". / 11.30 pm, Sun 10 pm.

Nopi W1 £56 ❷❷❸
21-22 Warwick St 7494 9584 3–2D
Thanks to Yottam Ottolenghi's "wonderfully colourful, fresh and inventively-flavoured small plates", this "beautiful" Soho two-year-old has quickly become a major destination; sceptics, though, can find prices "ludicrous" – "just go to Ottolenghi instead!" / W1B 5NE; www.nopi-restaurant.com; 10.15 pm, Sun 4 pm; closed Sun D.

Nordic Bakery £15 ❸④❸
14a, Golden Sq, W1 3230 1077 3–2D
37b, New Cavendish St, W1 7935 3590 2–1A
48 Dorset St, W1 7487 5877 2–1A
"Fabulous cinnamon buns", "delicious rye bread sarnies" and "fine coffee" – all highlights of the "Scandinavian delights" on offer at this refreshing small group. / Golden Square 8 pm, Sat 7 pm, Sun 7 pm; Cavendish Street & Dorset Street 6 pm.

The Norfolk Arms WC1 £45 ❸④④
28 Leigh St 7388 3937 8–4C
"Tucked-away near King's Cross", a boozer known for its "fantastic" tapas – "not in London's top tier, but a very solid performer". / WC1H 9EP; www.norfolkarms.co.uk; 10.15 pm.

North China W3 £40 ❷❷❷
305 Uxbridge Rd 8992 9183 7–1A
"Standards never drop", at this "good and reliable, if slightly-old-fashioned Chinese" – still Acton's greatest contribution to London gastronomy. / W3 9QU; www.northchina.co.uk; 11 pm, Fri & Sat 11.30 pm.

The North London Tavern NW6 £45 ④④❸
375 Kilburn High Rd 7625 6634 1–2B
Near the Tricycle Theatre, a "somewhat noisy" Kilburn boozer, praised for its "attractive" interior, and for food that's "better than average for a pub". / NW6 7QB; www.northlondontavern.co.uk; @NorthLondonTav; 10.30 pm, Sun 9.30 pm; set dinner £28 (FP).

North Sea Fish WC1 £37 ❸❸④
7-8 Leigh St 7387 5892 8–4C
"Still one of the most reliable – and most popular – chippies
in London"; "reassuringly", this Bloomsbury veteran "hasn't changed
in years", so such aspects as the "hideous" lighting have to be
deemed part of the 'charm'. / WC1H 9EW;
www.northseafishrestaurant.co.uk; 11 pm; closed Sun; no Amex.

The Northall WC2 £58 ❸❷❷
10a, Northumberland Ave 7321 3100 2–3C
The "spacious" dining room of this new hotel, near Embankment,
hasn't made many waves, but – with its "competent cooking, pleasing
service and impressive décor" – it makes a "can't-go-wrong" business
rendezvous. / WC2N 5AE; www.thenorthall.co.uk; 10.45 pm.

Northbank EC4 £54 ❸④❸
1 Paul's Walk 7329 9299 9–3B
A "stunning" riverside location – with "big windows overlooking the
Millenium Bridge and Tate" – is the highlight at this City stalwart;
the food (Cornish fish the speciality) can be a "knockout", but some
reporters are unimpressed, and service can be "slow". / EC4V 3QH;
www.northbankrestaurant.co.uk; @NorthbankLondon; 10 pm; closed Sun.

The Northgate N1 £42 ❷❷❸
113 Southgate Rd 7359 7392 1–1C
"If this is your local, lucky you!" – this "friendly" gastropub dishes
up "excellent, reasonably-priced" grub to De Beauvoir residents,
and the occasional 'visitor' too. / N1 3JS; 10 pm; D only, ex Sun open
L & D; no Amex.

Notes £18 ④❷❷
31 St Martin's Ln, WC2 7240 0424 4–4C
36 Wellington St, WC2 7240 7899 4–3D
6a, Tileyard Studios, N7 7700 0710 8–2C **NEW**
These handy Covent Garden cafés are most notable for the
wonderfully atmospheric outlet by the Coliseum – "one of the
best coffee bars in town", offering "excellent" brews, and snacks
which are rather incidental. / Wellington St Mon-Wed 10 pm, Thu-Fri
11 pm, Sun 6 pm; St Martin's Ln Mon-Wed 9 pm, Thu-Sat 10 pm, Sun 6 pm;
N7 closed Sat-Sun.

Notting Hill Kitchen W11 **NEW** £30 ❷❸❷
92 Kensington Park Rd 7313 9526 6–2B
A star Portuguese chef is now installed in the rambling townhouse site
most recently occupied by the Notting Hill Brasserie (RIP); our early-
days visit suggested it could become a top-grade all-rounder, but initial
press reaction has been mixed. / W11 2PN; Rated on Editors' visit;
www.nottinghillkitchen.co.uk; @NottingHillKTN; 10 pm; closed Mon & Tue.

Noura £56 ❸④❸
16 Hobart Pl, SW1 7235 9444 2–4B
17 Hobart Pl, SW1 7235 9696 2–4B
2 William St, SW1 7235 5900 5–1D
16 Curzon St, W1 7495 1050 3–4B
Generally "reliable", these Mayfair and Knightsbridge outlets dish
up "good Lebanese food" in a "French brasserie atmosphere".
/ www.noura.co.uk; 11.30 pm, Sun 10 pm; 16 Hobart Place closed Sun.

Novikov (Asian restaurant) W1   £76   ③④③
50A Berkeley St   7399 4330   3–3C
"You can easily spend over £100/head, without wine", in the
"crushed" pan-Asian section of this blingy Russian-backed Mayfair
yearling; it's "fun" though (in its way), the food can be "memorable",
and the people-watching is arguably "the best in town". / W1J 8HD;
www.novikovrestaurant.co.uk; 11.15 pm.

Novikov (Italian restaurant) W1   £78   ⑤⑤④
50 Berkeley St   7399 4330   3–3C
"Does Novikov think he's still in Moscow?" – prices in the "ridiculously
pricey" Italian dining room of this Eurotrash-central Mayfair scene are
just "off the clock"… especially when you bear in mind the
"pedestrian" cooking and "slipshod" service, and an atmosphere
reminiscent of "a Hilton breakfast room". / W1J 8HD;
www.novikovrestaurant.co.uk; 11.30 pm; set weekday L £44 (FP).

Nozomi SW3   £87   ④④⑤
14-15 Beauchamp Pl   7838 1500   5–1C
"The only place I've been with music so loud the table actually
vibrates!" – this pricey Japanese joint presumably hits the spot for
Knightsbridge scenesters, but reporters tend to find it a "soulless"
place that "trades on its location". / SW3 1NQ; www.nozomi.co.uk;
11.30 pm, Sun 10.30 pm; closed Mon L.

Numero Uno SW11   £53   ③②②
139 Northcote Rd   7978 5837   10–2C
"A rock-solid Italian", popular with the denizens of the Nappy Valley
– "it's the sort of local everyone would like to have", which
is presumably why it can get rather "crowded". / SW11 6PX; 11.30 pm;
no Amex.

Nuovi Sapori SW6   £43   ③0③
295 New King's Rd   7736 3363   10–1B
"A warm welcome" from the friendly owner sets the tone at this
"top local Italian", down Fulham way, which serves up some "great
dishes". / SW6 4RE; 11 pm; closed Sun.

Nusa Kitchen   £12   ②③④
9 Old St, EC1   7253 3135   9–1B
2 Adam's Ct, EC2   7628 1149   9–2C
"The queue is the only downside"; these City and Farringdon pit stops
offer a "wonderful variety" of "filling and delicious" soups,
with "lots of interesting garnishes". / www.nusakitchen.co.uk; 4 pm;
Sat & Sun; no booking.

The Oak   £50   ②③0
243 Goldhawk Rd, W12   8741 7700   7–1B **NEW**
137 Westbourne Park Rd, W2   7221 3355   6–1B
With its superbly "cool vibe" and its "brilliant wood-fired" pizzas this
former boozer has made itself quite a Notting Hill fixture – don't
miss the "funky and relaxed" bar upstairs; on an early visit, its airy
new Shepherd's Bush sibling seems a tad less "self-conscious" (but all
things are relative).

Obika £46 ❸❸❸
11 Charlotte St, W1 7637 7153 2–1C NEW
96 Draycott Ave, SW3 7581 5208 5–2C NEW
35 Bank St, E14 7719 1532 11–1C NEW
We're slightly mystified by the success of these "gimmicky" Italian operations, where many dishes are based on Mozzarella; they now have three locations, though, including the former Chelsea site of Ilia (RIP). / www.obika.co.uk; 10 pm - 11 pm; E14 Closed Sun.

Oblix
The Shard SE1 NEW £57 ❹❸❶
31 St Thomas St 7268 6700 9–4C
"Killer views" through "floor to ceiling windows" make it a "phenomenal" experience to visit this 32nd-floor South Bank eyrie (and the cocktails "get full marks too"); the cuisine so far has been "solid, but unspectacular", but optimists insist it "shows promise". / SE1 9RY; www.oblixrestaurant.com.

Odette's NW1 £58 ❸❹❸
130 Regent's Park Rd 7586 8569 8–3B
For a "high quality" neighbourhood experience, north London has few restaurants to rival this "intimate" Primrose Hill veteran, with Bryn Williams's deft cuisine; there are quibbles though — service can be "amateurish", it can seem "expensive", and it's still not a patch on Odette's in days of yore. / NW1 8XL; www.odettesprimrosehill.com; Mon-Thu 10 pm, Fri-Sat 10.30 pm, Sun 9 pm; no Amex; set weekday L & pre-theatre £37 (FP).

Okawari W5 £37 ❸❹❸
13 Bond St 8566 0466 1–3A
"A reliably good no-frills Japanese restaurant"; this Ealing café offers sushi that's "always of good quality", and "excellent-value" Bento boxes too. / W5 5AP; www.okawari.co.uk; 11.15 pm, Sun 10.45 pm.

The Old Brewery SE10 £48 ❹❹❷
The Pepys Building, Old Royal Naval College 3327 1280 1–3D
The impressive garden is usually "packed with tourists", but any visitor to this historic Greenwich site will be pleased by the formidable range of home-brews, plus the decent, if "basic", dishes to go with 'em. / SE10 9LW; www.oldbrewerygreenwich.com; @OldBrewery; 10 pm, Fri & Sat 10.30 pm; D only; no Amex.

The Old Bull & Bush NW3 £41 ❹❹❹
North End Rd 8905 5456 8–1A
Opposite Golder's Hill Park, a famous pub that's quite a local favourite; at busy times, however, it's seriously "hit-and-miss". / NW3 7HE; www.thebullandbush.co.uk; 9.30 pm, Sat 10 pm, Sun 9 pm; set weekday L £27 (FP).

Old Parr's Head W14 £23 ❸❸❹
120 Blythe Rd 7371 4561 7–1C
In the backstreets of Olympia, a pretty undistinguished-looking pub — its menu of Thai staples, however, offers "good value". / W14 0HD; www.theoldparrshead.co.uk; 10 pm, Sat & Sun 9.30 pm; no Amex.

The Old White Bear NW3 £48 ❸❷❸
Hampstead 7794 7719 8–1A
"A better-than-average gastropub", in an off-the-beaten-track Hampstead location; a "cosy" and "genuine" sort of place, it offers a menu that's both "interesting and varied". / NW3 1LJ; www.theoldwhitebear.co.uk; @OldWhiteBearNW3; 10.30 pm, Sun 9.30 pm; closed Mon L.

Oliveto SW1 £51 ❷④④
49 Elizabeth St   7730 0074   2–4A
"Incredibly busy" (and "very noisy" too), this "bright" and "child-friendly" Sardinian serves up some "superb" pizza and pasta; only by Belgravia standards, however, could this be called a "cheap 'n' cheerful" option! / SW1 9PP; www.olivorestaurants.com; 11 pm, Sun 10.30 pm; booking: max 7 at D.

Olivo SW1 £57 ❷❷④
21 Eccleston St   7730 2505   2–4B
A minimalist Sardinian fixture, near Victoria, which is "always packed with regulars", thanks to its "interesting" wines and "consistently good" cooking… "dreadful acoustics and dated décor" notwithstanding. / SW1 9LX; www.olivorestaurants.com; 10.30 pm; closed Sat L & Sun L.

Olivocarne SW1 NEW £52 ❸❷④
61 Elizabeth St   7730 7997   2–4A
"Go for steak – the rest of the food is unremarkable"; by the standards of Belgravia's impressive Olivo group, this meat-focused Italian is rather lacklustre – "lacking the vibe" of its siblings, and a touch "greedily priced" too. / SW1W 9PP; www.olivorestaurants.com; 10.30 pm; closed Sun D.

Olivomare SW1 £63 ❶❸❸
10 Lower Belgrave St   7730 9022   2–4B
Hidden-away in Belgravia, an "astoundingly authentic Sardinian seafood restaurant" ("the menu groans with crab, sea urchin and sumptuous whole fish"); not everyone, though, loves the "distinctly odd" '60s Sci-fi decor (even if it is "less noisy now they've changed the ceiling"). / SW1W 0LJ; www.olivorestaurants.com; 11 pm, Sun 10.30 pm; booking: max 10.

Olley's SE24 £39 ❷❸❸
65-69 Norwood Rd   8671 8259   10–2D
"You can't fault Olley's!"; this "very friendly" and "keenly priced" Brockwell Park institution is one of south London's best chippies. / SE24 9AA; www.olleys.info; 10 pm, Sun 9.30 pm; closed Mon; no Amex; SRA-70%.

Olympus Fish N3 £33 ❷❸④
140-144 Ballards Ln   8371 8666   1–1B
"Anyone who thinks the Two Brothers is Finchley's best chippy is missing out", say supporters of this "very popular" and "very friendly" – and now higher-rated – rival. / N3 2PA; 11 pm; closed Mon.

One Blenheim Terrace NW8 £60 ⑤④④
1 Blenheim Ter   7372 1722   8–3A
An ambitious St John's Wood venture that inspired a fair volume of feedback in its first year of operation; unfortunately, much of this suggests it's a "pretentious" place, where the food is "not as good as they think it is". / NW8 0EH; www.oneblenheimterrace.co.uk; 10.30 pm, Sun 3 pm; closed Mon.

One Canada Square E14 NEW £58
1 Canada Sq   7559 5199   11–1C
Opening as this guide goes to press, a new business-friendly brasserie at the foot of one of the Canary Wharf towers; if the Martin brothers get this one right, it could become quite a destination. / E14 5AB; www.onecanadasquarerestaurant.com; @OneCanadaSquare.

101 Thai Kitchen W6 £32 ❷❸⑤
352 King St 8746 6888 7–2B
"It's not the most elegant place", and "service isn't great", but this Hammersmith café has a loyal fan club, which insists that the Thai scoff it offers is "superb". / W6 0RX; www.101thaikitchen.com; 10.30 pm, Fri & Sat 11 pm.

1 Lombard Street EC3 £69 ④④❸
1 Lombard St 7929 6611 9–3C
This "airy" and "impressive" former banking hall, opposite the Royal Exchange, remains a key City rendezvous – "an excellent all-round breakfast or lunch option, even if prices do reflect the location"; for gravitas to the max, head for the 'fine-dining' room at the rear. / EC3V 9AA; www.1lombardstreet.com; 10 pm; closed Sat & Sun; 6 max in main restaurant.

One-O-One
Sheraton Park Tower SW1 £94 ❶❸⑤
101 Knightsbridge 7290 7101 5–1D
Is it "the best seafood in Europe"? Pascal Proyart "has a Midas touch with fish", and his "tremendously imaginative" cuisine inspires foodie adulation for his Knightsbridge HQ; pity about the room, though – "a weird space in a weird building", and "so soulless". / SW1X 7RN; www.oneoonerestaurant.com; @oneoone; 10 pm; booking: max 6; set weekday L £50 (FP).

The Only Running Footman W1 £49 ❸④❷
5 Charles St 7499 2988 3–3B
A handy option in pricey Mayfair – this "cheerful and stylish" gastropub offers affordable scoff, and inspires consistently upbeat feedback. / W1J 5DF; www.therunningfootmanmayfair.com; @theorfootman; 10 pm.

Opera Tavern WC2 £40 ❷❸❸
23 Catherine St 7836 3680 4–3D
"Iberico and foie-gras mini-burgers are a must", on a visit to this "cool" but "friendly" Covent Garden pub-conversion (a sibling to Salt Yard), whose "splendid" tapas and "interesting wines and sherries" are "great pre-theatre", but also make it a "top central rendezvous" at any time. / WC2B 5JS; www.operatavern.co.uk; @saltyardgroup; 11.15 pm; closed Sun D; SRA-63%.

The Orange SW1 £53 ❸❸❷
37 Pimlico Rd 7881 9844 5–2D
"Warm, wooden decor" contributes to the "always-great atmosphere" at this "airy" Pimlico gastropub; the food (majoring in "fantastic pizza") is "surprisingly good", and it comes at prices which are "reasonable... for the area". / SW1W 8NE; www.theorange.co.uk; 10 pm, Sun 9.30 pm; SRA-75%.

Orange Pekoe SW13 £26 ❷❷❷
3 White Hart Ln 8876 6070 10–1A
"Very popular, and it deserves it!"; this Barnes "gem" serves a wide range of "fragrant" teas and "delectable" baked goods, plus other "super", "light" dishes. / SW13 0PX; www.orangepekoeteas.com; 5 pm; L only.

The Orange Tree N20 £43 ④⑤❸
7 Totteridge Ln 8343 7031 1–1B
This large and inviting Totteridge gastropub is clearly a top destination in a thin area; reports are few, however, and remain mixed. / N20 8NX; www.theorangetreetotteridge.co.uk; @orangetreepub; 9.45 pm, Fri-Sat 10.30 pm, Sun 9 pm; set weekday L £28 (FP).

Orchard WC1 £41 ❸❸❸
11 Sicilian Ave 7831 2715 2–1D
This prettily-located Bloomsbury café, with nice al fresco tables, is a "welcoming" sort of place, offering "wonderfully seasonal" cuisine (and "great-looking cakes, too"); "your friends will never even notice it's vegetarian!" / WC1A 2QH.

Orpheus EC3 £41 ❷❷④
26 Savage Gdns 7481 1931 9–3D
"A little corner of Greece", unexpectedly nestling in a railway arch near Tower Hill; the style may evoke "a City lunch room of the 1960s", but the "diverse selection of top-quality fish" on offer is "a real treat". / EC3N 2AR; L only, closed Sat & Sun.

Orrery W1 £74 ❸❷❷
55 Marylebone High St 7616 8000 2–1A
"Beautiful and light" decor creates "a lovely space" (with "good views" over a churchyard) at this "peaceful", first-floor venture, in Marylebone; it's sometimes seen as the culinary flagship of the D&D group, and its "serious" Gallic cuisine rarely disappoints. / W1U 5RB; www.orreryrestaurant.co.uk; @orrery; 10.30 pm, Fri & Sat 11 pm; set weekday L £48 (FP); SRA-61%.

Orso WC2 £58 ④❸④
27 Wellington St 7240 5269 4–3D
Long-term fans still proclaim the "reliable" charms of this sometimes "noisy" Italian post-opera favourite, in a discreet Covent Garden basement; critics, though, find its "unchanging" style is becoming simply "jaded". / WC2E 7DB; www.orsorestaurant.co.uk; 11.30 pm; set pre theatre £38 (FP).

Oscar
Charlotte Street Hotel W1 £62 ④④❷
15 Charlotte St 7806 2000 2–1C
A "nice buzz" pervades this large and attractively decorated Fitzrovia haunt, whose bar is very popular with local media types; other than the "excellent breakfast", though, "the food is just average". / W1T 1RJ; www.charlottestreethotel.com; 10.45 pm, Sun 10 pm.

Oslo Court NW8 £60 ❷❶❶
Charlbert St, off Prince Albert Rd 7722 8795 8–3A
What "a hoot"!; this '70s-timewarp, at the foot of a Regent's Park apartment block, offers "an experience like no other"; it's the "terrific, old-fashioned service", and loyal north London clientele which really makes the place, but the food – with the almost surreal pudding trolley as the "climax" – is "surprisingly good" too. / NW8 7EN; 11 pm; closed Sun; no jeans or trainers.

Osteria Antica Bologna SW11 £40 ❸❸❸
23 Northcote Rd 7978 4771 10–2C
"A great local restaurant", near Clapham Junction – this "pleasant" fixture offers "classic Italian dishes at reasonable prices". / SW11 1NG; www.osteria.co.uk; 10.30 pm, Sun 10 pm.

Osteria Basilico W11 £55 ❸❸❷
29 Kensington Park Rd 7727 9957 6–1A
"A lively, fun and tasty Notting Hill stalwart!" – the "really busy, noisy and cramped" ground floor (where you can people-watch) is always the "preferred option" at this long-established "neighbourhood" Italian. / W11 2EU; www.osteriabasilico.co.uk; 11.30 pm, Sun 10.15 pm; no booking, Sat L.

Osteria Dell'Angolo SW1 £55 ❸②④
47 Marsham St 3268 1077 2–4C
Most reports on this Westminster Italian are of a "very slick" establishment, where "the high standards of food and service continue"; shame, though, that the ambience is so determinedly "sterile". / SW1P 3DR; www.osteriadellangolo.co.uk; 10.30 pm; closed Sat L & Sun.

Osteria dell'Arancio SW10 £54 ❸❸❸
383 King's Rd 7349 8111 5–3B
"An unusual, almost entirely Italian wine list, with many lesser known options" helps win fans for this "always-friendly" World's End fixture; the food is "dependable" too, if at "prices that match the neighbourhood". / SW10 0LP; www.osteriadellarancio.co.uk; 10.30 pm, Sun 9.30 pm; closed Mon L; set weekday L £33 (FP).

Ostuni NW6 NEW £42
43-45 Lonsdale Rd 7624 8035 1–2B
Out in Queen's Park, an impressively-scaled Italian newcomer, with an unusual regional specialisation (Puglia); sadly, we didn't have have the opportunity to visit before this guide went to press, but early critical reaction has been very favourable. / NW6 6RA; www.ostuniristorante.co.uk.

Otto Pizza W2 £29 ❷❷❷
6 Chepstow Rd 7792 4088 6–1B
"Tasty pizzas with a twist" (and a cornmeal crust) – secret of the success of this "fantastic pizzeria", on the Bayswater/Notting Hill border. / W2 5BH; www.ottopizza.com; @OttoPizzaUk; 11 pm, Sun 10 pm.

Otto's WC1 £55 ❷❷❸
182 Grays Inn Rd 7713 0107 2–1D
"A wonderful surprise in an unprepossessing part of Bloomsbury"; the "very cordial" Otto's "wonderfully eclectic" yearling has made quite a hit with its "determinedly old-fashioned" Gallic style (and its "astonishing" wine list!). / WC1X 8EW; www.ottos-restaurant.com; 10 pm; closed Sat L & Sun.

Ottolenghi £47 ❶❷❸
13 Motcomb St, SW1 7823 2707 5–1D
63 Ledbury Rd, W11 7727 1121 6–1B
1 Holland St, W8 7937 0003 5–1A
287 Upper St, N1 7288 1454 8–2D
Yotam Ottolenghi's Zeitgeisty deli/diners bewitch a large following with the "zingy and unusual" Middle Eastern flavours of their "colourful" and "alluring" dishes (not least "the best desserts"); "just a shame about the queues!" / www.ottolenghi.co.uk; N1 10.15 pm; W8 & W11 8 pm, Sat 7 pm, Sun 6 pm; N1 closed Sun D; Holland St takeaway only; W11 & SW1 no booking, N1 booking for D only.

Outlaw's Seafood and Grill
The Capital Hotel SW3 £80 ❷❶❸
22-24 Basil St 7589 5171 5–1D
The relaunch of this small dining room, near Harrods, under acclaimed Cornwall-based chef Nathan Outlaw, has made a relatively minor splash, but its "astounding" fish dishes are "top notch" and lunch in particular is "fantastic value"; for some tastes, though, the interior is a tad "Spartan" and "hotel-y". / SW3 1AT; www.capitalhotel.co.uk.

(Brasserie)
Oxo Tower SE1   £70   ⑤⑤④
Barge House St   7803 3888   9–3A

"An unrivalled position overlooking the Thames" is "entirely negated" by the "indescribably lacklustre" standards at this South Bank landmark, where service is "shockingly poor", and the food is "average at best"... and all at "crazy" prices! / SE1 9PH; www.harveynichols.com/restaurants/oxo-tower-london; 11 pm, Sun 10 pm; set weekday L & pre-theatre £52 (FP).

(Restaurant)
Oxo Tower SE1   £84   ⑤⑤④
Barge House St   7803 3888   9–3A

"Words cannot describe how bad this restaurant is!" – "overpriced" and "pompous", this top-floor South Bank fixture once again takes no end of flak from reporters; perhaps not entirely coincidentally, it does have a "great view". / SE1 9PH; www.harveynichols.com/restaurants/; 11 pm, Sun 10 pm; set weekday L £60 (FP).

The Oyster Shed EC4   £46   ④④❸
1 Angel Ln, Ground Floor   7256 3240   9–3C

River views, and a "lovely and light" (if Identikit) interior, justify a trip to this large Thames-side Geronimo Inn, which in particular is "a worthy, post-work, destination"; its fish and seafood can be "great", but "simple things can let it down". / EC4R 3AB; www.geronimo-inns.co.uk/theoystershed; 9.30 pm; closed Sat & Sun; SRA-60%.

Ozer W1   £48   ④❷④
5 Langham Pl   7323 0505   3–1C

Right by Broadcasting House, this "semi-formal" operation (flagship of the Sofra chain) certainly makes a handy standby for BBC luvvies, and its "wide-ranging Turkish, Middle Eastern and North African menu" offers "good value, especially given the location". / W1B 3DG; www.sofra.co.uk; 11 pm.

Le P'tit Normand SW18   £41   ❸❷❸
185 Merton Rd   8871 0233   10–2B

"It's nothing to look at from outside", but this age-old Southfields bistro has been on good form of late – "a great local", it feels "very French", and offers "welcoming" service and "fine" cooking too. / SW18 5EF; www.leptitnormand.co.uk; 10 pm, Sun 3 pm; closed Mon, Tue L, Wed L, Thu L & Sun D.

The Paddyfield SW12   £28   ❷❷❸
4 Bedford Hill   8772 1145   10–2C

"Great Balham value!" – this BYO hole-in-the-wall, serves "excellent Thai/Vietnamese food" at "low prices". / SW12 9RG; www.thepaddyfield.co.uk; 11 pm; D only, closed Mon; no credit cards.

Il Pagliaccio SW6   £38   ❸❷❸
182-184 Wandsworth Bridge Rd   7371 5253   10–1B

"Wonderful fresh pizza" is the culinary highlight of a visit to this family-friendly Sands End institution, to which the characterful service adds much charm. / SW6 2UF; www.paggs.co.uk; @pagliaccipizza; midnight; no Amex.

Le Pain Quotidien £37 ④④❸
Branches throughout London
*For their "delicious breads" and "the best Continental
breakfast in town", fans applaud these very "attractive" faux-rustic
cafés; "I sat next to Pippa Middleton, so it must be a good place!"*
/ www.painquotidien.com; most branches close between 7 pm-10 pm;
no booking at some branches, especially at weekends.

The Painted Heron SW10 £56 ❶❷❸
112 Cheyne Walk 7351 5232 5–3B
*"Simply stunning" dishes, "singing with spices", seem to have survived
the change of ownership at this surprisingly "superb" Indian, hidden
away off Chelsea Embankment; the ambience remains a little bit
"staid".* / SW10 0DJ; www.thepaintedheron.com; Mon-Sat 10.30 pm,
Sun 10 pm; no Amex.

The Palm SW1 £83 ④⑤④
1 Pont St 7201 0710 5–1D
*An "overpriced" Belgravia outpost of a US steakhouse chain where
the food is often as "boring" as the interior, and service is sometimes
in the style of "Fawlty Towers"; otherwise, it's fine.* / SW1X 9EJ;
www.thepalm.com/london; 11 pm, Sun 10 pm; Mon-Thu D only, Fri-Sun open
L & D.

The Palmerston SE22 £50 ❸④④
91 Lordship Ln 8693 1629 1–4D
*A "consumate gastropub" – this East Dulwich boozer
is "a modest and over-achieving" fixture, where the food is "genuinely
consistent".* / SE22 8EP; www.thepalmerston.net; @ThePalmerston; 10 pm,
Sun 9.30 pm; set weekday L £28 (FP).

Palmyra TW9 £41 ❷❷④
277 Sandycombe Rd 8948 7019 1–3A
*"Tucked-away" in Kew, a Lebanese restaurant that reporters reckon
"deserves to be busier"; the setting can seem "rather soulless",
but the food is "really tasty".* / TW9 3LU; www.palmyrarestaurant.co.uk;
11 pm; no Amex.

The Pantechnicon SW1 £56 ❸❸❷
10 Motcomb St 7730 6074 5–1D
*In the heart of Belgravia, this "posh gastropub" has an impressively
clubby upstairs dining room; fans find the food "a cut above",
but there's also a school of thought that it is "forgettable".*
/ SW1X 8LA; www.thepantechnicon.com; Weekdays 10 pm, Sun 9.30 pm;
SRA-75%.

Pantry SW18 £30 ❸❷❸
342 Old York Rd 8871 0713 10–2B
*A popular deli/café, in the villagey part of Wandsworth; "delicious
breakfasts, cooked to order" are the daily highlight.* / SW18 1SS;
www.thepantrylondon.com; @pantrycafe@pantrycafe; L only; no Amex.

Pappa Ciccia £39 ❸❸❸
105 Munster Rd, SW6 7384 1884 10–1B
41 Fulham High St, SW6 7736 0900 10–1B
*These "typical neighbourhood Italians" are "lively and fun", and very
"dependable" – they serve pizza and other fare (with "fab specials")
in "generous portions", or you can "just pop in for a great cappuccino
and cake"; BYO.* / www.pappaciccia.com; 11 pm, Sat & Sun 11.30 pm;
Munster Rd no credit cards.

Paradise by Way of Kensal Green W10 £47 ❸❸❷

19 Kilburn Ln   8969 0098   1–2B

*A hugely atmospheric and perennially hip Kensal Green fixture –
this rambling, shabby-chic tavern numbers amongst its many
attractions a "quirky" rear dining room, offering very "acceptable"
cooking. / W10 4AE; www.theparadise.co.uk; @weloveparadise; 10.30 pm,
Fri & Sat 11 pm, Sun 9 pm; closed weekday L; no Amex.*

Paradise Hampstead NW3 £30 ❶❷❸

49 South End Rd   7794 6314   8–2A

*A "first-class" South End Green favourite; one of north London's top
Indians, it offers "novel and delicious" curries, and the staff are
prepared to "go the extra mile". / NW3 2QB;
www.paradisehampstead.co.uk; 10.45 pm.*

El Parador NW1 £35 ❷❷❷

245 Eversholt St   7387 2789   8–3C

*"A little gem", in Camden Town, where the "outstanding" tapas
"never fail to please"; "the terrace garden at the back is particularly
wonderful on a warm summer's evening". / NW1 1BA;
www.elparadorlondon.com; 11 pm, Fri-Sat 11.30 pm, Sun 9.30 pm; closed
Sat L & Sun L; no Amex.*

Paramount
Centre Point WC1 £65 ❹❹❷

101-103 New Oxford St   7420 2900   4–1A

*For "superb views" and a cocktail, the 32nd floor of Centre Point has
its plus points; given the "mediocre" food and service, though,
its attractions for a full-blown meal are more dubious. / WC1A 1DD;
www.paramount.uk.net; 11 pm.*

Patara £54 ❷❸❸

15 Greek St, W1   7437 1071   4–2A
7 Maddox St, W1   7499 6008   3–2C
181 Fulham Rd, SW3   7351 5692   5–2C
9 Beauchamp Pl, SW3   7581 8820   5–1C

*"Authentic Thai food, elegantly presented in a calm and pleasant
atmosphere" – that's the deal that's long made a big hit of this
"reliable" chain; given the prices, though, critics can find the style
a touch "formulaic". / www.pataralondon.com; 10.30 pm; Greek St closed
Sun L.*

Paternoster Chop House EC4 £55 ⑤⑤⑤

Warwick Ct, Paternoster Sq   7029 9400   9–2B

*For a busy steakhouse near St Paul's, this D&D group operation
inspires amazingly little survey feedback; fans say it's a "buzzy" place
with "good meat" – critics that the acoustics are "dreadful"
("like sitting in a tin can"), service "in need of improvement", and the
food "disappointing". / EC4M 7DX; www.paternosterchophouse.co.uk;
10.30 pm; closed Sat & Sun D; SRA-72%.*

Patio W12 £35 ❹❷❶

5 Goldhawk Rd   8743 5194   7–1C

*"Like sitting in someone's home, and that's how you are treated" –
the food may be "heavy", but the vodka is cheap, at this
"very cheerful" Polish stalwart, right on Shepherd's Bush Green, which
offers an "outstanding-value" package overall. / W12 8QQ;
www.patiolondon.com; 11 pm, Sat & Sun 11.30 pm; closed Sat L & Sun L.*

Pâtisserie Valerie £27 ⑤⑤⑤
Branches throughout London
"Terrible, now it's a chain" – too often the verdict on the venture
capital-backed roll-out of these "once-delightful" and "quirky"
pâtisseries, which have been "formularised" and "had all charm
squeezed from them"; growth, however, continues unabated.
/ www.patisserie-valerie.co.uk; most branches close between 5 pm-8 pm;
no booking except Old Compton St Sun-Thu.

Patogh W1 £24 ❷❷④
8 Crawford Pl   7262 4015   6–1D
"One of the best meals you can find for under a tenner!" –
this "modest"-looking pit stop, just off the Edgware Road, offers
"some of the tastiest Persian food in town", and at "dead cheap"
prices too; BYO. / W1H 5NE; 11 pm; no credit cards.

Patty and Bun W1 NEW £21 ❶❸❸
54 James St   7487 3188   3–1A
"I waited over an hour in the cold for this burger... and boy was
it worth it!"; this "cramped" new burger joint, near Selfridges, inspires
lots of reports, all saying pretty much the same – "apart from the
perma-queue, it's brilliant"! / W1U 1HE; www.pattyandbun.co.uk;
@pattyandbunjoe; 10.15 pm, Sun 9.15 pm; closed Mon; no Amex.

Paul £27 ④⑤④
115 Marylebone High St, W1   7224 5615   2–1A
29-30 Bedford St, WC2   7836 3304   4–3C
"Pricier than others, but worth it" – these outposts of France's
biggest café/pâtisserie chain impress with their "wonderful, freshly-
made sandwiches", "great salads" and "delicious" pastries and
coffee; shame about the "slow" service though; (only the
largest branches are listed). / www.paul-uk.com; most branches close
between 7 pm-8.30 pm; no booking.

Pearl Liang W2 £43 ❷❸❸
8 Sheldon Sq   7289 7000   6–1C
This smart but "hard-to-find" basement, stuck out in Paddington
Basin, is known as "one of London's better Chinese options"
(with "incredible" dim sum a highlight); service can be "haphazard",
though, and the occasional reporter does sense "slippage" of late.
/ W2 6EZ; www.pearlliang.co.uk; 11 pm.

The Peasant EC1 £46 ❸❷❸
240 St John St   7336 7726   8–3D
In the '90s, the "very pleasant and comfortable" upstairs dining room
of this "lovely old gin palace", in Clerkenwell, was at the vanguard
of London's gastropub revolution; it still serves "solidly good,
sophisticated comfort food". / EC1V 4PH; www.thepeasant.co.uk;
@ThePeasant; 10.45 pm, Sun 9.30 pm.

Pellicano SW3 £58 ④❶④
19-21 Elystan St   7589 3718   5–2C
A "reliable Italian stalwart", in a Chelsea backstreet, where the staff
are "very friendly and welcoming"; the food "keeps up a good
standard, even if it does vary a bit from visit to visit". / SW3 3NT;
www.pellicanorestaurant.co.uk; 11 pm, Sun 9.30 pm; set weekday L £38 (FP).

E Pellicci E2 £21 ④❷❶
332 Bethnal Green Rd   7739 4873   12–1D
It's not just the famous (and listed) Art Deco interior that makes this
East End café a "classic" – "everyone is made to feel welcome and
invited to join in the banter!" / E2 0AG; 4.15 pm; L only, closed Sun;
no credit cards.

Pentolina W14 £43 ❷❷❸
71 Blythe Rd   3010 0091   7–1D
"The locals can't believe how lucky they are!" – this "simple and elegant" Olympia Italian, has "charming owners", and serves "fabulous" dishes made from "quality ingredients". / W14 0HP; www.pentolinarestaurant.co.uk; 10 pm; closed Mon & Sun; no Amex.

The Pepper Tree SW4 £27 ❸❷④
19 Clapham Common S'side   7622 1758   10–2D
"Tasty food at reasonable prices" – the mainstay of the "utterly dependable" formula that's long sustained this once-pioneering Thai canteen, near Clapham Common tube; service "in double-quick time" too. / SW4 7AB; www.thepeppertree.co.uk; 10.45 pm, Sun-Mon 10.15 pm; no Amex; no booking.

Pescatori £55 ❸❸④
11 Dover St, W1   7493 2652   3–3C
57 Charlotte St, W1   7580 3289   2–1C
For "well prepared fish in the Italian style", many more mature reporters find these slightly "old-fashioned" West End eateries a "very useful and reasonably-priced" option; the occasional 'off' report, however, is not unknown. / www.pescatori.co.uk; 11 pm; closed Sat L & Sun.

Petek N4 £31 ❸❷❷
94-96 Stroud Green Rd   7619 3933   8–1D
"The jewel of Finsbury Park!", say local fans; it "doesn't look much", but it's a "no-nonsense", "colourful" and "busy" operation serving "generous and juicy Turkish dishes". / N4 3EN; www.petekrestaurant.co.uk; 11 pm.

Petersham Hotel TW10 £65 ④❸❷
Nightingale Ln   8940 7471   1–4A
"Wonderful views of the River Thames" add lustre to the "old-fashioned" ("slightly stuffy") style of this Richmond hotel dining room; most reporters find a visit a "comforting" experience, though critics can find the approach a touch "complacent". / TW10 6UZ; www.petershamhotel.co.uk; @ThePetersham; 9.45 pm, Sun 8.45 pm.

Petersham Nurseries TW10 £72 ❸⑤❸
Church Ln, Off Petersham Rd   8940 5230   1–4A
"Primitive, scruffy, but oh-so-trendy" – this "ramshackle" venue (in the glasshouse of an upmarket garden centre) makes a famously "quirky" setting; since Skye Gyngell's departure, however, its performance seems ever more "smug and overpriced". / TW10 7AG; www.petershamnurseries.com; L only, closed Mon.

La Petite Maison W1 £84 ❷❸❷
54 Brook's Mews   7495 4774   3–2B
"Outstanding zest and freshness" characterise the "sensational" but simple-sounding sharing plates on offer at casually glamorous Nice-comes-to-Mayfair scene; the prices, though, are "crazy", and the whole "noisy" vibe is a bit "oligarchic" for some tastes. / W1K 4EG; www.lpmlondon.co.uk; 10.30 pm, Sun 9 pm.

Pétrus SW1 £92 ❷❶❸
1 Kinnerton St   7592 1609   5–1D
"Superb" ("if not especially innovative") food – "especially desserts" – figures in almost all reports on this "very professionally-run" Ramsay-outpost, in Belgravia, and the wines are "splendid" too; if there is a criticism, it is that the rather beige dining room "lacks soul". / SW1X 8EA; www.gordonramsay.com/petrus; 10.30 pm; closed Sun; no trainers; set weekday L £53 (FP).

Pham Sushi EC1 £37 ❶④⑤
159 Whitecross St 7251 6336 12–2A
"The most amazing fresh sushi and sashimi" justify the trip to this
"very basic" diner, north of the Barbican, and it's "so incredibly
cheap" – "the dishes are as good as Zuma or Nobu, but a third
of the price!" / EC1Y 8JL; www.phamsushi.co.uk; 10 pm; closed Sat L & Sun.

Pho £36 ❷❷❷
163-165 Wardour St, W1 7434 3938 3–1D
3 Great Titchfield St, W1 7436 0111 3–1C
Westfield, Ariel Way, W12 07824 662320 7–1C
48 Brushfield St, E1 7377 6436 12–2B
86 St John St, EC1 7253 7624 9–1A
"A brilliant homage to Vietnamese street-food"; you "can't fault" this
growing chain of "vibrant" pit stops, where "irresistible, yummy and
filling noodle soups" are "efficiently served" in a "fun" environment,
at "honest prices". / www.phocafe.co.uk; EC1 10 pm, Fri & Sat 10.30 pm;
W1 10.30 pm; W12 9 pm, Sat 7 pm, Sun 6 pm; EC1 closed Sat L & Sun;
W1 closed Sun; no Amex; no booking.

Phoenix Palace NW1 £51 ❸④④
5-9 Glentworth St 7486 3515 2–1A
"You could be in Hong Kong", at this glitzy-but-gloomy venture,
near Baker Street tube, which is "very popular with the Chinese
community", thanks to its "un-Anglicised" cooking and its "excellent
dim sum"; in recent years, however, "standards have slipped" a bit.
/ NW1 5PG; www.phoenixpalace.co.uk; 11.15 pm, Sun 10.30 pm.

Piccolino £51 ④❸④
21 Heddon St, W1 7287 4029 3–2C
11 Exchange Sq, EC2 7375 2568 12–2B
"A friendly and flexible chain, welcoming to all generations" –
the general view on this "safe" Italian group.
/ www.piccolinorestaurants.co.uk; 11 pm, Sun 10 pm; EC2 closed Sat & Sun.

Picture W1 NEW £32 ❷❷④
110 Great Portland St 7637 7892 2–1B
Very handy for Broadcasting House (and, at lunchtime, seemingly
entirely full of BBC staff), this cacophonous new restaurant offers
enjoyable small plates at reasonable prices. / W1W 6PQ; Rated
on Editors' visit; www.picturerestaurant.co.uk.

PIED À TERRE W1 £104 ❶❶❸
34 Charlotte St 7636 1178 2–1C
"An outstanding restaurant, with a team in full song!"; David Moore's
"sophisticated" Fitzrovia fixture offers not just Marcus Eaves's
"exquisite" cuisine, but also a "brilliant" wine list (including some
"great global discoveries"), and notably "discreet" and "friendly"
service too. / W1T 2NH; www.pied-a-terre.co.uk; 10.45 pm; closed
Sat L & Sun; booking: max 7; set weekday L £68 (FP).

Pig & Butcher N1 NEW £48 ❷❷❷
80 Liverpool Rd 7226 8304 8–3D
"A really great addition to Islington's gastropubs"; this "beautiful"
hostelry is a real pub (you can just drink), with "a huge list of ales",
but also turns out "fantastic", "solid" staples – meat dishes
in particular are "peerless". / N1 0QD; www.thepigandbutcher.co.uk;
@pigandbutcher; 10.30 pm; closed Mon L, Tue L & Wed L.

The Pig's Ear SW3 £50 ④④❸
35 Old Church St 7352 2908 5–3C
An Art Nouveau-themed Chelsea boozer, featuring a "delightful, old-fashioned upstairs dining room"; fans still laud its "honest British fare", but a worrying number of reports of late complain of food of "poor quality". / SW3 5BS; www.thepigsear.info; 10 pm, Sun 9 pm.

Pilpel £9 ❷❷④
38 Brushfield Street, London, E1 7247 0146 12–2B
Old Spitalfields Mkt, E1 7375 2282 12–2B
146 Fleet St, EC4 7583 2030 9–2A
Paternoster Sq, EC4 7248 9281 9–2B
"The best falafel this side of Tel Aviv" and "great service" too! – expect "massive" (but "fast-moving") queues if you make a lunchtime visit to a branch of this "slick" small chain. / www.pilpel.co.uk.

ping pong £32 ④❷❸
10 Paddington St, W1 7009 9600 2–1A
29a James St, W1 7034 3100 3–1A
45 Gt Marlborough St, W1 7851 6969 3–2C
48 Eastcastle St, W1 7079 0550 3–1C
74-76 Westbourne Grove, W2 7313 9832 6–1B
Southbank Centre, SE1 7960 4160 2–3D
St Katharine Docks, E1 7680 7850 9–3D
Bow Bells Hs, 1 Bread St, EC4 7651 0880 9–2B
"Fab, fresh fare and cocktails that really hit the spot" – many reporters like these stylish and "laid-back" dim sum hang-outs; service is "speedy" too (and "they deal effortlessly with young kids"). / www.pingpongdimsum.com; @pingpongdimsum; 10 pm-11.30 pm; EC2 & EC4 closed Sat & Sun; booking: min 8.

El Pirata W1 £38 ④❷❶
5-6 Down St 7491 3810 3–4B
"A really lively tapas bar in the depths of Mayfair" – a "fun" little dive, and one that's "surprisingly good value" for the area too. / W1J 7AQ; www.elpirata.co.uk; @elpirataw1; 11.30 pm; closed Sat L & Sun.

El Pirata de Tapas W2 £41 ❸❸❷
115 Westbourne Grove 7727 5000 6–1B
A "lovely" Bayswater bar; with its "finely flavoured" tapas and its "consistent high standards" all-round, it inspires only positive reports. / W2 4UP; www.elpiratadetapas.co.uk; @Pirate_de_Tapas; 11 pm, Sun 10 pm.

Pissarro W4 £49 ④④❶
Corney Reach Way 8994 3111 10–1A
"Make sure you ask for a conservatory table", at this "lovely" Chiswick location, which has a "beautiful, peaceful setting, right on the Thames" – "a wonderful place for a family weekend lunch", in particular. / W4 2UG; www.pissarro.co.uk; @pissarroW4; 9.45 pm; set weekday L £32 (FP).

Pitt Cue Co W1 £25 ❶❸❸
1 Newburgh St no tel 3–2D
"I actually enjoyed the queuing!" – such are the "happy" vibes at this tiny and "crowded" Carnaby Street BBQ – a "meaty-licious" heaven, where the pulled pork in particular is a "must-try". / W1F 7RB; www.pittcue.co.uk; SRA-57%.

Pizarro SE1 £47 ❷❷❶
194 Bermondsey St   7407 7339   9–4D
"Wonderful on all levels" – José P's Bermondsey "gem" is a "passionate" undertaking, serving tapas "almost as good as in Barcelona", and "interesting" wines too; unsurprisingly, it "can get very busy". / SE1 3TQ; www.josepizarro.com/restaurants/pizarro; @Jose_Pizarro; 11 pm, Sun 10 pm.

Pizza East £47 ❷❸❶
310 Portobello Rd, W10   8969 4500   6–1A
79 Highgate Rd, NW5   3310 2000   8–1B
56 Shoreditch High St, E1   7729 1888   12–1B
"Skinny jeans and face fur are 'de rigueur'" at these "warehousey" hang-outs (which now include a "painfully trendy" Kentish Town branch); its "reinvention of pizza", though, can come as a "genuine surprise" – "spot on". / www.pizzaeast.com; @PizzaEast; E1 Sun-Wed 11 pm, Thu 12 am, Fri-Sat 1am; W10 Mon-Thu 11.30 pm, Fri-Sat 12 am, Sun 10.30 pm.

Pizza Metro SW11 £45 ❷④④
64 Battersea Rise   7228 3812   10–2C
"As good as Naples' best!" – these "noisy" and "friendly" haunts (London pioneers of pizza-by-the-metre) are still sterling members of the capital's pizza 'hall of fame'; Notting Hill is just as highly-rated nowadays as the Battersea original. / SW11 1EQ; www.pizzametropizza.com; 11 pm; closed weekday L; no Amex.

Pizza Pilgrims W1 NEW £23
11-12 Dean St   667258   4–2A
A former pizza pop-up, now with its own proper base, in the heart of Soho; early-days press reviews have been encouraging. / W1D 3RP; @pizzapilgrims; 10.30 pm; closed Sun; no Amex.

Ciro's (Pizza Pomodoro) SW3 £48 ❸④❷
51 Beauchamp Pl   7589 1278   5–1C
An age-old Euro-hang-out, in a Knightsbridge basement, where the special attraction is the "great bar atmosphere" later on in the evening, with live music; OK pizza too. / SW3 1NY; www.pomodoro.co.uk; 1 am; D only.

PizzaExpress £38 ④④❸
Branches throughout London
"A bigger, more intelligent menu" (including the "lightweight pizzas with a hole in the middle"), plus constant reinvention of the "bright" decor maintain the benchmark status of this ever-faithful stand-by, not least as "a guaranteed success with kids". / www.pizzaexpress.co.uk; 11.30 pm-midnight; most City branches closed all or part of weekend; no booking at most branches.

Pizzeria Oregano N1 £40 ❷❷❸
18-19 St Albans Pl   7288 1123   8–3D
"Tucked-away down a side-alley off Islington's Upper Street", this family-run café knocks out "superb, crispy pizzas at great prices", plus other "delicious" pasta dishes and salads. / N1 0NX; 11 pm, Fri 11.30 pm, Sun 10.30 pm; closed weekday L.

Pizzeria Pappagone N4 £37 ❸❷❷
131 Stroud Green Rd   7263 2114   8–1D
"They love to sing Happy Birthday", at this "extremely noisy" Italian, in Stroud Green; a "fun" place, offering very dependable pizza and pasta, and which is "guaranteed always to be full". / N4 3PX; www.pizzeriapappagone.co.uk; midnight.

Pizzeria Rustica TW9 £38 ❸❸④
32 The Quadrant 8332 6262 1–4A
"Delicious thin-crust pizza" wins a fair-sized fan club for this
"cramped" Richmond Italian – a notably "dependable" destination.
/ TW9 1DN; www.pizzeriarustica.co.uk; 11 pm, Fri & Sat 11.30 pm,
Sun 10.30 pm.

PJ's Bar and Grill SW3 £53 ④❷❷
52 Fulham Rd 7581 0025 5–2C
"Busy" and "buzzing" at all hours, a "festive" Chelsea bar/restaurant
that's most tipped as a "brunch classic". / SW3 6HH;
www.pjsbarandgrill.co.uk; 10.30 pm, Sun 10 pm.

Plane Food TW6 £53 ④④④
Heathrow Airport, Terminal 5 8897 4545 1–3A
"Decent airport food at last!"; Gordon Ramsay's airside brasserie
provides a "bit of peace and quiet" within T5, and, by transport
catering standards, offers "good value", especially for breakfast.
/ TW6 2GA; www.gordonramsay.com; 9.30 pm.

Plateau E14 £58 ⑤④⑤
Canada Pl 7715 7100 11–1C
This "staid" Canary Wharf restaurant, part of the D&D group, gives
every impression of depending for business on its "convenient"
location and its "fabulous" outlook – otherwise, it can seem
"insultingly average in every respect". / E14 5ER;
www.plateau-restaurant.co.uk; 10.15 pm; closed Sat L & Sun; SRA-63%.

Plum + Spilt Milk
Great Northern Hotel N1 NEW £45 ❸❸❷
King's Cross 3388 0800 8–3C
This "nicely styled" new King's Cross dining room makes a surprisingly
funky 'find' for a railway station hotel; in the early days, though,
reports on the (simple) food have spanned the whole range from
"excellent" to "below par". / N1C 4TB; www.gnhlondon.com;
@PlumSpiltMilk; 11 pm, Sun 10 pm.

Plum Valley W1 £45 ❷❸❷
20 Gerrard St 7494 4366 4–3A
A "classy" Chinatown joint, in contemporary style, where the cuisine
is "truly different" from the local mainstream, and often
"very delicious" too. / W1D 6JQ; 11.30 pm.

Pod £14 ❸❸④
124 High Holborn, WC1 3174 0541 2–1D
Tooley St, SE1 3174 0374 9–4D
10 St Martin's Le Grand, EC1 3174 0399 9–2B
162-163 London Wall, EC2 7256 5506 9–2C
25 Exchange Sq, EC2 3174 0290 12–2B
Devonshire Sq, EC2 3174 0108 9–2D
5 Lloyds Ave, EC3 3174 0038 9–3D
1 Printer St, EC4 3174 0228 9–2A
75 King William St, EC4 7283 7460 9–3C
"A revelation"; fans of these health-conscious pit stops say their
"homestyle and very wholesome" scoff (wraps, salads, soups, small
plates) is "the best fast food on the high street". / www.podfood.co.uk;
3 pm-4 pm, WC2 7 pm, Sat 8 pm, Sun 5 pm; branches closed Sat & Sun,
St Martin's & City Rd closed Sun.

Poissonnerie de l'Avenue SW3 £69 ❷❷④
82 Sloane Ave 7589 2457 5–2C
*This "old-fashioned" Brompton Cross veteran is a fixed point in a
changing world; it generally appeals to a more mature crowd,
who know that its fish and seafood are "dependably first-rate".
/ SW3 3DZ; www.poissonneriedelavenue.co.uk; 11.30 pm, Sun 10.30 pm.*

**(Ognisko Polskie)
The Polish Club SW7** £54 ④④❷
55 Prince's Gate, Exhibition Rd 7589 4635 5–1C
*For time-warp grandeur at reasonable cost, few venues rival this
faded émigrés' club, in South Kensington; its dependable Polish fodder
is best enjoyed in summer on the "lovely balcony". / SW7 2PN;
www.ognisko.com; 11 pm; no trainers; set weekday L & Sun L £27 (FP).*

POLLEN STREET SOCIAL W1 £81 ❷❷❸
8-10 Pollen St 7290 7600 3–2C
*Jason Atherton's "genuinely exciting" cuisine – "fresh in every sense"
– again inspires adulation for his Mayfair two-year-old (where the
"amazing dessert bar" is a "highlight"); the décor is "a bit bland",
though, and some reporters can find dishes "over-engineered".
/ W1S 1NQ; www.pollenstreetsocial.com; 10.45 pm; closed Sun; set weekday L
£55 (FP).*

Polpo £36 ④❸❶
41 Beak St, W1 7734 4479 3–2D
6 Maiden Ln, WC2 7836 8448 4–3D
2-3 Cowcross St, EC1 7250 0034 9–1A
*A "cool NYC vibe" that's "easy, welcoming and democratic" –
plus lots of savvy marketing – has raised Russell Norman's "cramped"
Venetian-style tapas bars to cult status; "queueing is annoying",
though, and the quality of the dishes "does vary". / www.polpo.co.uk;
W1 & EC1 11 pm; WC2 11 pm, Sun 10.30 pm; W1 & EC1 closed D Sun.*

Le Pont de la Tour SE1 £72 ④④❷
36d Shad Thames 7403 8403 9–4D
*"Tower Bridge views to die for" (especially from outside tables) are
the undoubted plus of a meal at this stalwart D&D group South
Banker – a hotspot for business or romance; opinions on the cuisine,
however, range all the way from "brilliant" to "disappointing", though
the wine list is "second to none". / SE1 2YE; www.lepontdelatour.co.uk;
@lepontdelatour; 11 pm, Sun 10 pm; no trainers; set weekday L £52
(FP); SRA-58%.*

Popeseye £51 ④④⑤
108 Blythe Rd, W14 7610 4578 7–1C
277 Upper Richmond Rd, SW15 8788 7733 10–2A
*These "basic" west London dives have long had a name for "steaks
as good as you'll find", and "good-value" wines to go with 'em too;
recent times, however, have seen a number of "disappointing" reports
from former fans. / www.popeseye.com; 10.30 pm; D only, closed Sun;
no credit cards.*

La Porchetta Pizzeria £33 ❸❸❸
33 Boswell St, WC1 7242 2434 2–1D
141-142 Upper St, N1 7288 2488 8–2D
147 Stroud Green Rd, N4 7281 2892 8–1D
74-77 Chalk Farm Rd, NW1 7267 6822 8–2B
84-86 Rosebery Ave, EC1 7837 6060 9–1A
"Like a little outpost of chaotic Italian life" – these noisy,
and "authentic" north London stalwarts are long on "jolly"
atmosphere and "fast, family-friendly service"; they dish
up "satisfyingly big" pizza plus other "decent and cheapish fare".
/ www.laporchetta.net; last orders varies by branch; WC1 closed Sat L & Sun;
N1,EC1 & NW1 closed Mon-Fri L; N4 closed weekday L; no Amex.

Portal EC1 £56 ❹❹❸
88 St John St 7253 6950 9–1B
A potentially impressive Portuguese, in Clerkenwell, with a "light-filled
conservatory" and an "interesting" menu (and wine list); service can
be too "laissez-faire", however, and those who claim the food
is "nothing special" were more in evidence this year. / EC1M 4EH;
www.portalrestaurant.com; dine@portal; 10.15 pm; closed Sat L & Sun.

La Porte des Indes W1 £63 ❸❷❷
32 Bryanston St 7224 0055 2–2A
"Wow!"; this "enormous" and lavish basement, near Marble Arch,
certainly impresses first-timers, and its (French-colonial) "Indian food
with a twist" has been on "excellent" form of late; Sunday brunch,
in particular, is "well worth booking for". / W1H 7EG;
www.laportedesindes; 11.30 pm, Sun 10.30 pm.

Porters English Restaurant WC2 £44 ❹❸❸
17 Henrietta St 7836 6466 4–3C
Amidst all the 'boutique-ification' of Covent Garden, Lord Bradford's
English-themed diner seems ever-more retro nowadays (even despite
its recent more modern refurb); critics find the food "stodgy"... but
watch out for "excellent" pies, and "good-value special offers".
/ WC2E 8QH; www.porters.uk.com; 11.30 pm, Sun 10.30 pm; no Amex.

Il Portico W8 £49 ❹❸❸
277 Kensington High St 7602 6262 7–1D
"A large and loyal clientele" patronises this "traditional" Kensington
trattoria – "the very epitome of an Italian family place"; doubters,
though, are mystified by its popularity – "clearly there's a lot
of people out there nostalgic for the '60s!" / W8 6NA;
www.ilportico.co.uk; 11 pm; closed Sun.

Portobello Ristorante W11 £49 ❷❷❷
7 Ladbroke Rd 7221 1373 6–2B
"Not just great for pizza!" (by the metre) – this "friendly" spot,
just off Notting Hill Gate, is also of note for its "really good Italian
home cooking" and "charming" service; "sit on the patio in summer".
/ W11 3PA; www.portobellolondon.co.uk; 10.30 pm, Sun 10.15 pm.

**The Portrait
National Portrait Gallery WC2** £51 ❹❹❶
St Martin's Pl 7312 2490 4–4B
"Everything is secondary" to the "terrific" views ("over the Trafalgar
Square roofscape") of this mega-central top-floor dining room;
perhaps new caterers Company of Cooks will be able to make it a
gastronomic destination in its own right. / WC2H 0HE;
www.searcys.co.uk; Thu-Fri 8.30 pm; Sat-Sun closed L, Sun-Wed closed D.

Potli W6   £37   ❷④④
319-321 King St   8741 4328   7–2B
It may look "shabby" from the outside, but this "hospitable"
Hammersmith Indian serves up some "exciting and well-spiced"
dishes (including a "particularly delicious range of starters").
/ W6 9NH; www.potli.co.uk; 10.30 pm, Fri-Sat 11.30 pm.

La Poule au Pot SW1   £59   ❸❸❶
231 Ebury St   7730 7763   5–2D
"Home of Gallic cuisine, and amour" – for over half a century,
this "rustic" charmer (with its candle-light and "dark nooks"), on a
Pimlico corner, has been one of London's top choices for romance;
on the food front, the prix-fixe lunch offers particularly "amazing"
value. / SW1W 8UT; www.pouleaupot.co.uk; 11 pm, Sun 10 pm;
set weekday L £40 (FP).

Prawn On The Lawn N1 NEW   £27
220 St Paul's Rd   3302 8668   8–2D
Sadly, we didn't get the chance to visit this new Canonbury seafood
parlour before this guide went to press; the media reception, however,
has been enthusiastic. / N1 2LY; prawnonthelawn.com.

Pret A Manger   £15   ④❷④
Branches throughout London
"Unbeatable for consistency", thanks to its "always-fresh" snack
range, and its "super-efficient" service, this London-based sandwich
chain (now also in Paris, NYC and HK) is still the 'gold standard'; let's
hope the bargain 99p coffee will survive the economic upturn!
/ www.pret.com; generally 4 pm-6 pm; closed Sun (except some West End
branches); City branches closed Sat & Sun; no Amex; no booking.

Princess Garden W1   £59   ❶❷❸
8-10 North Audley St   7493 3223   3–2A
"Always delicious, and not as expensive as it looks" – this smart
Mayfair Chinese veteran is hailed in many reports for its "fresh" and
"delicate" cuisine, which includes some "fabulous and authentic dim
sum". / W1K 6ZD; www.princessgardenofmayfair.com; 10.45 pm,
Sun 10.45 pm.

Princess of Shoreditch EC2   £46   ❸④❸
76 Paul St   7729 9270   12–1B
"Full of Shoreditch luvvies", "a very pleasant" small dining room, up a
spiral staircase from "a very popular pub". / EC2A 4NE;
www.theprincessofshoreditch.com; @princessofs; 10 pm, Sun 8 pm; no Amex.

Princess Victoria W12   £46   ④❷❷
217 Uxbridge Rd   8749 5886   7–1B
An "oasis" at the far end of Shepherd's Bush, this "welcoming" gin
palace, which has been beautifully restored, has a big name locally
for its "refined" gastropub cuisine, and it offers a "surprisingly good"
wine selection too. / W12 9DH; www.princessvictoria.co.uk; @pvwestlondon;
10.30 pm, Sun 9.30 pm; no Amex.

Princi W1   £33   ❸④❷
135 Wardour St   7478 8888   3–2D
"Energetic" at all hours (and sometimes "hectic"), this "upscale"
Soho cafeteria-cum-bakery offers "Italian fast food at its best"
(now including table-service pizza). / W1F 0UT; www.princi.com; midnight,
Sun 10 pm; no booking.

F S A

Prix Fixe W1 £37 ❸②❸
39 Dean St 7734 5976 4–2A
A "cosy" and "reliable" Soho bistro, offering "great food, reasonably
priced" – no wonder it's always "lively"; there was a major refurb
in the summer of 2013. / W1D 4PU; www.prixfixe.net; 11.30 pm.

The Providores W1 £70 ❷④⑤
109 Marylebone High St 7935 6175 2–1A
"Challenging combinations producing amazing flavours" still inspire
applause for Peter Gordon's "tightly-packed" first-floor Marylebone
dining room; critics, though, do find prices unduly "hefty". / W1U 4RX;
www.theprovidores.co.uk; 10.30 pm; set weekday L £46 (FP); SRA-60%.

(Tapa Room)
The Providores W1 £52 ❷④❸
109 Marylebone High St 7935 6175 2–1A
Peter Gordon's Marylebone bar offers "deliciously crafted" Pacific-
fusion tapas and "outstanding" Kiwi wines, which help to "make up
for any unwanted cosiness" arising from its "cramped" lay-out;
brunch is "fantastic", but the queues for it "get ever worse".
/ W1U 4RX; www.theprovidores.co.uk; @theprovidores; 10.30 pm, Sun 10 pm.

Prufrock Coffee EC1 £13 ❷❷❸
23-25 Leather Ln 224 3470 9–2A
"Off-the-scale good!" – it's not just the coffee which makes this
Holborn spot of note, but also its "impressive" range of sandwiches
and snacks – "perfect for a pick-me-up during the working day".
/ EC1N 7TE; www.prufrockcoffee.com; 6 pm, Sat 5 pm; L only, closed Sun;
no Amex.

The Punch Tavern EC4 £37 ④❸❷
99 Fleet St 7353 6658 9–2A
"A real winner for value"; just off Ludgate Circus, this "busy" Victorian
boozer offers a good selection of food at competitive prices.
/ EC4Y 1DE; www.punchtavern.com; 10.30 pm, Sat & Sun 6.30 pm.

Punjab WC2 £27 ❷❷④
80 Neal St 7836 9787 4–2C
"Dead in the centre of town", this "old-established", "traditional" and
"solicitous" Indian fixture maintains a dedicated fan club. / WC2H 9PA;
www.punjab.co.uk; 11 pm, Sun 10.30 pm.

Quaglino's SW1 £65 ⑤④④
16 Bury St 7930 6767 3–3D
"A dinosaur!"; the early '90s – when this St James's basement was
a byword for glamour – are a bygone age, and this "tired" brasserie
can strike today's reporters as having "absolutely nothing
to commend it"; come on D&D – time for the revamp! / SW1Y 6AJ;
www.quaglinos.co.uk; 10.30 pm, Fri & Sat 11 pm; closed Sun; no trainers;
SRA-62%.

The Quality Chop House EC1 £40 ❷❷❷
94 Farringdon Rd 7278 1452 9–1A
"Off to a flying start"; the relaunch of this "vintage" Farringdon
'working class caterer' has "brought it back to life" with a bang,
thanks not least to its "deceptively simple and simply delicious" British
food, and its "fascinating" wine list. / EC1R 3EA;
www.thequalitychophouse.com; @QualityChop; 10.30 pm; closed Sun.

Quantus W4 £37 ❷❶❷
38 Devonshire Rd 8994 0488 7–2A
*"Leo, the owner, takes a personal interest in his customers", and his
"charming" welcome is a huge plus for this "cosy" Chiswick venture;
the South American-edged cuisine can sometimes seem a touch
"eccentric", but it's often "excellent" too. / W4 2HD;
www.quantus-london.com; 10 pm; closed Mon L, Tue L & Sun L.*

Queen's Head W6 £38 ❹❸❷
13 Brook Grn 7603 3174 7–1C
*A "quaint" tavern on Brook Green, which "has charm in spite of its
average food"; in particular, "you go here for the garden"… which
is surprisingly vast. / W6 7BL; www.queensheadhammersmith.co.uk; 10 pm,
Sun 9 pm.*

The Queens Arms SW1 £42 ❸❸❷
11 Warwick Way 7834 3313 2–4B
*In the Pimlico desert, this "friendly" and "consistent" boozer
is establishing itself as a "popular" destination; "standard pub food,
but well executed". / SW1V 1QT; www.thequeensarmspimlico.co.uk;
@thequeensarms; 11 pm, Sun 10.30 pm.*

Le Querce SE23 £39 ❶❷❸
66-68 Brockley Rise 8690 3761 1–4D
*An "unexpectedly fine" family-run Sardinian in Brockley Park;
fans cross town for its "truly fabulous" cooking, including "real and
rare Italian specialities"; "the ice-cream and sorbet list is absolutely
unbelievable". / SE23 1LN; 10 pm, Sun 8.30 pm; closed Mon & Tue L.*

Quilon SW1 £65 ❶❷❹
41 Buckingham Gate 7821 1899 2–4B
*"Magnificent" Keralan cuisine ("fish is particularly good") and
"courteous" service distinguish this "really impressive Indian",
near Buckingham Palace; the businesslike décor, though, is "rather
sterile". / SW1E 6AF; www.quilon.co.uk; 10.45 pm, Sun 10.15 pm; SRA-66%.*

Quirinale SW1 £61 ❶❷❹
North Ct, 1 Gt Peter St 7222 7080 2–4C
*"Tucked-away" in a Westminster backstreet, a "very professional"
(and arguably "under-rated") Italian, offering "superb" cooking and
"impeccable" service; the slightly "sepulchral" basement setting
is best when busy… typically with "lots of politicos pretending not
to be lobbied". / SW1P 3LL; www.quirinale.co.uk; @quirinaleresto; 10.30 pm;
closed Sat & Sun; set weekday L & pre-theatre £41 (FP).*

Quo Vadis W1 £55 ❸❸❷
26-29 Dean St 7437 9585 4–2A
*"Jeremy Lee has brought the fizz back to this elegant establishment",
say fans of this "sophisticated" Soho favourite; such "lavish praise",
however, leaves other reporters "bemused", and – overall – the food
is rated no better than "very competent". / W1D 3LL;
www.quovadissoho.co.uk; 10.45 pm; closed Sun; set weekday L & pre-theatre
£36 (FP).*

Racine SW3 £66 ❸❸❸
239 Brompton Rd 7584 4477 5–2C
*A reputation as "one of the best Gallic bistros in town" precedes
Henry Harris's "traditional" Knightsbridge fixture, which, for many
reporters, still offers a "special experience every time"; sadly,
however, the survey confirms that standards are "slipping", and quite
fast too. / SW3 2EP; www.racine-restaurant.com; 10.30 pm, Sun 10 pm;
set weekday L £35 (FP).*

Ragam W1 £27 **❶❸⑤**
57 Cleveland St   7636 9098   2–1B
"Some of the best South Indian cuisine I've eaten... and I'm South Indian!" – this *"terrific"* café veteran, near the Telecom Tower, is *"the real thing"*; OK, *"the decor sucks"* (*"and they've done it up!"*), but the *"fabulous"* dishes come at *"rock-bottom"* prices; BYO. / W1T 4JN; www.ragam.co.uk; 10.45 pm; essential Fri & Sat.

Randall & Aubin W1 £52 **❷❷❶**
16 Brewer St   7287 4447   3–2D
"A pretty much unique experience!"; offering *"delicious"* seafood, right in the sleazy heart of Soho, this *"cosily perfect"* (if *"loud"*) champagne and seafood bar is *"a real gem"*; *"get a window table to watch the goings-on outside"*. / W1F 0SG; www.randallandaubin.com; @edbaineschef; 11 pm, Sat midnight, Sun 10 pm; booking for L only; SRA-58%.

Rani N3 £27 **❸④④**
7 Long Ln   8349 4386   1–1B
"Terrific and great value" – it's the buffet offer which makes this *"homely"* Indian veggie veteran, in Finchley, of more than local interest. / N3 2PR; www.raniuk.com; 10 pm.

Ranoush £46 **❸❸④**
22 Brompton Rd, SW1   7584 6999   5–1D
338 King's Rd, SW3   7352 0044   5–3C
43 Edgware Rd, W2   7723 5929   6–1D
86 Kensington High St, W8   7938 2234   5–1A
"For a quick bite, you can't beat a salad and a chicken shawarma", at these *"comfy"* Lebanese pit stops – a less expensive part of the Maroush chain. / www.maroush.com; most branches close between 1 am-3 am.

Raoul's Café £45 **④❸❸**
105-107 Talbot Rd, W11   7229 2400   6–1B
113-115 Hammersmith Grove, W6   8741 3692   7–1C
13 Clifton Rd, W9   7289 7313   8–4A
The *"best eggs Benedict in town"* are the highlight attraction for fans of these chillaxed Notting Hill, Hammersmith and Maida Vale hang-outs; *"after a disastrous start, W6 is much better now"*. / www.raoulsgourmet.com; 10.15 pm, W11 6.15 pm; booking after 5 pm only.

Rasa £37 **❷❷❸**
6 Dering St, W1   7637 0222   3–2B
Holiday Inn Hotel, 1 Kings Cross, WC1   7833 9787   8–3D
55 Stoke Newington Church St, N16   7249 0344   1–1C
56 Stoke Newington Church St, N16   7249 1340   1–1C
"Outstanding" dishes – many of them veggie – have carved out a huge name for this small Keralan chain, with the original (55 S N Church St) still often voted one of London's best Indians; for some loyal fans, however, *"it's still a favourite"*, but has seemed *"less exciting and vibrant"* of late. / www.rasarestaurants.com; 10.45 pm; WC1 & W1 closed Sun.

Rasoi SW3 £101 **❷❸❸**
10 Lincoln St   7225 1881   5–2D
"Quite simply the best Indian food I've ever eaten!"; Vineet Bhattia is a *"magician"*, whose *"clever"* cuisine enchants almost all visitors to this *"classy and surprising"* Chelsea townhouse; it's an *"intimate"* experience, and the setting is on the *"quiet"* side for some tastes. / SW3 2TS; www.rasoirestaurant.co.uk; 10.30 pm, Sun 10 pm; closed Mon & Sat L.

The Real Greek £39 ⑤④④
56 Paddington St, W1   7486 0466   2–1A
60-62 Long Acre, WC2   7240 2292   4–2D
Westfield, Ariel Way, W12   8743 9168   7–1C
1-2 Riverside Hs, Southwark Br Rd, SE1   7620 0162   9–3B
6 Horner Sq, E1   7375 1364   12–2B
This "noisy" small chain does have its fans, who praise its "good, solid meze", but critics just find it "so poor in every respect" – "like a bad '70s-themed Greek restaurant". / www.therealgreek.com; 10.45 pm; WC2 10.30 pm, E1 Sun 7 pm; EC1 closed Sun, N1 closed Sun-Mon; WC2 no booking.

Red Dog Saloon N1 £40 ❸❷❷
37 Hoxton Sq   3551 8014   12–1B
"It's always a giggle watching someone take on one of the ridiculous Man vs Food challenges", at this "VERY hearty American BBQ" in Hoxton; the cooking's surprisingly "decent", though – the "devastator burger" rates special mention. / N1 6NN; www.reddogsaloon.co.uk; @reddogsaloonn1; 10.30 pm.

Red Fort W1 £65 ❸④④
77 Dean St   7437 2525   4–2A
This Soho stalwart – decorated nowadays "rather in international-hotel style" – no longer attracts the attention it once did; some loyalists still hail it as "London's best traditional Indian", but most assessments are more middle-of-the-road. / W1D 3SH; www.redfort.co.uk; 11.15 pm; closed Sat L & Sun L; set weekday L & pre-theatre £38 (FP).

The Red Pepper W9 £44 ❷❸④
8 Formosa St   7266 2708   8–4A
"Excellent pizzas… if you can get a seat" – "cramped" and "noisy" it may be, but this Maida Vale fixture has for many years been as "consistent" a destination as you'll find. / W9 1EE; theredpepper.net; Sat 11 pm, Sun 10.30 pm; closed weekday L; no Amex.

Refettorio
The Crowne Plaza Hotel EC4 £55 ❸❸④
19 New Bridge St   7438 8052   9–3A
A "staple" for business types, this Italian dining room, by Blackfriars Bridge, is "much better than the other restaurants in the immediate locality" – not, it should be noted, a particularly demanding test! / EC4V 6DB; www.refettorio.com; 10.30 pm, Fri & Sat 10 pm; closed Sat L & Sun.

Refuel
Soho Hotel W1 £70 ④④❷
4 Richmond Mews   7559 3007   3–2D
"A beautiful boutique hotel hidden-away in the middle of Soho", complete with "buzzing" bar, provides the "scintillating" setting for this "cool" dining room… where the food plays rather a supporting role. / W1D 3DH; www.firmdale.com; 11 pm, Sun 10 pm; set always available £41 (FP).

Le Relais de Venise L'Entrecôte   £42   ❸④❸
120 Marylebone Ln, W1   7486 0878   2–1A
18-20 Mackenzie Walk, E14   3475 3331   11–1C
5 Throgmorton St, EC2   7638 6325   9–2C
"You know what you'll get", at these "cheek-by-jowl" Gallic bistros,
whose "simple but very well executed" formula offers zero choice,
just "classic steak/frites", with secret sauce and salad (plus seconds);
"fun" too... aside from the "horrific" queues and "impersonal"
service. / www.relaisdevenise.com; W1 11 pm, Sun 10.30 pm; EC2 10 pm;
EC2 closed Sat & Sun; no booking.

Le Rendezvous du Café EC1   £47   ❸❸❸
22 Charterhouse Sq   7336 8836   9–1B
Looking for dinner in "good solid French style"? – you're unlikely to do
much better than this long-established Clerkenwell bistro, where
"the entrecôte is the star". / EC1M 6DX; www.cafedumarche.co.uk;
@cafedumarche; 10 pm; closed Mon, Tue D, Wed D, Thu D, Fri D, Sat & Sun.

Retsina NW3   £43   ④④❸
48-50 Belsize Ln   7431 5855   8–2A
A "friendly" family-run Belsize Park taverna, where the cuisine
is "reliable" (or better); "it can get a bit squashed and noisy,
especially at the end of the week". / NW3 5AR; www.retsina-london.com;
11 pm; closed Mon L; no Amex.

Reubens W1   £50   ❸④④
79 Baker St   7486 0035   2–1A
Is increased kosher competition making this Marylebone deli raise its
game? – after years of lacklustre feedback, it won consistent praise
this year for serving "the best" salt beef sandwiches (if still at toppish
prices). / W1M 1AJ; www.reubensrestaurant.co.uk; 10 pm; closed Fri D & Sat;
no Amex.

The Rib Man N1   £12   ❶❸–
KERB, King's Cross   no tel   8–3C
"Proof that street food need not be rubbish" – Mark Gevaux vends
"succulent and utterly delicious" pork, topped with "legendary" hot
sauces at his Kerb Food stall, behind King's Cross. / N1;
www.theribman.co.uk; @theribman.

Rib Room
Jumeirah Carlton Tower Hotel SW1   £100   ❸❷④
Cadogan Pl   7858 7250   5–1D
"An old classic given new life after a makeover"; this "clubby"
Belgravia dining room, renowned for beef long before the current
steakhouse trend, remains as "abominably expensive" as ever,
but more reporters this year felt that "the food matches up".
/ SW1X 9PY; www.jumeirah.com; 10.45 pm, Sun 10.15 pm.

RIBA Café
Royal Ass'n of Brit' Architects W1   £44   ④④❷
66 Portland Pl   7631 0467   2–1B
Looking for a "calm lunch location", not too far from the West End? –
this "spacious" high-ceilinged café, inside the architects' Art Deco
Marylebone HQ, is hard to beat; service is "unpredictable", but the
food "reasonable"; star attraction – the hidden-away summer terrace.
/ W1 4AD; www.riba-venues.com; @riba; 6 pm, Tue 9 pm; closed Mon D,
Wed D, Thu D, Fri D, Sat D & Sun.

Riccardo's SW3 £42 ⑤⑤④
126 Fulham Rd 7370 6656 5–3B
It's still "usually jammed", but this old-favourite Chelsea Italian
is "not what it used to be" – it's "hit 'n' miss" nowadays, and some
reports are truly "terrible". / SW3 6HU; www.riccardos.it; @ricardoslondon;
11.30 pm.

Riding House Café W1 £53 ④④❶
43-51 Great Titchfield St 7927 0840 3–1C
With its "straight-out-of-Brooklyn" vibe, this "buzzy" Fitzrovia
brasserie has "perfected the recipe for casual dining" at any time
of day (but particularly for brunch); no one seems to care that the
food is "pretty average" (and service too, for that matter).
/ W1W 7PQ; www.ridinghousecafe.co.uk; 11 pm, Sun 10.30 pm.

Rising Sun NW7 £43 ❸❷❸
137 Marsh Ln, Highwood Hill 8959 1357 1–1B
An Italian landlord who's "a real character" adds interest to this
"noisy" and sometimes "chaotic" Mill Hill gastropub; on a good day,
the food can be "excellent" too. / NW7 4EY; www.therisingsunmillhill.co.uk;
@therisingsunpub; 9.30 pm, Sun 8.30 pm; closed Mon L.

Il Ristorante
Bulgari Hotel SW7 NEW £85 ④❷④
171 Knightsbridge 7151 1025 5–1C
"What an anticlimax!"; this "ritzy" new Knightsbridge outpost of the
Roman bling brand too often offers a "diabolical" parody of the
design-hotel dining experience ("deafening" noise from the bar
included); shame – sometimes the food is "surprisingly excellent".
/ SW7 1DW; 10.30 pm.

(Palm Court)
The Ritz W1 £43 ❸❷❶
150 Piccadilly 7493 8181 3–4C
"One of those things to do before you die!"; "elegant and timeless",
this bastion of tradition certainly deliver up a "sense of occasion",
and its world-famous afternoon tea, is "very pricey, but worth it".
/ W1C 9BR; www.theritzlondon.com; 9.30 pm; jacket & tie.

The Ritz Restaurant
The Ritz W1 £119 ④❸❶
150 Piccadilly 7493 8181 3–4C
"Unbeatable for sheer romance", "London's most beautiful dining
room", in Louis XVI style, also "wows" some reporters with its food
and service; as ever, though, critics find the cooking "competent,
rather than memorable". / W1J 9BR; www.theritzlondon.com; 10 pm;
jacket & tie.

Riva SW13 £59 ❷❷④
169 Church Rd 8748 0434 10–1A
With its "astonishingly good" cuisine and its "slick" service, Andreas
Riva's Barnes Italian maintains its cult foodie following; even fans
concede the interior's on the "drab" side, though, and – as usual –
a small coterie of refuseniks dismisses the whole experience
as "snooty" and "cold". / SW13 9HR; 10.30 pm, Sun 9 pm; closed Sat L.

THE RIVER CAFÉ W6 £90 ❸④❷
Thames Wharf, Rainville Rd 7386 4200 7–2C
Downturn or not, it's still "horrendously hard to get a table" at this
"palpably buzzing" (and "crowded") Hammersmith Italian;
even many ardent fans of its "elegant" and "intensely flavoured"
Tuscan cuisine, however, feel bills are nothing short of "monstrous".
/ W6 9HA; www.rivercafe.co.uk; 9 pm, Sat 9.15 pm; closed Sun D.

The Riverfront
BFI Southbank SE1   £45   ④④❸
Southbank   7928 0808   2–3D
*"Always busy" ... but "not quite as full or tourists as everywhere else
nearby" – this attractive operation is one of the better budget options
on the South Bank; arguably, though, "it's not very exciting, and not
that cheap". / SE1 8XT; www.riverfrontbarandkitchen.com; @riverfront_bfi;
10.45 pm.*

Rivington Grill   £49   ④❸④
178 Greenwich High Rd, SE10   8293 9270   1–3D
28-30 Rivington St, EC2   7729 7053   12–1B
*Despite backing by the glamorous Caprice group, these nowadays
rather "tired" bar/brasseries, in Shoreditch and Greenwich,
have never made waves; for "simple" British dishes in casual
surroundings, though, they make an "OK" choice.
/ www.rivingtongrill.co.uk; 11 pm, Sun 10 pm; SE10 closed Mon,
Tue L & Wed L.*

Roast SE1   £70   ④④❸
Stoney St   0845 034 7300   9–4C
*This first-floor English dining room certainly has a "beautiful" setting
(especially on a sunny day), and it's "a great place for brunch after
browsing the stalls of Borough Market"; lunch and dinner are "less of
an attraction", though, and prices at any time are on the "grabby"
side. / SE1 1TL; www.roast-restaurant.com; 10.30 pm; closed Sun D;
SRA-71%.*

Rocca Di Papa   £42   ④④❸
73 Old Brompton Rd, SW7   7225 3413   5–2B
75-79 Dulwich Village, SE21   8299 6333   1–4D
*"Classic" pizza joints; these "family-friendly" South Kensington and
Dulwich Village spots may not be exciting, but they "make for
an enjoyable all-round experience". / SW7 11.30 pm; SE21 11 pm.*

Rocco SW5   £57   ④❷④
254-260 Old Brompton Rd   7259 2599   5–3A
*On the site of of Langan's Coq D'Or (RIP), this Italian newcomer
pleases fans with its "uncomplicated" but "serious" cooking,
and "attentive" service; the "stripped back" decor is not to all tastes
though, and "toppish" prices may explain why the place has not been
more of a hit. / SW5 9HR; www.roccopoint.co.uk.*

Rochelle Canteen E2   £40   ❷❷❷
Arnold Circus   7729 5677   12–1C
*"A former bike-shed" provides the "works-canteen-like" setting for this
"funky" Shoreditch outfit – a "great lunch venue" which attracts
some "seriously trendy" punters with its "simple" but "excellent"
daily-changing British dishes, "at really good prices"; BYO. / E2 7ES;
www.arnoldandhenderson.com; L only, closed Sat & Sun; no Amex.*

Rock & Rose TW9   £53   ⑤❺❸
106-108 Kew Rd   8948 8008   1–4A
*Supporters insist it offers "a good night out" (even if "the fun style
doesn't quite compensate for the uninspiring food"), but critics are
scathing about what they feel is a "pretentious" atmosphere at this
Richmond party scene. / TW9 2PQ; www.rockandroserestaurant.co.uk;
10 pm, Fri & Sat 10.30 pm.*

Rocket £45 ❸❸❸
2 Churchill Pl, E14   3200 2022   11–1C
201 Bishopsgate, EC2   7377 8863   12–2B
6 Adams Ct, EC2   7628 0808   9–2C
The E14 branch – with its "great views" – is the best-known of these "relaxed and fun" hang-outs, which serve an "interesting and creative" selection of pizzas and salads; for a cost-conscious Mayfair meal, however, the outlet tucked-away off Bond Street is also well worth knowing about. / 10.30 pm,Sun 9.30 pm; W1 closed Sun; EC2 closed Sat & Sun; SW15 Mon-Wed D only, Bishopsgate closed Sun D, E14.

The Roebuck W4 £41 ❹❸❸
122 Chiswick High Rd   8995 4392   7–2A
An "always-buzzy" Chiswick gastropub (with large garden); it has perhaps "slipped" a bit of late, but all reports are positive. / W4 1PU; www.theroebuckchiswick.co.uk; @the_roebuck; 11 pm, Sun 10.30 pm.

Roka £78 ❶❸❸
37 Charlotte St, W1   7580 6464   2–1C
Unit 4, Park Pavilion, 40 Canada Sq, E14   7636 5228   11–1C
"Extraordinary" Japanese-fusion dishes ("top-class" robata and "delectable" sushi) put the W1 original of this "slick" Asian duo ahead even of its famous sibling Zuma; does it need a revamp, though? – it has seemed a tad "impersonal" of late. / www.rokarestaurant.com; 11.15 pm, Sun 10.30 pm; booking: max 8.

Roots at N1 N1 £46 ❷❷❸
115 Hemingford Rd   7697 4488   8–3D
An out-of-the-way Islington pub-conversion provides the setting for this "hidden gem" – a "friendly and charming" outfit which offers, say fans, "all the excellence of London's top Indians, but without the crazy prices". / N1 1BZ; www.rootsatn1.com; @rootsatn1 @Rootsatn1; 10 pm, Sun 9 pm; closed Mon, Tue–Sat D only, Sun open L & D.

Rosa's £37 ❸❷❸
23a, Ganton St, W1   7287 9617   3–2C
48 Dean St, W1   7494 1638   4–3A
12 Hanbury St, E1   7247 1093   12–2C
"Canteen-like, but offering very good and filling food" – these Brick Lane and Soho Thais are "lovely" little places, and often "very busy". / www.rosaslondon.com; 10.30 pm, Fri & Sat 11 pm, Ganton St Sun 10 pm; some booking restrictions apply.

Rossopomodoro £38 ❸❸❸
50-52 Monmouth St, WC2   7240 9095   4–3B
214 Fulham Rd, SW10   7352 7677   5–3B
184a Kensington Park Rd, W11   7229 9007   6–1A
1 Rufus St, N1   7739 1899   12–1B NEW
10 Jamestown Rd, NW1   7424 9900   8–3B NEW
46 Garrett Ln, SW18   07931 9 20377   10–2B NEW
"Full of homesick Italians", these outposts of a Neapolitan chain impress most reporters with their "bubbly" and "authentic" style. / www.rossopomodoro.co.uk; 11.30 pm; WC2 Sun 11.30 pm.

Roti Chai W1 £46 ❷❸❸
3 Portman Mews South   7408 0101   3–1A
"Lip-smacking" Indian street food – "at great prices" – wins a big fan club for this "fun" year-old operation, near Selfridges; in the "more formal" basement, the cooking's "a little more complex, but equally flavoursome". / W1H 6HS; www.rotichai.com; @rotichai; 10.30 pm.

Rotunda Bar & Restaurant
Kings Place N1   £50   ④④❸
90 York Way   7014 2840   8–3C
*"Unbeatable when the weather is good"; this King's Cross office/arts
centre café boasts fine views of the canal, and a large terrace, plus a
menu well suited to "pre-concert dining". / N1 9AG;
www.rotundabarandrestaurant.co.uk; @rotundalondon; 10.30 pm,
Sun 6.30 pm.*

Roux at Parliament Square
RICS SW1   £76   ❸❷④
12 Great George St   7334 3737   2–3C
*With a view of the Palace of Westminster from some seats,
it's appropriate that this Gallic dining room has a "very discreet" style
well-suited to a lobbying lunch; the experience is "good all-round",
albeit in a mode which can ultimately seem "rather bland".
/ SW1P 3AD; www.rouxatparliamentsquare.co.uk; 10 pm; closed Sat & Sun.*

Roux at the Landau
The Langham W1   £91   ❸❸❷
1c, Portland Pl   7965 0165   2–1B
*"Beautiful" decor and "first-class" cuisine can make for "a splendid
experience" at this "classically styled" chamber, near Broadcasting
House; it's only the "excellent-value set lunch" which can really safely
be recommended, though – the à la carte offering is sometimes
"underwhelming". / W1B 1JA; www.thelandau.com; 10 pm; closed
Sat L & Sun; no trainers.*

Rowley's SW1   £69   ④④④
113 Jermyn St   7930 2707   3–3D
*With its charming premises inherited from the original Wall's
butcher's shop, this veteran St James's steakhouse has long been
a popular, and sometimes "overcrowded", destination – with its
"basic" and "overpriced" food, though, critics do feel it "trades on its
reputation". / SW1Y 6HJ; www.rowleys.co.uk; @rowleys_steak; 11 pm.*

Royal Academy W1   £53   ⑤④④
Burlington Hs, Piccadilly   7300 5608   3–3D
*This civilised café in the bowels of the RA has long been a handy
retreat from the Piccadilly mêlée, especially for afternoon tea;
it's slipped notably under Peyton & Byrne's management, however –
"slapdash", "pretentious" and "poor value". / W1J 0BD;
www.royalacademy.org.uk; 9 pm; L only, ex Fri open L & D; no booking at L.*

Royal China   £46   ❷④④
24-26 Baker St, W1   7487 4688   2–1A
805 Fulham Rd, SW6   7731 0081   10–1B
13 Queensway, W2   7221 2535   6–2C
30 Westferry Circus, E14   7719 0888   11–1B
*"Some of the best dim sum in the capital" – these "ever-reliable"
Chinese benchmarks remain a "rushed" and "very crowded"
weekend staple for legions of reporters; "service with a smile is an
alien concept", though, and the "darkly shiny" decor is not to all
tastes. / www.royalchinagroup.co.uk; 10.45 pm, Fri & Sat 11.15 pm,
Sun 9.45 pm; no booking Sat & Sun L.*

Royal China Club W1   £62   ❷❸④
40-42 Baker St   7486 3898   2–1A
*"Sophisticated" cooking has made quite a name for this "pricey"
(club-class) Marylebone Chinese; critics find service "inconsistent",
though, and wonder if the premium over the tourist-class Royal
Chinas is really justified. / W1U 7AJ; www.royalchinagroup.co.uk; 11 pm,
Fri & Sat 11.30 pm, Sun 10.30 pm.*

The Royal Exchange Grand Café
The Royal Exchange EC3 £54 ④❸❷
The Royal Exchange Bank 7618 2480 9–2C
With its "beautiful" atrium setting (with "luxury boutiques all around"), this City seafood bar is some reporters' favourite business-lunch venue "by a Square Mile"; it's "pricey", though, and critics find the fare "pedestrian". / EC3V 3LR; www.royalexchange-grandcafe.co.uk; 9.30 pm; closed Sat & Sun; SRA-58%.

RSJ SE1 £45 ❸❸④
33 Coin St 7928 4554 9–4A
An "encyclopaedic" list of Loire vintages helps compensate for the "austere" atmosphere of this South Bank stalwart; its Gallic cooking is "absolutely reliable" too, and the location is "very convenient for the National Theatre". / SE1 9NR; www.rsj.uk.com; 11 pm; closed Sat L & Sun.

Rugoletta N2 £37 ❸❸④
59 Church Ln 8815 1743 1–1B
"Good, honest rustic Italian cooking, like your Mama made"; "very cramped and chaotic" it may be, but this neighbourhood BYO in East Finchley is a "fun" destination too, and it's "always busy". / N2 8DR; 10.30 pm; closed Sun.

Rules WC2 £74 ❸❷❶
35 Maiden Ln 7836 5314 4–3D
"Full of wealthy tourists", it may be, but London's oldest restaurant (1798) has a genuinely "lovely", "old school" ambience, and still strikes many (if not quite all) of the natives as "living up to its history" – the beef, in particular, is "excellent", and the game "the best in town". / WC2E 7LB; www.rules.co.uk; 11.30 pm, Sun 10.30 pm; no shorts.

Le Sacré-Coeur N1 £35 ④❸❸
18 Theberton St 7354 2618 8–3D
"A reliable stand-by"; the basic charms of this "very French" Islington side street bistro continue to please most of the reporters who comment on it. / N1 0QX; www.lesacrecoeur.co.uk; 11 pm, Sat 11.30 pm, Sun 10.30 pm; set weekday L £23 (FP).

Sacro Cuore NW10 £31 ❷❷❸
45 Chamberlayne Rd 8960 8558 1–2B
"Perfect ingredients" and "paper-thin" bases help inspire rave reviews for this tiny year-old Kensal Rise pizzeria, which "does the simple things really well". / NW10 3NB.

Sagar £37 ❸❸④
17a, Percy St, W1 7631 3319 3–2B
31 Catherine St, WC2 7836 6377 4–3D
157 King St, W6 8741 8563 7–2C
"Dosas to die for!"; these "basic" cafés (Hammersmith is the best-known) "could convert the most die-hard carnivore" with their "interesting" South Indian dishes; "good value too". / www.sagarveg.co.uk; Sun-Thu 10.45 pm, Fri & Sat 11.30 pm.

Sager & Wilde E2 NEW £22
193 Hackney Rd no tel 12–1C
This Haggerston wine bar opened in the summer of 2013; we sadly didn't have have the opportunity to visit before this guide went to press, but the critical reaction has been very positive. / E2 8JP; www.sagerandwilde.com.

Saigon Saigon W6 £40 ❸④❸
313-317 King St 8748 6887 7–2B
*"Low lighting" and characterful decor help create a "warm"
atmosphere, at this long-standing Hammersmith Vietnamese, where
"very tasty" dishes come at "reasonable prices". / W6 9NH;
www.saigon-saigon.co.uk; @saigonsaigonuk; 11.30 pm, Sun & Mon 10 pm.*

St John EC1 £57 ❷❷❷
26 St John St 7251 0848 9–1B
*"You can order anything, no matter how off-putting it sounds, and it'll
be really good", say devotees of Fergus Henderson's infamously offal-
friendly Smithfield HQ — an "outstanding choice for aficionados
of unadulterated British food"; some fans are fretting though — "is the
menu becoming more mainstream?" / EC1M 4AY;
www.stjohngroup.uk.com; @SJRestaurant; 11 pm; closed Sat L & Sun D.*

St John Bread & Wine E1 £55 ❶❸❸
94-96 Commercial St 7251 0848 12–2C
*"The best of the St John stable"; with its "eclectic", "simple" and
"brilliant" British fare and its "interesting" wines too, this "cramped"
and "utterly unpretentious" Shoreditch canteen is — for fans — simply
"the perfect restaurant". / E1 6LZ; www.stjohngroup.uk.com/spitalfields;
10.30 pm, Sun 9.30 pm.*

St Johns N19 £47 ❸❷❶
91 Junction Rd 7272 1587 8–1C
*The "wonderful dining room" — a former ballroom —
adds considerable pizzazz to this large and "lively" Archway tavern;
the food is "far better than you might expect" too, but sliding ratings
tend to confirm recent concerns of "fallen" standards. / N19 5QU;
www.stjohnstavern.com; 11 pm, Sun 9.30 pm; Mon-Thu D only, Fri-Sun open
L & D; no Amex; booking: max 12.*

St Moritz W1 £53 ❸④❸
161 Wardour St 7734 3324 3–1D
*A "kitsch" Swiss-chalet-style Soho veteran, long popular for its
"friendly old-school" service and "quality" fondues (plus "excellent
game in season"); unusually, however, there were a couple of "really
disappointing" reports this year — hopefully a blip. / W1F 8WJ;
www.stmoritz-restaurant.co.uk; 11.30 pm, Sun 10.30 pm.*

St Pancras Grand
St Pancras Int'l Station NW1 £51 ⑤⑤④
The Concourse 7870 9900 8–3C
*"A terrible waste of a good space"; this briefly-glamorous brasserie,
on the way to Paris, again put in a "dismal" performance this year —
the food is "substandard", and "what on earth are the staff actually
doing?" / NW1 2QP; www.stpancrasgrand.com; @SearcysBars; 10.30 pm.*

Sakana-tei W1 £34 ❷❷⑤
11 Maddox St 7629 3000 3–2C
*"The setting may be dingy, but the place has a charm of its own!" —
this Mayfair basement Japanese offers "great value", and its menu
includes some items which are otherwise "hard to find". / W1S 2QF;
10 pm; closed Sun.*

Sake No Hana SW1 £69 ④❸④
23 St James's St 7925 8988 3–4C
*This style-conscious St James's Japanese deeply divides opinions;
fan hail it as a "great space" with "terrific" fusion fare that "leaves
other places standing" — to critics, though, it's a "strange" place,
offering "westernised" food that's "deeply average". / SW1A 1HA;
www.sakenohana.com; @sakenonhana; 11 pm, Fri-Sat 11.30 pm; closed Sun.*

Sakonis HA0 £20 ❷④⑤
127-129 Ealing Rd 8903 9601 1–1A
A Wembley Gujarati, where "you don't go for the ambience but for
the tasty vegetarian food"; no booking – "push and shove to get
a table, just like in India!" / HA0 4BP; www.sakonis.co.uk; @sakonis;
9.30 pm; no Amex.

Sakura W1 £32 ❸❸④
23 Conduit St 7629 2961 3–2C
A "no-frills" Japanese, well worth seeking out in pricey Mayfair for its
"authentic" dishes (including sushi), "prompt" service and "great
value for money". / W1S 2XS; 10 pm.

Salaam Namaste WC1 £34 ❷④④
68 Millman St 7405 3697 2–1D
"Hard to find, but worth discovering"; this "contemporary" Indian,
on a Bloomsbury backstreet, serves up "a few unusual, regional
dishes", plus some "adventurous interpretations" of more familiar
classics. / WC1N 3EF; www.salaam-namaste.co.uk; @SalaanNamasteUK;
11.30 pm, Sun 11 pm.

Sale e Pepe SW1 £65 ④④❸
9-15 Pavilion Rd 7235 0098 5–1D
"Very cramped and very noisy", "popular and dependable" – that's
how most reporters still see this old-favourite trattoria, near Harrods;
"it's got a bit left behind" in recent years, however, and the kitchen
"needs a shake-up". / SW1X 0HD; www.saleepepe.co.uk; 11.30 pm;
no shorts; set weekday L £43 (FP).

Salloos SW1 £59 ❷❷④
62-64 Kinnerton St 7235 4444 5–1D
"The best lamb chops anywhere" top the selection of "subtly-spiced"
dishes on offer at this "classy" Pakistani, hidden-away in a Belgravia
mews; its rather '60s styling, however, can strike critics as a touch
"stale". / SW1X 8ER; www.salloos.co.uk; 11 pm; closed Sun; need 5+ to book.

Salt Yard W1 £44 ❷❸❸
54 Goodge St 7637 0657 2–1B
"Seriously delicious" Mediterranean tapas and some "outstanding"
Italian/Spanish wines have carved out a big name for Dehesa's older
stablemate, in Fitzrovia; it's a "buzzy" operation, but critics can find
its cramped quarters a touch "claustrophobic". / W1T 4NA;
www.saltyard.co.uk; 11 pm; closed Sat L & Sun; SRA-63%.

The Salusbury NW6 £44 ④④❸
50-52 Salusbury Rd 7328 3286 1–2B
An endearing Queen's Park hang-out, where the food is "consistently
decent", even if the Mediterranean menu (including pizza) "doesn't
change much". / NW6 6NN; www.thesalusbury.co.uk; 10.30 pm; closed
Mon L.

Sam's Brasserie W4 £49 ④❸❷
11 Barley Mow Pas 8987 0555 7–2A
"A trusty favourite"; this "relaxed" and "buzzy" Chiswick haunt, in a
former factory, is a particular hit for weekend family brunches;
"the food is never bad… but rarely very good". / W4 4PH;
www.samsbrasserie.co.uk; @samsbrasserie; 10.30 pm, Sun 10 pm;
set weekday L £31 (FP); SRA-70%.

San Carlo Cicchetti W1 £46 ❸④④
215 Piccadilly 7494 9435 3–3D
Near Piccadilly Circus, a "buzzy" (and quite tightly-packed)
outpost of the glossy provincial Italian restaurant chain – useful for
a shopping or pre-theatre bite. / W1J 9HN; www.sancarlo.co.uk;
@SanCarlo_Group; midnight.

San Daniele del Friuli N5 £42 ❸❷❸
72 Highbury Park 7226 1609 8–1D
A "high-quality local" that's long been a fixture of Highbury Park,
this "fun" Italian offers "lots of menu variety". / N5 2XE;
www.sandanielehighbury.co.uk; 10.30 pm; closed Mon L, Tue L, Wed L & Sun;
no Amex.

San Lorenzo SW3 £66
22 Beauchamp Pl 7584 1074 5–1C
Once it was the epitome of an A-list haunt; nowadays this
Knightsbridge trattoria generates so little feedback, we've felt
it best to leave it un-rated. / SW3 1NH; 11 pm.

San Lorenzo Fuoriporta SW19 £61 ⑤⑤④
38 Wimbledon Hill Rd 8946 8463 10–2B
The "trip-down-Memory-Lane" charms of this Wimbledon trattoria
("last decorated in the 70s?") still win over some reporters, and its
"secret garden" can still impress; the journey can be an "expensive"
one, though, and too often "doesn't measure up". / SW19 7PA;
www.sanlorenzo.com; @fuoriporta; 10.40 pm.

The Sands End SW6 £50 ❸④❷
135 Stephendale Rd 7731 7823 10–1B
A "posh" but "friendly" Sands End boozer that "manages to cater for
all occasions"; "great bar snacks" – which include legendary Scotch
Eggs – are a highlight. / SW6 2PR; www.thesandsend.co.uk; @thesandsend;
11.30 pm, Thu-Sat midnight.

Santa Lucia SW10 £41 ❷❸❸
2 Hollywood Rd 7352 8484 5–3B
In a long-established 'restaurant row', in the Chelsea backwoods,
an outpost of the Made In Italy pizza group – it attracts only
a modest level of commentary, but all positive. / SW10 9HY;
www.madeinitalygroup.co.uk; 11.30 pm, Sun 10.30 pm; closed weekday L.

Santa Maria W5 £31 ❶❸❸
15 St Mary's Rd 8579 1462 1–3A
"A slice of heaven" – the pizzas at this "charming", "no-frills"
Neapolitan are arguably Ealing's biggest contribution to London
gastronomy (and are sometimes claimed as the city's best); it's a
"pokey" place, though, with "awfully cramped" seating and long
queues. / W5 5RA; www.santamariapizzeria.com; @SantaMariaPizza;
10.30 pm.

Santa Maria del Sur SW8 £50 ❸④❸
129 Queenstown Rd 7622 2088 10–1C
An Argentinian steakhouse that "has made its mark", down Battersea
way – "booking is essential"; even fans, though, may note that it's it's
"not cheap". / SW8 3RH; www.santamariadelsur.co.uk; @StaMariadelSur;
10 pm; no Amex.

Santini SW1 £68 ④④④
29 Ebury St   7730 4094   2–4B
A "spacious" Belgravia Italian, whose A-list status is now a dim '80s
memory; its still pretty pricey, though, and even some reporters who
tip it as "very good for a business lunch" say they "wouldn't spend
their own money" there. / SW1W 0NZ; www.santini-restaurant.com;
11 pm, Sun 10 pm; closed Sat L & Sun L.

Santore EC1 £42 ❷❷④
59 Exmouth Mkt   7812 1488   9–1A
"Authentic Neapolitan pizzas of the highest calibre", served by the
metre, inspire rave reviews for this "friendly", "busy" and "noisy"
joint, in Exmouth Market. / EC1R 4QL; www.santorerestaurant.co.uk;
11 pm.

Sapori Sardi SW6 £47 ❷❸④
786 Fulham Rd   7731 0755   10–1B
"Everyone wishes they had a family-run Italian like this round the
corner!" – this "lovely" small yearling offers "fresh home cooking
at extremely reasonable prices". / SW6 5SL; www.saporisardi.co.uk;
11 pm; closed Mon L; no Amex.

Sarastro WC2 £50 ⑤⑤❸
126 Drury Ln   7836 0101   2–2D
"Can't be beaten for entertainment value…" – just as well, as the
food and service at this OTT operatic-themed Theatreland experience
(accompanied by live arias) can be very lacking. / WC2B 5SU;
www.sarastro-restaurant.com; @SastroR; 10.30 pm, Fri & Sat 11.15 pm.

Sardo W1 £55 ❷❸④
45 Grafton Way   7387 2521   2–1B
"Top of the class for authenticity", this Fitzrovia fixture, just off
Tottenham Court Road, wins a consistent thumbs-up for its
"interesting Sardinian-based menu" and "excellent" wines.
/ W1T 5DQ; www.sardo-restaurant.com; 11 pm; closed Sat L & Sun.

Sarracino NW6 £41 ❷❸④
186 Broadhurst Gdns   7372 5889   1–1B
Neapolitan-style pizza by the metre is the main deal at this raucous
West Hampstead trattoria; limited feedback this year, but all
consistently upbeat. / NW6 3AY; www.sarracinorestaurant.com; 11 pm;
closed weekday L.

Sartoria W1 £58 ❸❸❸
20 Savile Row   7534 7000   3–2C
This "pleasantly laid out" D&D group establishment, just off Regent
Street, never sets the world on fire, but it's often tipped for business,
thanks to its "smart Italian food", and its "discreet and unobtrusive"
service. / W1S 3PR; www.sartoria-restaurant.co.uk; 10.45 pm; closed
Sat L & Sun; SRA-63%.

Satay House W2 £34 ❸④④
13 Sale Pl   7723 6763   6–1D
"Penang, minus the air travel!" – this Bayswater veteran is, for fans,
not just London's oldest Malaysian, but also the "most authentic".
/ W2 1PX; www.satay-house.co.uk; 11 pm.

Sauterelle
Royal Exchange EC3 £70 ❸❸❸
Bank 7618 2483 9–2C
"Good for a business lunch or dinner"; the first-floor D&D Group operation, looking into the atrium of the Royal Exchange, has always been a "discreet" sort of place; with its "improved" food of late, some fans reckon it can now be hailed as a "proper gastronomic destination" too! / EC3V 3LR; www.sauterelle-restaurant.co.uk; 9.30 pm; closed Sat & Sun; no trainers; set dinner £46 (FP); SRA-59%.

Savoir Faire WC1 £38 ❸❹④
42 New Oxford St 7436 0707 4–1C
A "quirky" and "good-value" bistro that makes "a perfect choice after a visit to the British Museum"; "useful pre-theatre" too. / WC1A 1EP; www.savoir.co.uk; 11 pm.

(Savoy Grill)
The Savoy Hotel WC2 £79 ④❸❸
Strand 7592 1600 4–3D
Under the 'stewardship' of Gordon Ramsay, this once-legendary Theatreland/power-dining rendezvous has become "a pale shadow of its former self"; it inspires wildly erratic commentary, too much of it to the effect that it is now "just another overpriced restaurant". / WC2R 0EU; www.gordonramsay.com/thesavoygrill/; 10.45 pm, Sun 10.15 pm; jacket required.

Scalini SW3 £75 ❸❷❷
1-3 Walton St 7225 2301 5–2C
Why is it "always mobbed"? – this "squashed-in" Knightsbridge stalwart Italian is just "fantastico", says fans of its "old-style" scoff, its "wonderfully friendly" service, and its "electric" buzz. / SW3 2JD; www.scalinionline.com; 11.30 pm, Sun 11 pm; no shorts.

Scandinavian Kitchen W1 £16 ❷❷❸
61 Great Titchfield St 7580 7161 2–1B
"Abba nice day!"; "appealing" open sandwiches, "delicious" pastries, "inventive" salads, "amazing" cakes, and gorgeous cinnamon rolls … – is there no end to the attractions of this "colourful and healthy" Fitzrovia "oasis"? / W1W 7PP; www.scandikitchen.co.uk; 7 pm, Sat 6 pm, Sun 4 pm; L only; no Maestro; no booking.

The Scarsdale W8 £39 ④❸❶
23a Edwardes Sq 7937 1811 7–1D
It's the "delightful location in a quiet Kensington square" which makes this ancient hostelry (with a "good terrace") really stand out, but its "good pub food" usually hits the spot too. / W8 6HE; 10 pm, Sun 9.30 pm.

SCOTT'S W1 £78 ❷❷❷
20 Mount St 7495 7309 3–3A
"Taking over where The Ivy left off" – Richard Caring's "suave and sophisticated" Mayfair all-rounder serves up "supreme" seafood (London's best, say some) to an A-list crowd; is it starting to coast, though? – ratings dipped a bit all-round this year. / W1K 2HE; www.scotts-restaurant.com; 10.30 pm, Sun 10 pm; booking: max 6.

The Sea Cow SE22 £30 ❷❸❸
37 Lordship Ln 8693 3111 1–4D
"Delicious basic fish and chips, but also stunning steamed and grilled options" – this "café-style" East Dulwich chippy invariably pleases; "great value when kids eat free at weekends" (before 4pm). / SE22 8EW; www.theseacow.co.uk; @seacowcrew; 11 pm, Sun-Mon 10 pm; closed Mon L, Tue L & Wed L; no Amex.

Sea Pebbles HA5 £28 ❸④❸
348-352 Uxbridge Rd 8428 0203 1–1A
"A place to go, if you find yourself in Hatch End" – a chippy that's
"always full", thanks to its "excellent fish", and its "great value for
money". / HA5 4HR; 9.45 pm; closed Sun; debit cards only; need 8+ to book.

Seafresh SW1 £36 ❸④⑤
80-81 Wilton Rd 7828 0747 2–4B
"Chips are never crisper, and the scampi tastes of the sea", say fans
of this "very reliable" Pimlico fish 'n' chips veteran (which offers
a menu of "unusual range"). / SW1V 1DL; www.seafresh-dining.com;
10.30 pm; closed Sun.

The Sea Shell NW1 £42 ❷❸④
49 Lisson Grove 7224 9000 8–4A
"Throw dietary caution to the wind", and have some "excellent fish,
chips 'n' mushy peas" at this famous Marylebone chippy; "now it's
been redecorated", some regulars say, the interior's "better" too.
/ NW1 6UH; www.seashellrestaurant.co.uk; 10.30 pm; closed Sun; SRA-50%.

Season Kitchen N4 [NEW] £37 ❷❷❸
53 Stroud Green Rd 7263 5500 8–1D
"A very good addition to the north London scene"; this "small but
very cosy" Finsbury Park spot offers some "thoughtful", seasonal
cooking, and local reporters find it "really lovely on all levels".
/ N4 3EF; www.seasonkitchen.co.uk; 10.30 pm, Sun 9 pm; D only.

Sedap EC1 £28 ④④④
102 Old St 7490 0200 12–1A
"Not cutting-edge but reliably satisfying and reasonably-priced" –
this Malaysian café, near Silicon Roundabout, makes a "great cheap
eat". / EC1V 9AY; www.sedap.co.uk; 10.30 pm, Sun 10 pm; closed
Sat L & Sun L; no Amex.

Seven Park Place SW1 £91 ❸❸❸
7-8 Park Pl 7316 1600 3–4C
William Drabble's "masterful" cooking – with real "artistry and
substance" – arguably deserves a wider audience than it finds in this
"niche" St James's chamber; the "opulent" but "odd" parlour-style
setting inspires mixed views, though – "intimate" to some tastes,
but too "staid" for others. / SW1A 1LP; www.stjameshotelandclub.com;
10 pm; closed Mon & Sun; set weekday L £55 (FP).

Seven Stars WC2 £29 ❸④❷
53 Carey St 7242 8521 2–2D
People come to Roxy Beaujolais's tavern behind the Royal Courts
of Justice "for the quirkiness (the cat with the ruff and so on),
and because it feels traditional"; that said, "the food, at pub prices,
is above usual pub standards". / WC2A 2JB; 9.30 pm.

Seventeen W11 £47 ❸❸❸
17 Notting Hill Gate 7985 0006 6–2B
Somewhat marooned on busy Notting Hill Gate, this "under-rated
Chinese" is worth seeking out; its styling, especially downstairs,
is "tasteful and modern", and the food "always delivers on the
classics, with some more exotic dishes too". / W11 3JQ;
www.seventeen-london.co.uk; 11.15 pm.

Shake Shack WC2 NEW   **£23**
23 The Mkt, Covent Garden   3598 1360   4–3D
Recently arrived in Covent Garden Market, an outpost of Danny Meyer's much-celebrated NYC-based burger bar chain; perhaps it's chauvinism, but the local press haven't been quite convinced that the burgers are so much better than the native offerings. / WC2E 8RD; www.shakeshack.com/location/london-covent-garden; @shakeshack; 11 pm, Sun 10.30 pm.

Shampers W1   **£45**   ❸❷❷
4 Kingly St   7437 1692   3–2D
An "unfailing" 80s wine bar, just off Regent Street; it's a "lively" but "relaxed" stalwart, offering "good old-fashioned food" plus "one of the most comprehensive wine lists you'll find". / W1B 5PE; www.shampers.net; 10.45 pm; closed Sun.

Shanghai E8   **£35**   ❸④❸
41 Kingsland High St   7254 2878   1–1C
"My Chinese friend makes a big detour to come here!"; "great dim sum" is the highlight at "Dalston's best Oriental", elegantly housed in a former pie 'n' eel shop – make sure you get a table at the front. / E8 2JS; www.shanghaidalston.co.uk; 11 pm; no Amex.

Shanghai Blues WC1   **£66**   ④⑤⑤
193-197 High Holborn   7404 1668   4–1D
Something seems to have gone awry at this once-admirable Holborn Chinese – formerly "cool" and "intriguing", it now too often just appears "cavernous", "pretentious" and "disappointing". / WC1V 7BD; www.shanghaiblues.co.uk; 11.30 pm.

The Shed W8 NEW   **£38**   ❸❷❶
122 Palace Gardens Ter   7229 4024   6–2B
"A brilliant new version of the old Ark"; this pint-sized, Notting Hill Gate landmark has been imaginatively re-born in "casual", faux-"rustic" style – its "delicious, British tapas-style" dishes may be no bargain, but most reporters think they are "wonderful", especially for a "cool brunch". / W8 4RT; www.theshed-restaurant.com; @theshed_resto; 11 pm; closed Mon & Sun.

J SHEEKEY WC2   **£70**   ❷❶❶
28-34 St Martin's Ct   7240 2565   4–3B
"A class act" par excellence; Theatreland's "elegant" fish-legend (opened 1896) is once again London's most talked-about restaurant; "superb fish pie" is the exemplar of the "utterly dependable" menu, served in its "clubby" (if squashed) series of rooms. / WC2N 4AL; www.j-sheekey.co.uk; midnight, Sun 11 pm; booking: max 6.

J Sheekey Oyster Bar WC2   **£63**   ❷❶❶
32-34 St Martin's Ct   7240 2565   4–3B
It's "pure gastronomic theatre" to grab a high stool in the Theatreland legend's "less formal" bar – many reporters prefer its combination of "real glamour" and "divine, simple but perfect seafood" to the full -blown experience next door. / WC2N 4AL; www.j-sheekey.co.uk; midnight, Sun 11 pm; booking: max 3.

Shilpa W6   **£30**   ❷❸⑤
206 King St   8741 3127   7–2B
"Excellently-spiced" Keralan food at "incredible" prices inspires ardent praise for this "dull and utilitarian" café, on Hammersmith's main drag; "somehow its scruffiness makes it feel more authentic!" / W6 0RA; www.shilparestaurant.co.uk; 11 pm, Thu-Sat midnight.

The Shiori W2 NEW £84 ❶❷④
45 Moscow Rd 7221 9790 6–2C
"Exceptional kaiseki-style food" (including "stunning" sushi) offers lovers of Japanese food a "sublime" experiences at this Bayswater newcomer; sadly, though, the setting is decidedly "sterile". / W2 4AH; www.theshiori.com; 8.30 pm; closed Mon & Sun.

The Ship SW18 £47 ④④❸
41 Jews Row 8870 9667 10–2B
Come summertime, this "understandably popular" boozer, by Wandsworth Bridge, is rammed, thanks to the attractions of its large Thames-side terrace and dependable BBQ – "the food is nothing special". / SW18 1TB; www.theship.co.uk; @shipwandsworth; 10 pm; no booking, Sun L.

Shoryu Ramen £27 ❷❸❸
9 Regent St, SW1 no tel 3–3D NEW
3 Denman St, W1 no tel 3–2D NEW
"Getting very close to Tokyo chain standards!" – this "cheap", "cheerful" and "tightly-packed" ramen parlour is hailed by most reporters as a "superb" pit stop... and just a few moments from Piccadilly Circus too; now also in Soho. / Regent St 11.30 pm, Sun 10.30 pm – Soho midnight, Sun 10.30 pm.

Shrimpy's N1 £49 ④④❸
King's Cross Filling Station, Good's Way 8880 6111 8–3C
A former petrol station, in redeveloping King's Cross, that's become quite a "hipster heaven", despite its "patchy" service, and its food which can "promise a lot, and deliver little". / N1C 4UR; www.shrimpys.co.uk; @shrimpysloves; 11 pm.

Siam Central W1 £31 ④❸❸
14 Charlotte St 7436 7460 2–1C
"Inexpensive, fresh, and speedy" – a Fitzrovia Thai that's "ideal for a casual meal". / W1T 2LX; 10.45 pm, Sun 10.15 pm.

Sichuan Folk E1 £43 ❷❸⑤
32 Hanbury St 7247 4735 12–2C
A "superb gastronomic experience" ("if you like hot and spicy Sichuan food") awaits those who seek out this decidedly no-frills East Ender; "shame about the cold atmosphere..." / E1 6QR; www.sichuan-folk.co.uk; 10.30 pm; no Amex; set weekday L £23 (FP).

The Sign of the Don EC4 NEW
21 St Swithin's Ln 7626 2606 9–3C
Opening in late-2013, a neighbouring offshoot of City favourite The Don, offering a more casual style, and the wine emphasis for which the parent establishment is known; decor relates to the Sandeman Port & Sherry heritage of the site. / EC4N 8AD; www.thesignofthedon.com.

Signor Sassi SW1 £66 ④❸❸
14 Knightsbridge Grn 7584 2277 5–1D
This "buzzy" ("noisy") old-time Knightsbridge Italian is still a "favourite" for some reporters; it's the "attentive" service which really makes the place, but the food, if no bargain, is "always enjoyable". / SW1X 7QL; www.signorsassi.co.uk; 11.30 pm, Sun 10.30 pm.

Simpson's Tavern EC3　　　　£37　　④❸❶
38 1/2 Ball Ct, Cornhill　7626 9985　9–2C
*A "wonderful" hang-over from the time of Dickens – an "ancient"
chophouse delivering "old-school grub at very fair prices", dispensed
by matronly staff who are "matter-of-fact and witty, to the point
of being cheeky and abrupt". / EC3V 9DR; www.simpsonstavern.co.uk;
@SimpsonsTavern; 3 pm; L only, closed Sat & Sun.*

Simpsons-in-the-Strand WC2　　　£75　　④④❸
100 Strand　7836 9112　4–3D
*For fans, these grand and very English dining rooms, on the fringe
of Covent Garden, still offer "a great trip down memory lane to the
days of good old roast beef" (and the breakfast is "super" too);
as ever, though, critics proclaim a "jaded" institution, run "mainly for
tourists". / WC2R 0EW; www.simpsonsinthestrand.co.uk; 10.45 pm,
Sun 9 pm; no trainers.*

Singapore Garden NW6　　　　£43　　❷❸④
83a Fairfax Rd　7624 8233　8–2A
*A "very dependable" Swiss Cottage fixture which continues to please
the locals with its "tasty, well spiced dishes from a range of SE Asian
countries". / NW6 4DY; www.singaporegarden.co.uk; 11 pm, Fri & Sat
11.30 pm.*

(Gallery)
Sketch W1　　　　　　　　£75　　④④④
9 Conduit St　7659 4500　3–2C
*This Mayfair fashionista favourite is "just amazing", say those who
feel this "eclectic" party scene is a notably "fun" destination for
"sociable dining"; for almost every fan, though, there's a foe who finds
the whole style "uncomfortably pretentious", and with "prices
to match". / W1S 2XG; www.sketch.uk.com; 11 pm; D only; booking:
max 10.*

(Lecture Room)
Sketch W1　　　　　　　　£119　　④❸❶
9 Conduit St　7659 4500　3–2C
*A "quite extraordinary" Mayfair dining room offering an experience
which is "ostentatious" to an extent rarely seen; its "terrific" cuisine –
created by Parisian über-chef Pierre Gagnaire – comes with "lots of
twists", but leaves some reporters unconvinced that the "mega-buck"
pricing is justified. / W1S 2XG; www.sketch.uk.com; @sketchlondon;
10.30 pm; closed Mon, Sat L & Sun; no trainers; booking: max 8.*

(The Parlour)
Sketch W1　　　　　　　　£62　　④④❷
9 Conduit St　7659 4533　3–2C
*"Like Alice in Wonderland" – this "eternally quirky" Mayfair parlour
is, for fans, a "fun" experience, and "recommended for afternoon
tea" or a "chilled breakfast"; to sceptics, though, it's just "massively
overpriced and ordinary". / W1S 2XG; www.sketch.uk.com; 10 pm;
no booking.*

Skipjacks HA3　　　　　　　£39　　❶❷④
268-270 Streatfield Rd　8204 7554　1–1A
*A "really down-to-earth" and "hectic but friendly" Harrow chippy,
acclaimed for its "brilliant fish 'n' chips" in "huge portions". / HA3 9BY;
10.30 pm; closed Sun.*

Skylon
South Bank Centre SE1   £59   ④④❷
Belvedere Rd   7654 7800   2–3D
If you can get a table by the massive windows, this vast South Bank chamber offers "surely the most romantic view in London"; other aspects of this D&D group operation, however, are very missable – for the "distinctly so-so" food, the bills can sometimes seem "unbelievable". / SE1 8XX; www.skylonrestaurant.co.uk; 10.30 pm, Sun 10 pm; no trainers; SRA-64%.

Skylon Grill SE1   £56   ❸❸❷
Belvedere Rd   7654 7800   2–3D
With its "gigantic windows for watching the sunset", this "buzzy" cheaper section of the D&D group's massive South Bank dining room is "better value than the adjacent restaurant"; the grill fare is "reliably good" and the view is just the same as next door. / SE1 8XX; 11 pm.

Smiths Brasserie E1 NEW   £51   ❷❸❷
22 Wapping High St   7488 3456   11–1A
"An excellent addition to the Wapping restaurant scene" – this new outpost of a popular Essex brasserie wins praise for its "wonderfully fresh fish"; "stunning views of Tower Bridge" too. / E1W 1NJ; 10 pm; closed Sun D.

(Ground Floor)
Smiths of Smithfield EC1   £32   ④④❸
67-77 Charterhouse St   7251 7950   9–1A
"Sunday brunch at Smith's is a must", or at least so say long-term fans of this "atmospheric" hang-out, "slap bang in the middle of Smithfield"; of late, however, not all reporters have been that impressed. / EC1M 6HJ; www.smithsofsmithfield.co.uk; L only; no bookings.

(Dining Room)
Smiths of Smithfield EC1   £53   ④④④
67-77 Charterhouse St   7251 7950   9–1A
"Reliable", "professional" and "no-nonsense" – that's why most reporters like the "noisy" first floor of this Smithfield warehouse-complex, where simple char-grilled fare is the stock-in-trade; there's also a feeling, however, that "for the price, nothing really stands out". / EC1A 6HJ; www.smithsofsmithfield.co.uk; 10.45 pm; closed Sat L & Sun; booking: max 12.

(Top Floor)
Smiths of Smithfield EC1   £72   ⑤④④
67-77 Charterhouse St   7251 7950   9–1A
A City-fringe rooftop steak venue, with an impressive view; it's the vista you pay for, though – with its "very standard" cooking and "aloof" service, its standards are "not a patch on the modern competition". / EC1M 6HJ; www.smithsofsmithfield.co.uk; 10.45 pm; closed Sat L & Sun D; booking: max 10.

The Smokehouse Islington N1 NEW   £45
63-69 Canonbury Rd   7354 1144   8–2D
On the former Canonbury site of the House (RIP), this large new gastropub opened just before this guide went to press; we didn't have the opportunity to visit, but there has been some very positive commentary in the media. / N1 2RG; www.smokehouseislington.co.uk.

Social Eating House W1 NEW   £55   ❸❸❸
58-59 Poland St   7993 3251   3–2D
On most accounts, Jason Atherton's latest "buzzy" baby is "a really
great addition to the Soho scene", offering "inventive" British fare
that's both "excellent" and "artistic"; the occasional report of "bland"
cuisine, however, slightly undercuts its ratings. / W1F 7NR;
www.socialeatinghouse.com; 10 pm; closed Sun.

Sofra   £35   ❹❸❹
1 St Christopher's Pl, W1   7224 4080   3–1A
18 Shepherd St, W1   7493 3320   3–4B
36 Tavistock St, WC2   7240 3773   4–3D
These "useful" Turkish "fall backs" are ideal for "a quick, reliable"
meal – "nothing's amazing but meze are done well", and there are
some "good-value set-price deals". / www.sofra.co.uk; 11 pm-midnight.

Soho Diner W1 NEW   £37   ❸❷❷
19 Old Compton St   7734 5656   4–2A
Brooklyn comes to the heart of Soho; this fast-service, small-menu
diner (on the former site of Bohème Kitchen RIP) really only offers
simple American 'bar' food, but it makes a good place to watch the
world go by. / W1D 5JJ; Rated on Editors' visit; www.sohodiner.com;
SohoDinerLDN.

Soho Japan NW1   £40   ❷❷❹
195 Baker St   7486 7000   2–1B
Once an Irish pub – and little changed decor-wise – this Japanese
diner (north of Oxford Street) is well-rated for "cheap 'n' cheerful"
sushi. / NW1 6UY; www.sohojapan.co.uk; @sohojapan; 10.30 pm; closed
Mon & Sun L; no Amex.

Soif SW11   £46   ❹❹❹
27 Battersea Rise   7223 1112   10–2C
Like its parent, Terroirs, this Battersea bistro undoubtedly offers some
"interesting biodynamic wines"; otherwise, though, feedback on all
aspects of operations in this "awkwardly-shaped" room is rather
ambivalent. / SW11 1HG; 10 pm; closed Mon L, Tue L, Wed L.

Solly's NW11   £44   ❸❹❹
146-150 Golders Green Rd   8455 0004   1–1B
A Golder's Green landmark – this "popular" Israeli café/take-away
(with upstairs restaurant) serves "good-quality" wraps and meze,
sometimes rather brusquely. / NW11 8HE; 10.30 pm; closed
Fri D & Sat L; no Amex.

Somerstown Coffee House NW1   £39   ❸❷❸
60 Chalton St   7387 7377   8–3C
"A perfect meeting-place, between Euston and St Pancras" –
this "friendly and competent" gastropub operates a "mainly tapas"
formula that generally satisfies. / NW1 1HS;
www.somerstowncoffeehouse.co.uk; 10 pm; no Amex.

Sông Quê E2   £33   ❸❺❹
134 Kingsland Rd   7613 3222   12–1B
"Crazy menu, crazy choices, crazy green decor sometimes crazy
queues!" – this "authentic" Shoreditch Vietnamese "marches to its
own, no-frills beat"; some long-term fans, though, think it's "gone way
downhill" in recent years. / E2 8DY; www.sonque.co.uk; 11 pm; no Amex.

Sonny's Kitchen SW13   £52   ④④④
94 Church Rd   8748 0393   10–1A
This Barnes linchpin (newly a 'Kitchen') has put in an inconsistent performance since its 2012 re-launch – fans feel it has recaptured the "informal and lively" mojo of old, with "stunning", "simple" fare, whereas sceptics, just see a "noisy" place with "disjointed" cooking and "slipshod" service. / SW13 0DQ; www.sonnyskitchen.co.uk; 10 pm, Fri-Sat 11 pm, Sun 9.30 pm; set weekday L £32 (FP), set Sun L £39 (FP).

La Sophia W10   £46   ❷③④
46 Golborne Road   8968 2200   6–1A
Still less commentary than we'd like on this North Kensington two-year-old; such as it is, though, suggests that this Middle Eastern/Mediterranean spot is a notably "consistent" all-rounder. / W10 5PR; www.lasophia.co.uk; Mon-Thu 10 pm, Fri & Sat 10.30 pm, Sun 9 pm; closed Mon L & Tue L.

Sophie's Steakhouse   £52   ④④④
29-31 Wellington St, WC2   7836 8836   4–3D
311-313 Fulham Rd, SW10   7352 0088   5–3B
Fans of these "straightforward" hang-outs applaud their "fab cocktails", "succulent" steaks and "buzzing atmosphere"; "with so many great steakhouses around" nowadays, however, the formula can seem rather "tired" in comparison. / www.sophiessteakhouse.com; SW10 11.45 pm, Sun 11.15 pm; WC2 12.45 am, Sun 11 pm; no booking; set weekday L £31 (FP).

Sotheby's Café W1   £57   ④❷❷
34-35 New Bond St   7293 5077   3–2C
For "a people-watching lunch", this café off the foyer of the famous Mayfair auction house has its attractions (particularly on sale or pre-sale days); the lobster club-sandwich is a highlight of the rather "limited" menu. / W1A 2AA; www.sothebys.com; L only, closed Sat & Sun; booking: max 8.

Spianata & Co   £11   ❸❷❸
3 Hay Hill, W1   no tel   3–3C
Tooley St, SE1   8616 4662   9–4D
41 Brushfield St, E1   7655 4411   12–2B
20 Holborn Viaduct, EC1   7248 5947   9–2A
17 Blomfield St, EC2   7256 9103   9–2C
73 Watling St, EC4   7236 3666   9–2B
A "friendly" Italian take-away (mainly) chain, where the focus is on "authentic focaccia sandwiches" and "the best coffee ever". / www.spianata.com; 3.30 pm; EC3 11 pm; closed Sat & Sun; E1 closed Sat; no credit cards; no booking.

Spice Market
W Hotel London W1   £75   ④④④
10 Wardour St   7758 1088   4–3A
Very mixed (and remarkably few) reports on this heart-of-the-West-End outpost of the empire of top NYC chef Jean-Georges Vongerichten... which all tends to support the view that it's "not a patch" on the Manhattan Meatpacking District original. / W1D 6QF; www.spicemarketlondon.co.uk; 11 pm, Thu-Sat 11.30 pm; set weekday L £46 (FP).

Spuntino W1   £40   ❷③❷
61 Rupert St   no tel   3–2D
Russell Norman's "very hip" ("Brooklyn-style") bar, in the sleazy heart of Soho, offers "great cocktails" and a snack menu that includes "great sliders" (mini-burgers) – "worth the queue!" / W1D 7PW; www.spuntino.co.uk; 11.30 pm, Sun 10.30 pm.

THE SQUARE W1 £104 ❷❶❸
6-10 Bruton St 7495 7100 3–2C
Phil Howard's "consistently assured" cuisine "surprises even the most jaded palette", and the appeal of his "calm" Mayfair HQ for some "serious dining" — especially for expense accounters — is completed by a wine list "to drain a sovereign wealth fund"; fans insist the suit-heavy ambience is "getting more lively" too. / W1J 6PU; www.squarerestaurant.com; 9.45 pm, Sat 10.15 pm, Sun 9.30 pm; closed Sun L; booking: max 8.

Sree Krishna SW17 £27 ❷❸④
192-194 Tooting High St 8672 4250 10–2C
"Unchanging, in a good way" — this 40-year-old south Indian in Tooting is admittedly "unatmospheric", but the food is "great, and very good value"; BYO. / SW17 0SF; www.sreekrishna.co.uk; @SreeKrishnaUk; 10.45 pm, Fri & Sat 11.45 pm; set weekday L £13 (FP).

Star of India SW5 £51 ❷④④
154 Old Brompton Rd 7373 2901 5–2B
"No longer fashionable, but not forgotten!"; this "quirky" Earl's Court subcontinental, with its 'Sistine Chapel' interior, is still — for its many fans — "one of the best"; service, though, is "up-and-down". / SW5 0BE; www.starofindia.eu; 11.45 pm, Sun 11.15 pm.

Stick & Bowl W8 £22 ❷❷❸
31 Kensington High St 7937 2778 5–1A
"Real, honest Cantonese food" makes this "unique, little noodle house", near Kensington Palace, a mightily handy 'value' destination — "don't let the scruffy, cramped, shared tables put you off!" / W8 5NP; 10.45 pm; no credit cards; no booking.

Sticks'n'Sushi £47 ❸❸❷
11 Henrietta St, WC2 3141 8800 4–3D NEW
58 Wimbledon Hill Rd, SW19 3141 8800 10–2B
A "hugely popular" yearling, serving up "really enjoyable Japanese fare with a Scandi twist", in a setting that "looks like it should be somewhere much trendier than Wimbledon" (and which even fans can find "pricey" for what it is); a new branch opens in Covent Garden in late-2013. / www.sticksnsushi.com; Sun - Tues 10 pm, Wed -Sat 11 pm.

Sticky Fingers W8 £42 ❸❸❸
1a Phillimore Gdns 7938 5338 5–1A
"Rolling Stones memorabilia drips from every wall, staff are really helpful... and the burgers aren't bad either" — this Kensington backstreet burger parlour remains a "great" destination (especially "with kids"). / W8 7QR; www.stickyfingers.co.uk; 10.45 pm.

STK Steakhouse
ME by Meliá London WC2 £68 ④④❸
336-337 The Strand 7395 3450 4–3C
This "night-clubby and cool" new arrival, on the fringe of Covent Garden gets mixed reports; to fans it's "a sleek and sexy place, just like being back in NYC", but foes (many) say it's "ridiculously pricey" and "pretentious", and "so loud you can't think". / WC2R 1HA; www.stkhouse.com.

Stock Pot £27 ④❸❸
38 Panton St, SW1 7839 5142 4–4A
273 King's Rd, SW3 7823 3175 5–3C
"Get away from fancy meals, and get in touch with the real world!" – these *"friendly, noisy, busy and fun"* canteen-veterans offer *"basic"* fodder at *"fabulous"* prices; they provide *"a trip down memory lane"* too… *if you're old enough to recall the '60s! / SW1 11.30 pm, Wed-Sat midnight, Sun 11 pm SW3 10.15 pm, Sun 9.45 pm; no Amex.*

Story SE1 NEW £65 ❶❶❸
201 Tooley St 7183 2117 9–4D
Tom Sellers's *"sensational"* food with a *"theatrical"* twist (*"everyone will want to try the dripping candle"*) has made his *"NOMA-style"* spot the best of the 2013 newcomers – brave the *"awful"* location, south of Tower Bridge, and you'll find an *"interesting"* Scandi-style room where staff simply *"buzz with enthusiasm". / SE1 2UE; www.restaurantstory.co.uk; 9.15 pm; closed Mon & Sun.*

Story Deli E2 £42 ❷④❷
123 Bethnal Green Rd 819 7352 12–2B
"Get the East London vibe at this cool hangout" (still near Brick Lane, but moved from the Truman Brewery a couple of years ago), where thin-crust pizza is the main event food-wise. */ E2 7DG; www.storydeli.com; 10.30 pm; no credit cards.*

Strada £41 ④④④
Branches throughout London
A *"patchy"* performance by this pizza/pasta chain – fans find it *"reliable"* and *"family-friendly"*, but those who remember its one-time culinary pre-eminence feel it's *"really gone downhill". / www.strada.co.uk; 10.30 pm-11 pm; some booking restrictions apply.*

Street Kitchen EC2 £18 ❷❸–
Broadgate Circle no tel 12–2B
Proof positive that food vans are mainstream – this silver Airstream, run by celeb chefs Mark Jankel and Jun Tanaka, serves *"great daily specials"* from their lunchtime perch at Broadgate Circle; other locations (with other more dude-foodish menus) too. */ EC2; www.streetkitchen.co.uk/home.shtml; @Streetkitchen.*

Suda WC2 £45 ❸❸❸
23 Slingsby Pl, St Martin's Ct 7240 8010 4–3C
OK, it has 'chain prototype' written all over it, but this *"handy"* Covent Garden-fringe Thai still impresses all who report on it with its *"simple but tasty"* cuisine. */ WC2E 9AB; www.suda-thai.com; 10.30 pm, Thu-Sat 11 pm.*

Sufi W12 £30 ❸❷❸
70 Askew Rd 8834 4888 7–1B
"You won't find better bread" than the tandoori-baked offering at this *"ever-friendly and welcoming"* Persian spot, deep in Shepherd's Bush; dishes are *"fairly simple"*, but they offer *"such good value". / W12 9BJ; www.sufirestaurant.com; 11 pm.*

Suk Saran SW19 £51 ❸④⑤
29 Wimbledon Hill Rd 8947 9199 10–2B
"Very good" food (*"amazing"*, say fans) makes this Wimbledon Town Thai a handy local standby. */ SW19 7NE; www.sukhogroup.com; 11 pm; booking: max 20.*

Sukho Fine Thai Cuisine SW6 £50 ❶❶④
855 Fulham Rd 7371 7600 10–1B
"The best Thai food in West London" – arguably the whole capital – is to be had at this "wonderful" little outfit, in deepest Fulham; staff are ultra-"charming" too, leaving the "cramped" setting as the only real downside. / SW6 5HJ; www.sukhogroup.co.uk; 11 pm.

The Summerhouse W9 £55 ④❸❷
60 Blomfield Rd 7286 6752 8–4A
"A lovely canalside setting" is the particular attraction of this "great find" in Little Venice (which is nowadays open all year) – the fish-centric cuisine very much plays second fiddle. / W9 2PA; www.thesummerhouse.co.uk; 10.30 pm, Sun 10 pm; no Amex.

Sumosan W1 £76 ❷④④
26b Albemarle St 7495 5999 3–3C
"Wonderful" Japanese-fusion fare, including "fabulous" sashimi and sushi, top the bill at this style-conscious, and "outrageously expensive" Mayfair Japanese; though it's sometimes "buzzy", it never seems to have attracted the following of the likes of Nobu and Zuma. / W1S 4HY; www.sumosan.com; @sumosan_; 11.30 pm, Sun 10.30 pm; closed Sat L & Sun L; set weekday L £51 (FP).

The Surprise SW3 £45 ④❸❷
6 Christchurch Ter 7351 6954 5–3D
Hidden-away in Chelsea, this "lovely little pub" is something of a "gem"; it serves a "simple but imaginative" menu of British 'tapas'. / SW3 4AJ; www.geronimo-inns.co.uk/thesurprise; 10 pm, Sun 9 pm; SRA-60%.

Sushisamba EC2 £76 ❸④❷
Heron Tower, 110 Bishopsgate 3640 7330 9–2D
"Peerless" views and "the best terrace in town" have certainly made this "showy" bar/restaurant complex, on the 38th/39th floors of the City's Heron Tower, an "exceptional" destination; although it's "wildly expensive", the "sumptuous" Latino/Asian cuisine is "surprisingly good" too. / EC2N 4AY; Sun-Thu midnight, Fri & Sat 1 am.

Sushi Tetsu EC1 £54 ❶❶❸
12 Jerusalem Pas 3217 0090 9–1A
"Having lived in Tokyo for 5 years, this is the only sushi bar in the UK that bears comparison!" – this Clerkenwell hole-in-the-wall is "a labour of love" which "redefines Japanese food in London"; "unfortunately the word is out and, as there are only 7 seats, it is impossible to get a booking". / EC1V 4JP; www.sushitetsu.co.uk.

Sushi-Say NW2 £43 ❶❷④
33b Walm Ln 8459 7512 1–1A
Don't let the unlikely Willesden Green location fool you – this unassuming café is "definitely one of London's best Japanese restaurants", and "proof that authentic Japanese grub needn't leave you hungry and bankrupt!" / NW2 5SH; 10 pm, Sat 10.30 pm, Sun 9.30 pm; closed Mon, Tue, Wed L, Thu L & Fri L; no Amex.

Sushinho £57 ❷❸❸
312-314 King's Rd, SW3 7349 7496 5–3C
9a, Devonshire Sq, EC2 7220 9490 9–2D
"Surprisingly fantastic" Japanese/Brazilian fusion cuisine, and "excellent cocktails" too – this alluring Chelsea bar/restaurant makes a good, if pricey, destination for a night out; remarkably, though, the new City branch has "no ambience". / www.sushinho.com; SW3 12 am, EC2 10.30 pm; SW3 closed Sun-Fri L, EC2 closed Sat L.

The Swan W4 — £44 — ❷❷❶
119 Acton Ln   8994 8262   7–1A
The food shows impressive "attention to detail" and the service is really "lovely", but it's the "fabulous" atmosphere – and "the best pub garden" – which primarily underpin the popularity of this "traditional" Chiswick boozer. / W4 5HH; www.theswanchiswick.co.uk; 10 pm, Fri & Sat 10.30 pm, Sun 10 pm; closed weekday L.

Swan & Edgar NW1 — £39 — ❹❸❷
43 Linhope St   7724 6268   2–1A
"A nice hidden secret" – this "quirky" and "cosy" bolt-hole, near Marylebone station, dishes up very decent food, as well as "good wines by the glass". / NW1 6HL; www.swanandedgar.co.uk; 10 pm, Sun 9 pm; D only, ex Sun open L & D.

The Swan at the Globe SE1 — £54 — ❹❹❷
21 New Globe Walk   7928 9444   9–3B
With its view of St Paul's, this "romantic" South Bank first floor operation strikes fans as a "really great dining room"; even they may concede that "the food doesn't match the setting", though, and harsher critics say "you might do better at the local Pizza Express!" / SE1 9DT; www.loveswan.co.uk; @swanabout; 9.45 pm, Sun 4.45 pm; closed Sun D.

Sweet Thursday N1 NEW — £33 — ❷❸❷
95 Southgate Rd   7226 1727   1–2C
In De Beauvoir, this "excellent" new pizzeria has won instant local acclaim; the formula? – "huge" thin crust pizza, with "interesting combos", "great wine" (they do tastings) and "a wonderful homely vibe". / N1 3JS; www.sweetthursday.co.uk; @Pizza_and_Pizza; 10 pm, Sat 10.30 pm, Sun 9 pm.

Sweetings EC4 — £58 — ❸❸❷
39 Queen Victoria St   7248 3062   9–3B
If you're looking for "a real institution that never changes", it would be hard to beat this "eccentric" Victorian "national treasure" – "a classic City fish bar" whose "enduring" nature is "part of its appeal"; arrive early for a table, or have a sandwich at the counter. / EC4N 4SA; www.sweetingsrestaurant.com; 3.30 pm; L only, closed Sat & Sun; no booking.

Taberna Etrusca EC4 — £50 — ❸❷❸
9 Bow Churchyard   7248 5552   9–2C
"Well-executed food in a charming location"; this long-established City Italian – which has some particularly nice al freso tables – has been dishing up some unusually good meals of late. / EC4M 9DQ; www.etruscarestaurants.com; 10 pm; closed Mon D, Sat & Sun.

The Table SE1 — £45 — ❸❹❹
83 Southwark St   7401 2760   9–4B
A "fantastic" lunch or brunch-stop, particularly good pre-Tate Modern – so claim fans of this "chilled" canteen-like space, on the ground floor of a major architectural practice; you can't book, though, and prices can seem high, given the "basic" setting, and sometimes "rushed" service. / SE1 0HX; www.thetablecafe.com; @thetablecafe; 10.30 pm; closed Mon D & Sun D; SRA-64%.

Taiwan Village SW6 £34 ❶❶❸
85 Lillie Rd 7381 2900 5–3A
*"An extraordinary find for the area!"; this "welcoming"
Chinese/Taiwanese, behind an "unassuming shopfront" off the North
End Road, "deserves to be much better known"; the "leave-it-to-the-
chef" menu, in particular, is "an absolute treat". / SW6 1UD;
www.taiwanvillage.com; 11.30 pm, Sun 10.30 pm; closed weekday L; booking:
max 20.*

Tajima Tei EC1 £35 ❷❸❸
9-11 Leather Ln 7404 9665 9–2A
*Looking for "a quick Japanese lunch", in the heart of legal-land? –
this "authentic" fixture offers an experience "like being back
in Tokyo", offering a "well-priced" menu that includes "consistently
excellent sushi". / EC1N 7ST; www.tajima-tei.co.uk; 10 pm; closed Sat & Sun;
no booking, L.*

Talad Thai SW15 £31 ❸④⑤
320 Upper Richmond Rd 8246 5791 10–2A
*"It's canteen-like and functional to look at", and service is "slightly
haphazard", but this Putney Thai wins acclaim for its "authentic and
tasty" scoff at "cheap" prices. / SW15 6TL; www.taladthairestaurant.com;
10.30 pm, Sun 9.30 pm; no Amex.*

Tamarind W1 £72 ❷❸④
20 Queen St 7629 3561 3–3B
*This Mayfair veteran is still on top of its game, and its "masterful"
evolved Indian cuisine still pleases most reporters; "the negatives are
that you're in a basement, and prices are high". / W1J 5PR;
www.tamarindrestaurant.com; 10.45 pm, Sun 10.30 pm; closed Sat L;
set weekday L £41 (FP), set pre-theatre £48 (FP).*

Tandoori Nights SE22 £37 ❸❷❸
73 Lordship Ln 8299 4077 1–4D
*"Lovely" owners make it worth seeking out this "consistent"
East Dulwich fixture, whose "ambiance is pretty much what one
would expect in a local Indian", but where the curries are
"very tasty". / SE22 8EP; www.tandoorinightsdulwich.co.uk; 11.30pm, Fri &
Sat midnight; closed weekday L & Sat L.*

Tapas Brindisa £42 ❷❸❸
46 Broadwick St, W1 7534 1690 3–2D
18-20 Southwark St, SE1 7357 8880 9–4C
*"Iberico and olive oil alone justify the trip!"; this tapas bar duo, run by
the Spanish food importers, serve up "authentic" dishes from "high-
quality ingredients"; the always "rammed" Borough Market original
is much better known than the more modern Soho spin-off.
/ 10.45 pm, Sun 10 pm; W1 booking: max 10.*

Taqueria W11 £34 ❸❸④
139-143 Westbourne Grove 7229 4734 6–1B
*"Everything you could ask of a Mexican restaurant!"; thanks to its
small dishes with "authentic" flavours, plus brilliant margaritas and
cocktails, this snug Notting Hill hang-out "feels just like eating in a
cantina in Mexico". / W11 2RS; www.taqueria.co.uk; 11 pm, Fri & Sat
11.30 pm, Sun 10.30 pm; no Amex; no booking Fri-Sun.*

Taro £34 ❸❸❸

10 Old Compton St, W1   7439 2275   4–2B
61 Brewer St, W1   7734 5826   3–2D
44a, Cannon St, EC4   7236 0399   9–3B

Mr Taro's "no-frills" and usually "jam-packed" Soho canteens are "straightforward and quick" for a "filling, yummy and cheapish" Japanese snack. / www.tarorestaurants.co.uk; 10.30 pm, Sun 9.30 pm; no Amex; Brewer St only small bookings.

Tartufo SW3 NEW £50 ❶❷❸

11 Cadogan Gdns   7730 6383   5–2D

"Hard to find, but worth it!"; Alexis Gauthier's new establishment, in the "cosy" basement of a small hotel near Sloane Square, has opened to huge acclaim for its "first-class" cooking, and at "reasonable prices" too! / SW3 2RJ; www.tartufolondon.co.uk; 10 pm; closed Mon & Sun.

Tas £36 ❹❸❸

22 Bloomsbury St, WC1   7637 4555   2–1C
33 The Cut, SE1   7928 2111   9–4A
72 Borough High St, SE1   7403 7200   9–4C
76 Borough High St, SE1   7403 8557   9–4C
97-99 Isabella St, SE1   7620 6191   9–4A
37 Farringdon Rd, EC1   7430 9721   9–1A

"Cheap", "cheerful" and "dependable", this Turkish bistro chain is hailed by pretty much all reporters as at least a "good stand-by", especially "for a late meal". / www.tasrestaurant.com; 11.30 pm, Sun 10.30 pm.

Tas Pide SE1 £33 ❹❸❸

20-22 New Globe Walk   7928 3300   9–3B

"Stick to the signature Anatolian pizzas and the Turkish desserts and you won't go wrong" – not bad advice if you visit this "bustling" spot near Shakespeare's Globe; it's still hailed as a "value-for-money" destination, but critics do fear it's "not as good as it used to be". / SE1 9DR; www.tasrestaurant.com/tas_pide; 11.30 pm, Sun 10.30 pm.

(Rex Whistler)
Tate Britain SW1 £53

Millbank   7887 8825   2–4C

Re-opening in late-2013, this famous dining room is being given a major refurb; its renowned Whistler murals will survive, of course – we trust the almost equally famous wine list will also be intact. / SW1 4RG; www.tate.org.uk; L & afternoon tea only.

(Restaurant, Level 7)
Tate Modern SE1 £48 ❺❹❸

Bankside   7887 8888   9–3B

"Fabulous views across the river to St Paul's plus not especially memorable food" – that's the 'middle view' on the the top-floor restaurant of the world's most-visited modern art gallery; reports, however, span the whole range from "classy" to "shocking". / SE1 9TG; www.tate.org.uk; @TateFood; 9.30 pm; Sun-Thu closed D, Fri & Sat open L & D; SRA-61%.

Taylor St Baristas £15 ❷❸❸
22 Brooks Mews, W1 7629 3163 3–2B
Unit 3 Westminster Hs, Kew Rd, TW9 07969798650 1–4A
1 Harbour Exchange Sq, E14 3069 8833 11–2C
8 South Colonnade, E14 no tel 11–1C
110 Clifton St, EC2 7929 2207 12–2B
Unit 3, 125 Old Broad St, EC2 7256 8668 9–2C
2 Botolph Alley, EC3 7283 1835 9–3C
"Beware too big a caffeine-hit!", when you visit this "small chain out of Oz" – you may also avail yourself of some of the "brilliant" cakes and snacks to complement the "superb" coffee. / EC2M 4TP; www.taylor-st.com; All branches 5 pm; Old Broad ST, Clifton St, W1, E14 closed Sat & Sun; New ST closed Sat; TW9 closed Sun.

Tayyabs E1 £28 ❶❺❸
83 Fieldgate St 7247 9543 9–2D
"Too popular, but otherwise perfect!"; this "seriously addictive" East End Pakistani continues to dish up "incredible" dishes (including "the best lamb chops ever") at "bargain" prices, and it's a BYO too; service can be "chaotic", but it's all part of the experience. / E1 1JU; www.tayyabs.co.uk; 11.30 pm.

Telegraph SW15 £39 ❹❹❸
Telegraph Rd 8788 2011 10–2A
The sign at this Putney Heath boozer – 'A Country Pub in London' – doesn't lie; service is "haphazard" at busy weekends, but the food is decent, and it's all very cosy (though "upstairs rather lacks atmosphere"). / SW15 3TU; www.thetelegraphputney.co.uk; 9 pm, Fri & Sat 9.30 pm.

The 10 Cases WC2 £55 ❹❶❷
16 Endell St 836 6801 4–2C
"Incredible" wines (from a short but ever-changing list) have made a major hit of this "terrific", if "cramped", Covent Garden yearling (which has already expanded into the shop next door); "the food's not bad either". / WC2H 9BD; www.the10cases.co.uk; 11 pm; closed Sun.

10 Greek Street W1 £46 ❷❶❸
10 Greek St 7734 4677 4–2A
"Atmosphere, charm, style and originality" – this "cramped" Soho yearling has them all, plus "unshowy" but "wonderfully-flavoured" cooking at "incredible-value" prices; no booking. / W1D 4DH; www.10greekstreet.com; @10GreekStreet; 11.30 pm; closed Sun.

Tendido Cero SW5 £45 ❷❷❷
174 Old Brompton Rd 7370 3685 5–2B
"Continues to impress on all fronts..."; Cambio de Tercio's "buzzy" and "noisy" younger sibling serves "designer" tapas to a "sleek thirty-something clientele", at this "accommodating" Earl's Court spot. / SW5 0BA; www.cambiodetercio.co.uk; @CambiodTercio; 11 pm.

Tendido Cuatro SW6 £41 ❷❷❸
108-110 New King's Rd 7371 5147 10–1B
Cambio de Tercio's "buzzy", "friendly" and "slightly cramped" Fulham outpost attracts consistent praise for its "excellent tapas and very good wine". / SW6 4LY; www.cambiodetercio.co.uk; 11 pm, Sun 10.30 pm.

Tentazioni SE1 £51 ❸❸❸
2 Mill St 7394 5248 11–2A
"The best-kept secret in Shad Thames!"; this "welcoming", "no-fuss" Italian has "quite a reputation on the gourmet trail" for its "proper" cooking (pasta in particular). / SE1 2BD; www.tentazioni.co.uk; @TentazioniWorld; 10.45 pm; closed Sat L & Sun.

Terroirs WC2 £46 ❸❸❸
5 William IV St 7036 0660 4–4C
"Hidden-away" near Charing Cross, this "stylishly simple" Gallic bistro
has won fame with its earthy, "big-flavoured" dishes (often in small-
plate format), and its "almost perversely unusual" range of organic
wines; its ratings, however, continue to drift gently. / WC2N 4DW;
www.terroirswinebar.com; @terroirswinebar; 11 pm; closed Sun.

Texture W1 £93 ❷❷❸
34 Portman St 7224 0028 2–2A
Agnar Sverrisson's "incredible Noma-like food" ("marvellous subtleties
of flavours"), with "superb wine choices" too, are carving out an ever-
bigger reputation for this "eclectic" venture, near Selfridges –
a "vibrant" spot that's a little hard-edged and "noisy" for some tastes.
/ W1H 7BY; www.texture-restaurant.co.uk; 10.30 pm; closed Mon & Sun.

Thai Corner Café SE22 £21 ❸❸❸
44 North Cross Rd 8299 4041 1–4D
"A small corner Thai restaurant" in the depths of East Dulwich;
the food's "good" and "fresh", but it's "the great bonus of BYO"
which makes locals seek it out. / SE22 9EU; www.thaicornercafe.co.uk;
10.30 pm; closed Mon L & Tue L; no credit cards.

Thai Garden SW11 £31 ❸❸④
58 Battersea Rise 7738 0380 10–2C
A low-profile neighbourhood Thai, near Clapham Junction, that's
proved very reliable over many years; as a "cheap 'n' cheerful"
option, it remains a consistent local recommendation. / SW11 1EG;
www.thaigarden.co.uk; @thaigardenuk; 10.30 pm; D only, closed Mon.

Thai Square £40 ④④④
21-24 Cockspur St, SW1 7839 4000 2–3C
27-28 St Annes Ct, W1 7287 2000 3–1D
5 Princess St, W1 7499 3333 3–1C
148 The Strand, WC2 7497 0904 2–2D
166-170 Shaftesbury Ave, WC2 7836 7600 4–1B
229-230 Strand, WC2 7353 6980 2–2D
19 Exhibition Rd, SW7 7584 8359 5–2C
347-349 Upper St, N1 7704 2000 8–3D
2-4 Lower Richmond Rd, SW15 8780 1811 10–1A
563 Fulham Rd, SW6 7610 0055 5–4A
136-138 Minories, EC3 7680 1111 9–3D
1-7 Great St Thomas Apostle, EC4 7329 0001 9–3B
"Convenient", "solid", "nice" – such are the virtues fans see in this
Thai stand-by chain (and the SW15 branch has "great views" of the
Thames too). / www.thaisquare.net; 10 pm-11.30 pm; SW1 Fri & Sat 1 am;
EC3, EC4 & St Annes Ct closed Sat & Sun, Strand branches and Princess
St closed Sun.

Thali SW5 £43 ❷❸④
166 Old Brompton Rd 7373 2626 5–2B
"The owner's family recipes" are used as the basis for some
"fantastic" North Indian dishes, with "clean and crisp flavours",
at this "slightly poncy" Earl's Court venture. / SW5 0BA;
www.thali.uk.com; 11.30 pm, Sun 10.30 pm.

The Thatched House W6 £44 ❸④❸
115 Dalling Rd 8748 6174 7–1B
"Improved since the relaunch", this "friendly" Hammersmith
gastroboozer offers an "awesome" Sunday lunch, a "good choice
of beers" and a "lovely little garden". / W6 0ET; www.thatchedhouse.com;
@thethatched; Thu-Sat midnight, Sun-Wed 11pm.

Theo Randall
InterContinental Hotel W1   £83   ❷❸④
1 Hamilton Pl   7318 8747   3–4A
"Sublime" Italian dishes, "cooked with panache", have won renown
for this ex-River Café chef's Mayfair HQ; gripes about
"unspectacular" meals and "incredible" prices rose this year, though,
and the windowless room is notoriously "unatmospheric". / W1J 7QY;
www.theorandall.com; 11 pm; closed Sat L & Sun; set weekday L & pre-theatre
£57 (FP).

34 W1   £74   ④❸❸
34 Grosvenor Sq   3350 3434   3–2A
Richard Caring's year-old grill-house "looks great", say fans, and –
with its "tender" steaks and "awesome" burgers – it "never fails
to impress"; those who find the cooking "not particularly memorable",
though, may be inclined to notice the decidedly Mayfair prices.
/ W1K 2HD; www.34-restaurant.co.uk; 10.30 pm.

Thirty Six
Duke's Hotel SW1   £88   ❸⑤④
35-36 Saint James's Pl   7491 4840   3–4C
Mixed feedback this year on this "quiet" St James's basement;
most reporters still say it's a "hidden gem" with "well-executed"
cuisine, but sceptics can find it "rather dull", and the service
is "rather flaky" too often for comfort. / SW1A 1NY; www.dukeshotel.com;
@dukeshotel; 9.30 pm; closed Mon L & Sun D; set weekday L £57 (FP), set
pre-theatre £61 (FP).

The Thomas Cubitt SW1   £60   ❸❸❷
44 Elizabeth St   7730 6060   2–4A
This "always-buzzing" Belgravian rendezvous is, say fans, "a pub
in the same way a diamond is a rock"; this said, the food – both on
the ground floor and in the restaurant above – has "gone backwards"
of late. / SW1W 9PA; www.thethomascubitt.co.uk; 10 pm; closed
Sat L & Sun D; booking only in restaurant; SRA-75%.

3 South Place
South Place Hotel EC2   £60   ④❸④
3 South Pl   3503 0000   12–2A
A "something-for-everyone" menu makes the ground-floor dining
room of this contemporary-style D&D group hotel a handy City
standby; for more atmosphere, though, head for the top-floor Angler
(see also). / EC2M 2AF; www.southplacehotel.com.

Tian Fu W12   £32   ❸⑤⑤
37 Bulwer St   8740 4546   7–1C
"Spicy" and "unusual" Sichuan dishes at "low" prices, and in
an "unexpected" location by Westfield too – the formula that's made
a hit of this Shepherd's Bush Chinese. / W12 8AR; 11 pm; no Amex.

tibits W1   £34   ❸❸❸
12-14 Heddon St   7758 4110   3–2C
"Always fresh and interesting"; the veggie buffet concept of this "cool"
Swiss outlet, near Piccadilly Circus, pleases all who report on it;
it offers an "impressive array" of dishes, for which "you pay by weight
at the check-out". / W1B 4DA; www.tibits.co.uk; 11.30 pm, Sun 10 pm;
no Amex; Only bookings for 8+.

Tierra Peru N1 £40 ④❸④
164 Essex Rd 7354 5586 8–3D
*This "closely-packed" Islington yearling offers an "excellent take
on Peruvian cooking" (with ceviche rating particular mention);
it doesn't impress all reporters, though, and a disgruntled minority say
it's "a real let-down". / N1 8LY; www.tierraperu.co.uk; @tierraperu; 11 pm;
set weekday L £26 (FP).*

Tinello SW1 £47 ❷❷❸
87 Pimlico Rd 7730 3663 5–2D
*"Meaty and hearty" Tuscan food "with a nice light touch" combines
with "very friendly and efficient" service to make this "elegant",
Locatelli-backed Pimlico Italian a major hit; if there's a quibble it's that
it can feel a tad "subdued". / SW1W 8PH; www.tinello.co.uk; 10.30 pm;
closed Sun.*

Toasted SE22 NEW £45
38 Lordship Ln 8693 9021 1–4D
*A long way from Charing Cross, this East Dulwich newcomer is the
latest outpost of the Terroirs empire, but in a style that's more 'classic
wine bar' than usual; it opened just as our survey for the year was
concluding – the first reporter was very impressed! / SE22 8HJ;
toastdulwich.co.uk; toastdulwich.*

Toff's N10 £39 ❷❷④
38 Muswell Hill Broadway 8883 8656 1–1B
*"The freshest fish, simply served" ("and not just the usuals") –
this "cramped" and "crowded" Muswell Hill "institution" is hailed
by many locals as "surely the best chippy in town"; BYO. / N10 3RT;
www.toffsfish.co.uk; @toffsfish; 10 pm; closed Sun.*

Toku
Japan Centre SW1 £40
16 Regent St 3405 1246 3–3D
*"It's pretty much a canteen" in style, but this café within Japan's
West End cultural outpost serves a good range of "well-priced and
authentic dishes"; a move to Shaftesbury Avenue is scheduled for
late-2013. / SW1Y 4PH; 9.45 pm, Sun 8.45 pm; no Amex; no booking Sat.*

Tokyo Diner WC2 £26 ❸❷❸
2 Newport Pl 7287 8777 4–3B
*"Unassuming, small and basic", this diner on the edge of Chinatown
is well worth knowing about – "decent" sushi and noodles
at "good prices", and "very fast and polite" service too. / WC2H 7JJ;
www.tokyodiner.com; 11.30 pm; no Amex; no booking, Fri & Sat.*

Tom Aikens SW3 £91 ❷❸❸
43 Elystan St 7584 2003 5–2C
*"Vastly improved since the refurbishment", Tom Aikens' "pared-down"
but "stylish" HQ is back on true crowd-pleasing form; it's still very
pricey, but offers "wonderfully creative" food from its "imaginative"
small-plates menu, and "exciting" wines too. / SW3 3NT;
www.tomaikens.co.uk; @TomAikensRest; 10.45 pm; closed Sat L & Sun;
booking: max 8; set weekday L £55 (FP).*

Tom's Deli W11 £35 ❸❸❸
226 Westbourne Grove 7221 8818 6–1B
*"Best eggs Benedict ever" – the sort of attraction that means
"you may have to queue" for brunch at Tom Conran's ever-popular
Notting Hill deli/diner. / W11 2RH; www.tomsdeli.co.uk; 5.30 pm; L only;
no Amex; no booking.*

Tom's Kitchen £63 ④❸❸
Somerset House, 150 Strand, WC2 7845 4646 2–2D
27 Cale St, SW3 7349 0202 5–2C
11 Westferry Circus, E14 3011 1555 11–1C **NEW**
*From the "buzzy" (if "squashed") Chelsea original to the "lovely"
Somerset House outlet, Tom Aikens's branded spin-offs have potential
as "fun" hang-outs, especially for brunch; in truth, though, standards
are pretty "ordinary". / 10 pm - 10.45 pm; WC2 closed Sun D.*

Tommi's Burger Joint W1 **NEW** £18 ❷④④
30 Thayer St awaiting tel 3–1A
*For many reporters, this "too-cool-for-school" Marylebone ex-pop-up
newcomer offers "truly great burgers", perhaps even
"the best in town"; a few refuseniks, though, just can't see it.
/ W1U 2QP; www.burgerjoint.co.uk; @BurgerJointUk; 10.30 pm, Sun 9.30 pm.*

Tonkotsu W1 £31 ❸❸❸
63 Dean St 7437 0071 4–2A
*"It took me back to Tokyo"; "ramen bars don't come better than
this", say fans of this "hip" and somewhat "cramped" Soho noodle-
spot, instantly "rammed with cool kids". / W1D 4QG;
www.tonkotsu.co.uk; 10.30 pm, Sun 10 pm.*

Tortilla £18 ❸❸❸
6 Market Place, W1 7637 2800 3–1C
460 The Strand, WC2 7930 0269 4–3D
6a, King St, W6 8741 7959 7–2C
13 Islington High St, N1 7833 3103 8–3D
106 Southwark St, SE1 7620 0285 9–4B
22 The Broadway, SW19 8947 3589 10–2B
18 North Colonnade, E14 7719 9160 11–1C
213 The Balcony, Westfield Stratford City, E20 8555 3663 1–3D
28 Leadenhall Mkt, EC3 7929 7837 9–2D
*Of the many burrito joints springing up around town, this "pleasant"
chain is amongst the better options to "grab and go" – "portions are
generous", and there's "a large choice of fillings". / www.tortilla.co.uk;
W1 & N1 11 pm, Sun 9 pm, SE1 & E14 9 pm, EC3 7 pm, E14 Sun 7 pm;
SE1 & EC3 closed Sat & Sun, N1 closed sun; no Amex; SRA-52%.*

Tosa W6 £41 ❷④④
332 King St 8748 0002 7–2B
*A "friendly" Hammersmith café, offering "great yakitori and other
grills" plus "some interesting Japanese dishes you don't often see".
/ W6 0RR; www.tosauk.com; 10.30 pm.*

Tozi SW1 **NEW** £40 ❷❷❷
8 Gillingham St 7769 9771 2–4B
*"A great addition to Pimlico"; this "friendly" Venetian-influenced small-
plates specialist is a big and bustling venture that manages
to transcend the fact that it's attached to a hotel. / SW1V 1HN;
www.tozirestaurant.co.uk; @ToziRestaurant; 10 pm.*

Tramontana Brindisa EC2 £36 ❸④❸
152-154 Curtain Rd 7749 9961 12–1B
*"A buzzy Shoreditch addition to the Brindisa stable"; it offers "a slight
twist on your typical tapas, with more of a Catalan feel". / EC2A 3AT;
Mon-Sat 11 pm, Sun 9 pm.*

F S A

The Tramshed EC2 £56 ④④❸
32 Rivington St 7749 0478 12–1B
"Eat under the watchful gaze of Damien Hurst's cow!"; Mark Hix's "enormous" grill menu is certainly a "sensational transformation" of a Shoreditch industrial space, but the food – steak or chicken 'n' chips – is no more than "OK", and service can be a bit of a let-down too. / EC2A 3LX; www.chickenandsteak.co.uk.

Trinity SW4 £66 ❶❶❷
4 The Polygon 7622 1199 10–2D
"How lucky are we to have this in our 'hood!"; with its "wonderful" cuisine that's "perfectly balanced, fresh and delicious at every turn" and its "polished" but "friendly" service, Adam Byatt's "unassuming" foodie Mecca, in Clapham, goes "from strength to strength". / SW4 0JG; www.trinityrestaurant.co.uk; @TrinityLondon; 10.30 pm; closed Mon L & Sun D; set weekday L £46 (FP).

Trishna W1 £53 ❷❸❸
15-17 Blandford St 7935 5624 2–1A
The "complex flavours" of "the finest, authentic Indian cooking" – particularly from the tasting menu with wine pairings – again win acclaim for this Marylebone outpost of the famous Mumbai fish restaurant; critics do feel, though, that the setting is "not the most atmospheric". / W1U 3DG; www.trishnalondon.com; @TrishnaLondon; 10.45 pm, Sun 9.45 pm; set pre theatre £38 (FP).

Les Trois Garçons E1 £70 ❸❶❶
1 Club Row 7613 1924 12–1C
"Ravishing" decor that's "as camp as it comes" makes this East End pub-conversion a "magical" destination, which will "amaze any romantic date", and the Gallic fare can be "superb" too… if at a price. / E1 6JX; www.lestroisgarcons.com; @lestroisgarcons; 9.30 pm, 10.30 pm; closed Mon L, Tue L, Wed L, Sat L & Sun; need credit card to book £25 deposit; set weekday L £38 (FP).

La Trompette W4 £65 ❷❷❸
5-7 Devonshire Rd 8747 1836 7–2A
A revamp and expansion have divided opinion on this "Chiswick star", which is historically one of the survey's top performers; for fans it's still "the best example of a fine dining neighbourhood restaurant in town", but doubters say the cooking's "lost wow factor" of late, with service seeming "harassed" too. / W4 2EU; www.latrompette.co.uk; 10.30 pm, Sun 9.30 pm.

Troubadour SW5 £42 ④④❶
263-267 Old Brompton Rd 7370 1434 5–3A
"Bohemian, lively and loud, but still relaxed" – this Earl's Court café/music venue is not a foodie experience, but it's an "amusing" hang-out, and "the ambience is always special". / SW5 9JA; www.troubadour.co.uk; 11 pm.

Trullo N1 £51 ❷❷❷
300-302 St Paul's Rd 7226 2733 8–2D
Jordan Trullo's "skilful" Italian cuisine has helped this Highbury two-year-old quickly become one of north London's foodie hotspots; "a superb compendium of Italian wines", "charming" service and a "lovely" atmosphere add to the all-round appeal. / N1 2LH; www.trullorestaurant.com; 10.30 pm; closed Sun D; no Amex.

Tsunami £48 ❷④④
93 Charlotte St, W1   7637 0050   2–1C
5-7 Voltaire Rd, SW4   7978 1610   10–1D
"Sarf London's answer to Zuma!"; with its "surprisingly complex" Japanese cuisine, this Clapham fixture (with less interesting Fitzrovia spin-off) is a "top-notch" destination; the "tacky" dining room, however, is rather beginning to show its age.
/ www.tsunamirestaurant.co.uk; @Tsunamirest; SW4 10.30 pm, Fri & Sat 11 pm, Sun 9.30 pm; W1 11 pm; SW4 closed Mon - Fri L; W1 closed Sat L and Sun; SW4 no Amex.

28-50 £52 ❸❷❸
15 Maddox St, W1   7495 1505   3–2C **NEW**
15-17 Marylebone Ln, W1   7486 7922   3–1A
140 Fetter Ln, EC4   7242 8877   9–2A
"An unbelievable, affordable wine list" – an "ever-changing selection, available by the glass" – has made a big name for this "classy" chain of "very metropolitan" modern wine bars (from the Texture team); the food offer is "narrow", but the "simple" dishes are "well cooked".
/ www.2850.co.uk; EC4 9.30 pm; W1 Mon-Wed 10 pm, Thu-Sat 10.30 pm, Sun 9.30 pm; EC4 closed Sat-Sun.

2 Amici SW1 £46 ④❸④
48a Rochester Rw   7976 5660   2–4C
A "relaxed", if somewhat unatmospheric, Italian – handy for Westminster locals in a restaurant desert. / SW1P 1JU; www.2amici.org; 11 pm; closed Sat L & Sun.

Two Brothers N3 £41 ❸④④
297-303 Regent's Park Rd   8346 0469   1–1B
"Always long queues" for this famous Finchley chippie (nowadays no longer owned by the two founding brothers); on most accounts, the food offers "incredible value", but a few doubters discern "a lowering of standards" in the last year or so, and say the chips "are no longer the best ever!" / N3 1DP; www.twobrothers.co.uk; 10 pm, Sun 8 pm; closed Mon.

2 Veneti W1 £46 ④❷④
10 Wigmore St   7637 0789   3–1B
This "comfortable" Marylebone Venetian is "handy for the Wigmore Hall", and serves "straightforward" food that's "very consistent", if perhaps "expensive, for what it is". / W1U 2RD; www.2veneti.com; 10.30 pm, Sat 11 pm; closed Sat L & Sun.

Umu W1 £102 ❸④❸
14-16 Bruton Pl   7499 8881   3–2C
"The best kaiseki menu this side of Japan" delivers "a startling array of flavours", say fans of Marlon Abela's "classy" operation, hidden away in a Mayfair mews; even they concede, though, that it might be "cheaper to fly to Kyoto". / W1J 6LX; www.umurestaurant.com; 11 pm; closed Sat L & Sun; no trainers; booking: max 14.

The Union Café W1 £50 ④④④
96 Marylebone Ln   7486 4860   3–1A
It my be "densely-packed" and sometimes rather "noisy", but this Marylebone bistro retains its impressive following; the food, though, is merely "straightforward" – it's the good-value wine which is "the main attraction". / W1U 2QA; www.brinkleys.com; @BrinkleysR; 11 pm; closed Sun D.

Union Jacks £42 ⑤④④
4 Central St Giles Piazza, WC2 3597 7888 4–1B
57 The Market, WC2 awaiting tel 4–3D
217-221 Chiswick High Rd, W4 3617 9988 7–2A
'English pizza' may be "laudable as a patriotic act", but the execution
at Jamie O's latest money-spinner is notably "ramshackle" –
"shocking to pay so much for such astonishingly bad food", say critics.
/ www.unionjacksrestaurants.com; 11 pm, Sun 10.30 pm.

Union Street Café SE1 £48
Harling Hs, Union St 7592 7977 9–4B
Gordon Ramsay's first London début for quite a while belatedly
opened its doors, in Southwark, in late-2013, to a fairly middle-of-the-
road reception from the critics; David Beckham – much touted as a
co-proprietor – seems to have made his excuses shortly before the
launch. / SE1 0BS.

Upstairs SW2 £52 ❷❷❷
89b Acre Ln (door on Branksome Rd) 7733 8855 10–2D
"Behind an anonymous door", in Brixton, a "cool" and "mysterious"
find, seemingly reserved for those "in the know"; "apart from the bill,
it's like the best-ever dinner party", with "inspired" and
"sophisticated" cooking, and "knowledgeable" service too. / SW2 5TN;
www.upstairslondon.com; @Upstairslondon; 9.30 pm, Thu-Sat 10.30 pm;
D only, closed Mon & Sun.

Le Vacherin W4 £57 ❸❸❸
76-77 South Pde 8742 2121 7–1A
"A classic, traditional establishment", which wouldn't look out
of place in 'la France profonde', but which seems quite a find opposite
Acton Green; critics can find the fare a touch "unexciting", though,
and the interior is "closely packed". / W4 5LF; www.levacherin.co.uk;
9.45 pm, Fri & Sat 10.45 pm; closed Mon L.

Vanilla Black EC4 £55 ❸0❸
17-18 Tooks Ct 7242 2622 9–2A
"Outstanding" staff serve up some "unusual" and "exquisite" veggie
dishes at this smart legal-land spot; if there is a criticism, it is that the
cuisine can sometimes seem a little "over-complicated". / EC4A 1LB;
www.vanillablack.co.uk; @vanillablack1; 10 pm; closed Sat L & Sun.

Vapiano W1 £25 ❸❸❸
19-21 Great Portland St 7268 0080 3–1C
"Crazy busy" and sometimes "chaotic" it may be, but – with its
"fresh" fare (pizza, pasta, salads), all "cooked in front of you"
to order – this Continental-style food court, near Oxford Circus,
makes a "great choice for a cheap and tasty meal". / W1W 8QB;
www.vapiano.co.uk; 11 pm, Sun 10 pm.

Vasco & Piero's Pavilion W1 £58 ❷❷❸
15 Poland St 7437 8774 3–1D
"Still going strong, and long may it continue"; this "delightful"
(if "crowded") old-Soho fixture has been in the same ownership for
decades, and its "chummy" staff still serve up Umbrian dishes which
are "simple" but "well-cooked". / W1F 8QE; www.vascosfood.com;
10.15 pm; closed Sat L & Sun.

Veeraswamy W1 £71 ❷❷❷
Victory Hs, 99-101 Regent St   7734 1401   3–3D
"Maybe it is on the tourist route", but London's longest-established Indian restaurant, handily located near Piccadilly Circus, offers a "refined" and "very modern" experience, including some "really fine" cuisine. / W1B 4RS; www.realindianfood.com; 10.30 pm, Sun 10 pm; booking: max 12.

El Vergel SE1 £32 ❷❸❷
132 Webber St   7401 2308   9–4B
"The steak sandwiches are a winner", say fans of this "airy" Borough canteen; more generally, its menu comprises "simple" but "consistently very good" Latino dishes. / SE1 0QL; www.elvergel.co.uk; 2.45pm, Sat-Sun 3.45 pm; closed D, closed Sun; no Amex.

Verru W1 £51 ❷❷❸
69 Marylebone Ln   7935 0858   2–1A
"Baltic cuisine merges with Nordic flavours" to create some "fantastic" dishes at this "small, quiet and professional" two-year-old, in Marylebone. / W1U 2PH; www.verru.co.uk; 10.30 pm; set weekday L £33 (FP).

Vertigo 42
Tower 42 EC2 £66 ⑤④❷
25 Old Broad St   7877 7842   9–2C
Despite all the recent elevated competition, this 42nd-floor City eyrie is "still a great place to see the view and have a glass of fizz"; pity, though, that the food is so "pretentious, pricey and uninspired". / EC2N 1HQ; www.vertigo42.co.uk; @vertigo42bar; 10.45 pm; closed Sat L & Sun; no shorts; booking essential.

Viajante E2 £106 ❷❸❸
Patriot Sq   7871 0461   1–2D
"A real thrill", "unexpected delights", "gastronomic story-telling" – Nuno Mendes's "passionate" Bethnal Green venture inspires lyrical praise; its "quirky" setting may sometimes seem "a little sterile", and the bill can "shock"… but, for many reporters, this is "London's most interesting dining". / E2 9NF; www.viajante.co.uk; 9.30 pm; closed Mon, Tue, Wed L & Thu L; set weekday L £59 (FP).

Il Vicolo SW1 £49 ❸❷④
3-4 Crown Passage   7839 3960   3–4D
Hidden away in a pedestrian lane, this "good, local and friendly" Sicilian is an oddity in the heart of St James's; the worst anyone can say about it is that it makes a "decent fallback". / SW1Y 6PP; www.vicolo.co.uk; 10 pm; closed Sat L & Sun.

The Victoria SW14 £49 ❸❷❸
10 West Temple   8876 4238   10–2A
Handy for Richmond Park, a big and "friendly" East Sheen gastroboozer, where the "imaginative" and "very appealing" dishes are realised "with a sophistication worthy of pricier establishments". / SW14 7RT; www.thevictoria.net; @thevictoria_pub; 10 pm, Sat 10 pm; closed Sun D; no Amex; set weekday L £32 (FP).

Viet W1 £20 ❸④④
34 Greek St   7494 9888   4–3A
A "cheap 'n' cheerful" Soho café, offering "fresh and delicious" Vietnamese scoff, for which you may have to queue; BYO. / W1D 5DJ; 10.30 pm, Fri 11 pm; closed Sun; no Amex; no booking.

Viet Grill E2 £37 ❷④❸
58 Kingsland Rd   7739 6686   12–1B
"The best of the many restaurants in Little Vietnam"; this "lively" and "stylish" Shoreditch spot is "fast-paced, but un-rushed if you want to linger", and its fare is "authentic and of good quality". / E2 8DP; www.vietnamesekitchen.co.uk; 11 pm, Fri & Sat 11.30 pm, Sun 10.30 pm.

Viet Hoa E2 £32 ❷⑤④
70-72 Kingsland Rd   7729 8293   12–1B
"One of the best Vietnamese cafés along Kingsland Road"; this ever-"noisy" EastEnder is once again firing on all cylinders. / E2 8DP; www.viethoarestaurant.co.uk; 11.30 pm.

Vijay NW6 £30 ❸❷④
49 Willesden Ln   7328 1087   1–1B
A decidedly "un-posh" Kilburn survivor, where a "flavour adventure" is pretty much guaranteed, and "at prices so low you could almost be in southern India"; BYO. / NW6 7RF; www.vijayrestaurant.co.uk; 10.45 pm, Fri & Sat 11.45 pm.

Villa Bianca NW3 £60 ⑤④④
1 Perrins Ct   7435 3131   8–2A
In its mega-cute Hampstead sidestreet location, this Italian veteran has long got away with being on the cheesy side; of late, however, even fans have felt that it has become "excessively pricey", and seems to "lack soul". / NW3 1QS; www.villabiancanw3.com; 11.30 pm, Sun 10.30 pm; set weekday L £38 (FP).

Village East SE1 £55
171-173 Bermondsey St   7357 6082   9–4D
This large but "friendly" hang-out takes some credit for helping to make Bermondsey the "buzzy" place it is today; let's hope it emerges stronger than ever from the major refurb that closed it for a major part of 2013. / SE1 3UW; www.villageeast.co.uk; @villageeastse1; 10 pm, Sun 9.30 pm.

Villandry W1 £51 ④④④
170 Gt Portland St   7631 3131   2–1B
It's as a "good business lunch venue" that the dining room of this grand Marylebone deli often finds favour with reporters – foodies may simply bemoan the fact that "the wonderful groceries are not reflected in the dull menus!" / W1W 5QB; www.villandry.com; 10.30 pm; closed Sun D.

The Vincent Rooms
Westminster Kingsway College SW1 £31 ❸❸❸
76 Vincent Sq   7802 8391   2–4C
"Service may depend on which year students are in", at this elegant dining room, which is part of a Westminster catering college; most reporters find playing guinea pig "a delightful experience", and it's not an expensive one. / SW1P 2PD; www.thevincentrooms.com; 7.15 pm; closed Mon D, Tue D, Fri D, Sat & Sun; no Amex.

VQ £46 ④❸④
St Giles Hotel, Great Russell St, WC1   7300 3000   4–1A **NEW**
325 Fulham Rd, SW10   7376 7224   5–3B
A Chelsea fixture; London's original 24/7 restaurant is "pretty good" for somewhere that never sleeps, and breakfast, in particular, is "superb"; as we to go press, a new branch is set to open in Bloomsbury. / www.vingtquatre.co.uk; open 24 hours.

F S A

Vinoteca £44 ④❸❷

15 Seymour Pl, W1   7724 7288   2–2A
55 Beak St, W1   3544 7411   3–2D
18 Devonshire Rd, W4   3701 8822   7–2A **NEW**
7 St John St, EC1   7253 8786   9–1B

"A stunning wine list with fair mark-ups" (and available by the glass too) is the mainstay of these "always packed" (rather "cramped") wine bars; their straightforward food is "a bit more variable" than in the early days, but usually "very decent". / www.vinoteca.co.uk; 11 pm, Seymour Pl Sun 5 pm; EC1 Sun; Seymour Pl Sun D.

Vivat Bacchus £52 ④④④

4 Hay's Ln, SE1   7234 0891   9–4C
47 Farringdon St, EC4   7353 2648   9–2A

The menu may be quite "interesting" (kangaroo anyone?), and there's an "inspirational" selection of cheeses, but "you don't go for the food" to these City-fringe and South Bank bars – it's all about the dazzling array of South African wines. / www.vivatbacchus.co.uk; 9.30 pm; EC4 closed Sat & Sun; SE1 closed Sat L & Sun.

Vrisaki N22 £35 ④❸❸

73 Middleton Rd   8889 8760   1–1C

An "old-favourite" Bounds Green taverna, renowned for its "massive portions" (if, perhaps, favouring "quantity over quality") and "good value" – "ignore the fact that, from outside, it looks like a cheap take-away". / N22 8LZ; 11.30 pm, Sun 9 pm; closed Mon; no Amex.

Wagamama £37 ④❸④

8 Norris St, SW1   7321 2755   4–4A
Harvey Nichols, Knightsbridge, SW1   7201 8000   5–1D
101a Wigmore St, W1   7409 0111   3–1A
10a Lexington St, W1   7292 0990   3–2D
4a Streatham St, WC1   7323 9223   2–1C
1 Tavistock St, WC2   7836 3330   4–3D
14a Irving St, WC2   7839 2323   4–4B
26a Kensington High St, W8   7376 1717   5–1A
N1 Centre, 37 Parkfield St, N1   7226 2664   8–3D
11 Jamestown Rd, NW1   7428 0800   8–3B
Royal Festival Hall, Southbank Centre, SE1   7021 0877   2–3D
50-54 Putney High St, SW15   8785 3636   10–2B
46-48 Wimbledon Hill Rd, SW19   8879 7280   10–2B
Jubilee Place, 45 Bank St, E14   7516 9009   11–1C
1a Ropemaker St, EC2   7588 2688   12–2A
22 Old Broad St, EC2   7256 9992   9–2C
Tower Pl, EC3   7283 5897   9–3D
109 Fleet St, EC4   7583 7889   9–2A
30 Queen St, EC4   7248 5766   9–3B

With their "hustle and bustle", "speedy" service and "large platefuls of freshly prepared Asian fare", these ubiquitous and "cheap" canteens are, for most reporters, "a formula that works" (and "super-friendly to kids"); for some sceptics, however the whole idea is a bit "past its sell-by date". / www.wagamama.com; 10 pm-11 pm; EC4 & EC2 closed Sat & Sun; no booking.

Wahaca £32 ❸❸❷
19-23 Charlotte St, W1   7323 2342   2–1C
80-82 Wardour St, W1   7734 0195   3–2D
66 Chandos Pl, WC2   7240 1883   4–4C
Westfield, Ariel Way, W12   8749 4517   7–1C
68-69 Upper St, N1   3697 7990   8–3D
Southbank Centre, SE1   7928 1876   2–3D
Unit 4, Park Pavilion, 40 Canada Sq, E14   7516 9145   11–1C
6 Chestnut Plaza, Westfield Stratford City, E20   3288 1025   1–1D
"It's an achievement in this country to make Mexican food worth eating", and most reports are full of praise for Thomasina Myers's "fun" and "surprisingly funky" chain, and its array of "street food with a twist"; a "menu update", though, might not go amiss. / www.wahaca.com; WC2 & W1 & E14 11 pm, Sun 10.30 pm; W12 11 pm, Sun 10 pm; no booking; SRA-73%.

The Wallace
The Wallace Collection W1 £56 ❹❺❶
Hertford Hs, Manchester Sq   7563 9505   3–1A
A "surprising" modern atrium behind an 18th-century palazzo provides a "stunning" setting for this Marylebone venue; shame that – with its too often "appalling" service – it can seem such a "missed opportunity". / W1U 3BN; www.thewallacerestaurant.com; Fri & Sat 9.15 pm; Sun-Thu closed D; no Amex.

The Walmer Castle W11 £39 ❸❸❷
58 Ledbury Rd   7229 4620   6–1B
Perennially popular and trendy, this Notting Hill boozer has a dining room "tucked-away" upstairs, which has long served "great Thai food". / W11 2AJ; www.walmercastle.co.uk; 11 pm, Fri & Sat midnight, Sun 10.30 pm.

Wapping Food E1 £51 ❹❹❶
Wapping Power Station, Wapping Wall   7680 2080   11–1A
Surprisingly little feedback on this "amazing" post-industrial Wapping restaurant and art-space – "so unusual it makes a great place to take visitors"; the food can seem a touch "variable", but "lovely" brunches are a highlight, and there are some "good Australian wines" too. / E1W 3SG; www.thewappingproject.com; 10.45 pm; Mon-Fri D only, Sat open L & D, closed Sun D.

Waterloo Bar & Kitchen SE1 £48 ❹❸❹
131 Waterloo Rd   7928 5086   9–4A
"Useful for the Old Vic"; this straightforward eatery may be somewhat "hangar-like", but the food it offers is "reliable" enough, and service is "helpful" too. / SE1 8UR; www.barandkitchen.co.uk; 10.30 pm.

The Waterway W9 £51 ❹❺❸
54 Formosa St   7266 3557   8–4A
The canalside terrace is undoubtedly "outstanding", but this "buzzy" Maida Vale hang-out otherwise inspires some irreconcilable reviews – all the way from "top-notch" to "disastrous and uncaring". / W9 2JU; www.thewaterway.co.uk; 10.30 pm, Sun 10 pm.

The Wells NW3 £47 ❸❸❷
30 Well Walk   7794 3785   8–1A
"A credit to Hampstead" – with a "cosy first-floor" restaurant, and "more bar-like" downstairs, this "very busy and buzzy" tavern makes a "lovely" destination; it offers a "high standard of cooking" too (even for your canine companion!). / NW3 1BX; www.thewellshampstead.co.uk; @WellsHampstead; 10 pm, Sun 9.30 pm; set Sun L £36 (FP).

The Wet Fish Cafe NW6 £46 ❸❷❷
242 West End Ln   7443 9222   1–1B
"In a street full of restaurants no one really wants to go to, this one shines out!" – this "friendly" West Hampstead "hide-away" (in a former fishmongers) is a "reliable" spot any time, but brunch is a particular highlight. / NW6 1LG; www.thewetfishcafe.co.uk; @thewetfishcafe; 10 pm; no Amex.

The Wharf TW11 £47 ④❸❷
22 Manor Rd   8977 6333   1–4A
"A lovely location, overlooking Teddington Lock" is the crown-jewel feature of this large, modern bar/brasserie – a "fun place", offering "good-value set meals". / TW11 8BG; www.thewharfteddington.com; 10 pm; closed Mon L & Tue L.

White Horse SW6 £51 ④④❸
1-3 Parsons Grn   7736 2115   10–1B
Fulham's most famous boozer, the 'Sloaney Pony', "can be very loud", and its "average" pub grub is arguably "too dear"; there's a "great selection of beers", though (plus excellent wines), and few would deny that this is a characterful destination. / SW6 4UL; www.whitehorsesw6.com; 10.30 pm.

White Rabbit N16 NEW £27 ❶❶❷
125 Stoke Newington Church St   3556 3350   1–1C
"A wonderfully refreshing take on the tapas revolution"; this "cool" Stoke Newington newcomer offers a "diverse and continually evolving menu of small plates designed for sharing" – just the trick, for most reporters. / N16 0UH; www.whiterabbitlondon.co.uk; 9.30 pm; D only, closed Mon.

The White Swan EC4 £53 ❸❸❸
108 Fetter Ln   7242 9696   9–2A
A bustling Fleet Street boozer, "transformed a few years ago from humdrum pub to gastronomic treat"; "very sound" cooking is served in the restaurant upstairs (which is completely insulated from the noisy bar below). / EC4A 1ES; www.thewhiteswanlondon.com; 10 pm; closed Sat & Sun.

Whitechapel Gallery Dining Room
Whitechapel Gallery E1 £47 ❸❸❸
77-82 Whitechapel High St   7522 7896   12–2C
This "intimate" café, off the gallery's foyer, serves a "small menu that's well thought-out, and well priced"; "it's not quite the experience you might expect, given Angela Hartnett's involvement, but a welcome addition to the Whitechapel wasteland". / E1 7QX; www.whitechapelgallery.org/dine; 9.30 pm; closed Mon, Tue D & Sun D.

Whits W8 £47 ❷❶❷
21 Abingdon Rd   7938 1122   5–1A
"A warm and personal welcome" from the "wonderful owner" helps make this cute Gallic bistro one of Kensington's "hidden gems"; "come hungry, as portions are generous!" / W8 6AH; www.whits.co.uk; 10.30 pm; D only, closed Mon & Sun.

Whyte & Brown W1 NEW £36
Kingly Ct, Kingly St   3747 9820   3–2C
Chicken every which way – that's the deal at this new all-day restaurant, just off Carnaby Street; early-days press reviews are rather mixed. / W1B 5PW; www.whyteandbrown.com.

Wild Honey W1 £68 ❸④④
12 St George St 7758 9160 3–2C
Sad to record "a dive in quality" at this one-time Mayfair foodie hotspot; the food is still "perfectly enjoyable", but it "doesn't stand out from the crowd" any more, and service can be "hit 'n' miss". / W1S 2FB; www.wildhoneyrestaurant.co.uk; 11 pm, Fri & Sat 11.30 pm, Sun 10 pm.

William Curley £18 ❷❸❸
198 Ebury St, SW1 7730 5522 5–2D
10 Paved Ct, TW9 8332 3002 1–4A
"A truly dangerous place to enter!" – these deluxe chocolatiers, in Belgravia and Richmond, offer a wide choice of enticing treats from the "excellent dessert bar". / www.williamcurley.co.uk; 6.30 pm.

Wiltons SW1 £98 ❸④❷
55 Jermyn St 7629 9955 3–3C
"The best turbot", "excellent Dover sole", "seafood of superb quality" – such are the delicacies which still win a major following for this "civilised" but "absurdly overpriced" bastion of the St James's plutocracy – est 1742, and on this site since 1984. / SW1Y 6LX; www.wiltons.co.uk; 10.30 pm; closed Sat & Sun; jacket required; set pre-theatre £58 (FP), set weekday L £67 (FP).

The Windmill W1 £37 ❸④❸
6-8 Mill St 7491 8050 3–2C
"The best pies in the West End" are the big deal at this well-preserved ancient hostelry, on what's effectively the continuation of Savile Row. / W1S 2AZ; www.windmillmayfair.co.uk; @tweetiepie_w1; 9.30 pm, Sat 4 pm; closed Sat & Sun; no Amex.

The Windsor Castle W8 £42 ④④❷
114 Campden Hill Rd 7243 8797 6–2B
Just off Notting Hill Gate, this ancient pub – named after the landmark once visible from the front door – boasts a snug interior and, as a star attraction, a "very pleasant" garden; the food is "competent", but not really the point. / W8 7AR; www.thewindsorcastlekensington.co.uk; @windsorcastlew8; 10 pm, Sun 9 pm.

Wine Gallery SW10 £46 ④❸❸
47 Hollywood Rd 7352 7572 5–3B
"Lovely" wines buoy the "lively" buzz at John Brinkley's deepest-Chelsea old favourite; not everyone's impressed by the scoff, but the overall package still seems "great value for money". / SW10 9HX; www.brinkleys.com; @BrinkleysR; 11.30 pm; booking: max 12.

The Wine Library EC3 £26 ❺❷❶
43 Trinity Sq 7481 0415 9–3D
"A liquid lunch doesn't come any better" than at this "steadfast favourite" – ancient and "lovely" City cellars where the food (a buffet of pâté and cheese) is "entirely secondary" to "the best wine list in town", sold at "excellent prices"; book. / EC3N 4DJ; www.winelibrary.co.uk; 8 pm, Mon 6 pm; closed Mon D, Sat & Sun.

Wishbone SW9 £18 ❺④④
Brixton Village, Coldharbour Ln 7274 0939 10–2D
This year-old Brixton "chicken shop", from the mega-trendy MEATshop team, is seen by many reporters as a "heinous hipster hang-out" – "loud", "soulless" and "overrated", and "expensive" too! / SW9 8PR; www.wishbonebrixton.co.uk.

Wolfe's WC2 £47 ❸④④
30 Gt Queen St 7831 4442 4–1D
This grand and comfortable Covent Garden diner may seem a bit dated, but fans insist it's still "a good place for a simple meal" – "delicious burgers" a highlight. / WC2B 5BB; www.wolfes-grill.net; @wolfesbargrill; 10 pm, Fri-Sat 10.30 pm, Sun 9 pm.

The Wolseley W1 £59 ❸②❶
160 Piccadilly 7499 6996 3–3C
"Captains of industry rub shoulders with A-listers" at Corbin & King's perennially "exciting" grand café/brasserie, by the Ritz – its "old-school glamour" makes it "great for impressing people"; the "hit 'n' miss" food is not really the point, but absolutely everyone agrees this is the home of "the most glamorous breakfast in town". / W1J 9EB; www.thewolseley.com; midnight, Sun 11 pm; SRA-63%.

Wong Kei W1 £29 ④⑤⑤
41-43 Wardour St 7437 8408 4–3A
The waiters, sadly, are "not quite as rude as they used to be" at this vast and notorious Chinatown fixture; it still serves the same old "cheap 'n' cheerful" chow, though, at "very decent prices". / W1D 6PY; 11.30 pm, Fri & Sat 11.45 pm, Sun 10.30 pm; no credit cards; no booking.

Woodlands £40 ❸④④
37 Panton St, SW1 7839 7258 4–4A
77 Marylebone Ln, W1 7486 3862 2–1A
102 Heath St, NW3 7794 3080 8–1A
"Very reliable"; these low-key veggie stalwarts (part of an international chain) are worth seeking out for "a different take on a standard curry", including "a fine range" of "fresh and flavourful" dishes from South India. / www.woodlandsrestaurant.co.uk; 10 pm; NW3 no L Mon.

Workshop Coffee EC1 £44 ❸❸②
27 Clerkenwell Rd 7253 5754 9–1A
"Another winning Oz-style café"; with its "wonderful array of brunch and lunch dishes", as well as "incredible coffee", this "hip" Clerkenwell two-year-old has quickly won quite a following. / EC1M 5RN; www.workshopcoffee.com; 10 pm; closed Mon D, Sat D & Sun D.

Wright Brothers £52 ②❸②
13 Kingly St, W1 7434 3611 3–2D
11 Stoney St, SE1 7403 9554 9–4C
8 Lamb St, E1 awaiting tel 9–2D **NEW**
"Fabulous fresh oysters" and "perfect fish" have made a smash hit of this "casual", if "cramped", Borough Market bistro, which "oozes atmosphere"; "stick with SE1", however – the grander Soho offshoot is not nearly as well rated. / 10.30 pm, Sun 9 pm; booking: max 8.

XO NW3 £47 ④④④
29 Belsize Ln 7433 0888 8–2A
"A suburban staple where the menu could do with some jazzing up" – this Belsize Park fusion restaurant is "not as good as its siblings" (including the ever-fashionable E&O), and it can seem "a little over-priced" too. / NW3 5AS; www.rickerrestaurants.com; 10.30 pm.

Yalla Yalla   £34   ❸④❸
1 Green's Ct, W1   7287 7663   3–2D
12 Winsley St, W1   7637 4748   3–1C
186 Shoreditch High St, E1   07725841372   8–3C
"Brilliant flavours in dishes it's fun to share" still win rave reviews for
this Lebanese street food chain; feedback was less enthusiastic this
year, though, with the "very small" original branch – "down a Soho
porn alley" – remaining reporters' favourite. / www.yalla-yalla.co.uk;
Green's Court 11 pm, Sun 10 pm; Winsley Street 11.30 pm, Sat 11 pm;
W1 Sun.

Yashin   £82   ❶❸❸
117-119 Old Brompton Rd, SW7   awaiting tel   5–2B **NEW**
1a, Argyll Rd, W8   7938 1536   5–1A
The "sensational" sushi and other "refined" Japanese fare are
"like works of modern art", say fans of this Manhattan-esque
(and quite un-Japanese) Kensington two-year-old; the prices, however,
"will make your eyes water more than the wasabi"; a new spin-off,
'Ocean House', opened in late-2013. / www.yashinsushi.com; 11 pm.

Yauatcha W1   £68   ❶④❷
Broadwick Hs, 15-17 Broadwick St   7494 8888   3–2D
"Exemplary" dim sum and "fabulous" cocktails remain unchanging
features at this "night-clubby" Soho mainstay (as, sadly, does the
"strict table turning" policy); the "blingy", "oligarch-chic" basement
is generally preferred to the ground floor. / W1F 0DL; www.yauatcha.com;
11.15 pm, Sun 10.30 pm.

The Yellow House SE16   £43   ❷❷④
126 Lower Rd   7231 8777   11–2A
A popular Rotherhithe local where the "passionate" cooking
"just keeps getting better"; highlights – "brilliant" pizza from a wood-
fired oven… and "home-made fudge that's out of this world!"
/ SE16 2UE; www.theyellowhouse.eu; @theyellowhousejazz; 10.30 pm,
Sun 9.30 pm; closed Mon, Tue–Sat closed L, Sun open L & D.

Yi-Ban E16   £44   ❸❸④
London Regatta Centre, Royal Albert Dock   7473 6699   11–1D
The setting may feel a bit "tired" nowadays, but this bizarrely-located
Docklands Chinese can offer some "great" food (including dim
sum)… and you do get to watch the planes taking off and landing
at London City Airport. / E16 2QT; www.yi-ban.co.uk; 10.45 pm.

Yipin China N1   £41   ❶❷⑤
70-72 Liverpool Rd   7354 3388   8–3D
"The surroundings are very stark, but it doesn't matter, as the focus
is the food", at this "amazing" Chinese yearling, in Islington, serving
"wonderful and different" Hunan/Sichuan cuisine at a fraction
of prices in the West End. / N1 0QD; www.yipinchina.co.uk.

Yming W1   £44   ❷❷④
35-36 Greek St   7734 2721   4–2A
"Always a star for 30 years" – Christine Yau's "calm" and "rock-solid"
Soho Chinese "marches serenely on", and head waiter William
"always has a warm welcome"; main complaint about the
"consistently high-quality food"? – it's "too good to be so cheap!"
/ W1D 5DL; www.yminglondon.com; 11.45 pm.

Yo Sushi £28 ⑤⑤④
Branches throughout London
"I only go because my children beg to see the conveyor belt!" –
this gimmicky chain is definitely a hit with kids; but *"gourmet it ain't"*,
and too many critics decry *"shocking"* food as part of a *"grim"*
overall experience. / www.yosushi.co.uk; 10.30 pm; no booking.

Yoisho W1 £44 ②④⑤
33 Goodge St 7323 0477 2–1C
"Excellent" dishes come *"thick and fast"* at this *"utterly authentic"*
izakaya-style Fitzrovia Japanese – just as well, as service is *"so-so"*,
and the décor *"appallingly shabby"*. / W1T 2PS; 10.30 pm; D only, closed
Sun; no Amex.

York & Albany NW1 £57 ④④④
127-129 Parkway 7388 3344 8–3B
A potentially *"classy"* operation, in an imposing former boozer near
Regent's Park; sadly, however, it has *"gone downhill"*, and is now
just *"another example of overpriced and average food, riding on the
back of Gordon Ramsay's name"*. / NW1 7PS; www.gordonramsay.com;
10.30 pm, Sun 8 pm.

Yoshino W1 £43 ③①⑤
3 Piccadilly Pl 7287 6622 3–3D
Perhaps it's *"not as good as in its distant heyday"*, but this *"austere"*
spot, hidden away in a Piccadilly side-alley, still serves up a decidedly
genuine Japanese formula, including *"tasty"* fare (with *"delicious"*
sushi) at *"reasonable prices"*. / W1J 0DB; www.yoshino.net; 10 pm;
closed Sun.

Young Turks at the Ten Bells E1 £50 ③①③
84 Commercial St 492986 12–2C
Above a Shoreditch pub, an *"achingly cool"* ex-pop-up, whose *"smart
and inventive"* dishes are *"consistently good and interesting"*;
"the front-of-house staff are great" too – *"not so hip they can't
be nice and friendly"*. / E1 6LY; www.tenbells.com; 11 pm; closed
Mon & Sun D; no Amex.

Yum Yum N16 £39 ②③②
187 Stoke Newington High St 7254 6751 1–1D
"A go-to destination when you need a good Thai" – this large Stoke
Newington fixture still generates pretty consistent reports... but they
have been surprisingly few in number of late. / N16 0LH;
www.yumyum.co.uk; @yumyum; 10.30 pm, Fri & Sat 11.30 pm; set weekday L
£24 (FP).

Zafferano SW1 £71 ③③④
15 Lowndes St 7235 5800 5–1D
This once-famous Belgravia Italian can still offer some *"lovely"* dishes,
and is still a *"favourite"* for some reporters; in spite of the *"eye-
watering"* bills, however, its no longer the culinary destination it once
was, and the room, since its enlargement, has lost much of its former
charm. / SW1X 9EY; www.zafferanorestaurant.com; 11 pm, Sun 10.30 pm.

Zaffrani N1 £44 ②②②
47 Cross St 7226 5522 8–3D
A *"charming"* Islington Indian, *"off the Upper Street beaten track"*,
which all reports praise for its *"sophisticated"* cuisine – *"it satisfies all
five flavour centres, rather than carpet bombing them in cream
or chilli"*. / N1 2BB; www.zaffrani-islington.co.uk; 10.30 pm.

Zaika W8 £66 ❷❸❸
1 Kensington High St   7795 6533   5–1A
"Sophisticated Indian fine dining" is to be found at this "spacious" former banking hall, in Kensington, (even if the odd "stumble" was not unknown this year); fans find the interior "magnificent", but it "helps the ambience considerably when it's full". / W8 5NP; www.zaika-restaurant.co.uk; 10.45 pm, Sun 9.45 pm; closed Mon L; set weekday L £43 (FP).

Zayna W1 £52 ❷❷④
25 New Quebec St   7723 2229   2–2A
"Not your usual curry!"; "great twists" on North Indian and Pakistani dishes win praise for this low-key outfit near Marble Arch; "make sure you sit upstairs". / W1H 7SF; www.zaynarestaurant.co.uk; 11.15 pm, Fri & Sat 11.45 pm.

Zero Degrees SE3 £42 ❸④④
29-31 Montpelier Vale   8852 5619   1–4D
"The food is better than you'd expect", at this buzzy (if slightly "clinical") Blackheath microbrewery, where "reliable" pizzas and moules-frites complement the "excellent" home brews. / SE3 0TJ; www.zerodegrees.co.uk; midnight, Sun 11.30 pm.

Ziani's SW3 £51 ❸❷❷
45 Radnor Walk   7351 5297   5–3C
"Tables are crowded, the food can be average, but you always have a good time!" – this "squashed" and "noisy" Chelsea Italian is a "long-standing local favourite"; prepare, though, for service that can be "almost too speedy"! / SW3 4BP; www.ziani.co.uk; 11 pm, Sun 10.30 pm.

Zizzi £46 ④④④
Branches throughout London
"Generally OK, and you know what you will get" – this "decent, if unspectacular" pizza chain remains a useful stand-by for most reporters, especially those with kids in tow. / www.zizzi.co.uk; 11 pm.

Zoilo W1 NEW £50 ❷❷④
9 Duke St   7486 9699   3–1A
Not far from Selfridges, a new Argentinian small-plates specialist, which includes "an interesting selection of wine" and "delightful" service among its attractions; some reporter, though, find conditions "overcrowded" and "awkward". / W1U 3EG; www.zoilo.co.uk; @Zoilo_London; 10.30 pm, Sun 9.30 pm.

Zucca SE1 £49 ❶❷❷
184 Bermondsey St   7378 6809   9–4D
"London's best Italian" – Sam Harris's "phenomenal" Bermondsey three-year-old is "on a par with the River Café" yet "at a fraction of the cost"; it's a surprisingly "civilised" experience too (for which you must book months ahead). / SE1 3TQ; www.zuccalondon.com; 10 pm; closed Mon & Sun D; no Amex.

Zuma SW7 £80 ❶❸❷
5 Raphael St   7584 1010   5–1C
"WAGs and men with mortgageable wrist watches" help power the "great vibe" at this "sexy" Mayfair canteen; "although the people-watching is enjoyable", though, it's "quickly forgotten" with the arrival of "divine" Japanese-fusion fare that's still amongst London's best. / SW7 1DL; www.zumarestaurant.com; 10.45 pm, Sun 10.15 pm; booking: max 8.

INDEXES

BREAKFAST
(with opening times)

Central

Abokado:WC2 (7.30)
Al Duca (9)
Amaranto (6.30, Sun 7)
Apsleys (7)
aqua nueva (Sun brunch 12 pm)
Asia de Cuba (7)
Athenaeum (7)
Aubaine:W1 (8, Sat 10)
Automat (Mon-Fri 7.30)
Baker & Spice:SW1 (7)
Balans: all central branches (8)
Bar Italia (6.30)
Bentley's (Mon-Fri 7.30)
Benugo: all central branches (7.30)
Bistro 1: Beak St W1 (Sun 11)
Black & Blue: Berners St W1 (9)
The Botanist (8, Sat & Sun 9)
La Bottega: Eccleston St SW1 (8, Sat & Sun 9);
    Lower Sloane St SW1 (8, Sat 9, Sun 10)
Boulevard (9)
Brasserie Max (7)
Browns (Albemarle) (7, Sun 7.30)
Browns:WC2 (9, 10 Sat & Sun)
Café Bohème (8, Sat & Sun 9)
Café in the Crypt (Mon-Sat 8)
Caffé Vergnano:WC1 (6.30 am, Sun 8.30
    am);WC2 (8, Sun 11)
Canteen:W1 (8, Sat & Sun 9)
Cecconi's (7 am, Sat & Sun 8 am)
Christopher's (Sat & Sun 11.30)
The Cinnamon Club (Mon-Fri 7.30)
Comptoir Libanais:Wigmore
    St W1 (8.30); Broadwick St W1 (8 am)
Côte:W1 (8, Sat & Sun 10)
The Courtauld Gallery Café (10)
Cut (7am, Sat & Sun 7.30 am)
Daylesford Organic:SW1 (8, Sun 10)
Dean Street Townhouse (Mon-Fri
    7, Sat-Sun 8)
The Delaunay (7, Sat & Sun 11)
Diner:W1 (10, Sat & Sun 9);
    WC2 (9.30 am)
Dishoom:WC2 (8, Sat & Sun 10)
Dorchester Grill (7, Sat & Sun 8)
Ed's Easy Diner: Sedley Pl, 14 Woodstock
    St W1 (Sat 9.30 am)
Fernandez & Wells: Beak St W1 (7.30,
    sat& sun 9); Lexington St W1 (7 am);
    St Anne's Ct W1 (8, sat 10);WC2 (8am, sat-
    sun 9am)
Flat White (8, Sat & Sun 9)
Fleet River Bakery (7, Sat 9)
The Fountain (Fortnum's) (7.30,
    Sun 11)
Franco's (7, Sat 8)
La Fromagerie Café (8, Sat & Sun 10)
Fuzzy's Grub: SW1 (7)
Gelupo (Sat & Sun 12)
Giraffe:W1 (7.45, Sat & Sun 9)
The Goring Hotel (7, Sun 7.30)
Grazing Goat (7.30)
Hélène Darroze (Sat 11)
Homage (7)
Hush:WC1 (8 am)
Indigo (6.30)
Inn the Park (8, Sat & Sun 9)
JW Steakhouse (6.30, Sat & Sun 7)
Kaffeine (7.30, Sat 8.30, Sun 9.30)

Kaspar's Seafood and Grill (7)
Kazan (Cafe):Wilton Rd SW1 (8 am,
    Sun 9 am)
Konditor & Cook:WC1 (9.30);W1 (9.30,
    Sun 10.30)
Kopapa (8.30, Sat & Sun 10)
Ladurée:W1 (9); SW1 (Mon - Sat
    9, Sun noon - 1.30)
Lantana Cafe (8, Sat & Sun 9)
Leon:WC2 (7.30, Sat 9, Sun 10);
    Gt Marlborough St W1 (9.30, Sat & Sun
    10.30)
Maison Bertaux (8.30, Sun 9.15)
maze Grill (6.45)
Monmouth Coffee Company:WC2 (8)
The National Dining Rooms (10)
National Gallery Café (8, Sat & Sun 10)
Natural Kitchen:W1 (8, Sat 9, Sun 11)
Nopi (8, Sat & Sun 10)
Nordic Bakery: Dorset St W1 (8 am, Sat-
    Sun 9); Golden Sq W1 (Mon-Fri 8, Sat 9,
    Sun 11)
The Northall (6, Sat & Sun 7)
Noura:William St SW1 (8)
One-O-One (8)
The Only Running Footman (7.30,
    Sat & Sun 9.30)
The Orange (8)
Oscar (7, Sun 8)
Ottolenghi: SW1 (8, Sun 9)
Ozer (8)
The Pantechnicon (Sat & Sun 9)
Paramount (8)
Paul:WC2 (7.30);W1 (7.30, Sat & Sun 8)
The Portrait (10)
Princi (8, 8.30)
Providores (Tapa Room) (9, Sat
    & Sun 10)
Ranoush: SW1 (9)
Refuel (7, Sun 8)
Rib Room (7, Sun 8)
RIBA Café (8)
Riding House Café (7.30, Sat & Sun 9)
The Ritz Restaurant (7, Sun 8)
Roux at the Landau (8)
Royal Academy (10)
Scandinavian Kitchen (8, Sat & Sun 10)
Simpsons-in-the-Strand (Mon-Fri 7.30)
The Sketch (Parlour) (Mon-Fri 8, Sat 10)
Sophie's Steakhouse: all branches (Sat &
    Sun 11)
Sotheby's Café (9.30)
Spice Market (7, Sat & Sun 8)
Stock Pot: SW1 (9.30)
Tate Britain (Rex Whistler) (Sat-
    Sun 10)
Taylor St Baristas:W1 (8 am)
Thirty Six (7)
tibits (9, Sun 11.30)
Tom's Kitchen:WC2 (Sat & Sun 10)
The Union Café (Sat & Sun 11)
Villandry (Sat 8 am, Sun 9 am)
The Wallace (10)
William Curley: all branches (9.30,
    Sun 10.30)
Wolfe's (9)
The Wolseley (7, Sat & Sun 8)
Yalla Yalla: Green's Ct W1 (Sat-Sun 10)

West

Adams Café (7.30 am)
Angelus (10)

Annie's: W4 *(Tue - Thu 10, Fri & Sat 10.30, Sun 10)*
Aubaine: SW3 *(8, Sun 9)*; W8 *(Mon-Sat 8 am, 9 am Sun)*
Baker & Spice: *all west branches (7, Sun 8)*
Balans West: SW5, W4, W8 *(8)*
Bedlington Café *(8.30)*
Beirut Express: W2 *(7)*
Benugo: W12 *(9)*
Best Mangal: SW6 *(10-12)*
Bluebird Café *(8)*
La Brasserie *(8)*
Bumpkin: SW7 *(11 am)*
Bush Dining Hall *(Tue-Fri 8.30 am)*
The Cabin *(Fri 12, Sat 11, Sun 10)*
Chelsea Bun Diner *(7, Sun 9)*
The Chelsea Kitchen *(Sun 8)*
Comptoir Libanais: SW7 *(8.30 am)*; W12 *(9.30)*
Daylesford Organic: W11 *(8, Sun 11)*
Ffiona's *(Sat & Sun 10)*
Gail's Bread: W11 *(7, Sat & Sun 8)*
Gallery Mess *(Sat & Sun 10)*
Geales Chelsea Green: SW3 *(9 am Sat & Sun)*
Giraffe: W4, W8 *(7.45, Sat & Sun 9)*; W11 *(8, Sat & Sun 9)*
Granger & Co *(7)*
The Hampshire Hog *(8, Sat& Sun 9)*
The Henry Root *(Sat & Sun 9)*
High Road Brasserie *(7, Sat & Sun 8)*
Joe's Brasserie *(Sat & Sun 11)*
Julie's *(10)*
Kensington Square Kitchen *(8, Sun 9.30)*
Lisboa Pâtisserie *(7)*
Lola & Simón *(8, Sat & Sun 9.30)*
Lucky Seven *(Mon noon, Tue-Thu 10, Fri-Sun 9)*
Mona Lisa *(7)*
Ottolenghi: W11 *(8, Sun 8.30)*
Pappa Ciccia: Fulham High St SW6 *(7 am)*
Pizza East Portobello: W10 *(8)*
PJ's Bar and Grill *(Sat & Sun 10)*
Ranoush: W8 *(10)*; W2 *(9)*; SW3 *(noon)*
Raoul's Café & Deli: W11 *(8.30)*; W9 *(8.30 am)*
Il Ristorante *(9)*
Sam's Brasserie *(9)*
Sophie's Steakhouse: *all branches (Sat & Sun 11)*
Stock Pot: SW3 *(8)*
Tom's Deli *(8, Sun 9)*
Tom's Kitchen: SW3 *(8, Sat & Sun 10)*
Troubadour *(9)*
VQ: SW10 *(24 hrs)*
The Waterway *(10 Sat & Sun)*
White Horse *(9.30)*

North

The Almeida *( )*
Assiette Anglaise *(Sat-Sun 9 am)*
Banners *(9, Sat & Sun 10)*
Benito's Hat: N1 *(7 am)*
Blue Legume: N1 *(8.30 am)*; N16 *(9.30)*
The Clissold Arms *(Mon-Sat 9 am)*
Diner: N1, NW10 *(sat, sun 9)*
Dirty Burger: NW5 *(Mon-Thu 7, Sat & Sun 9)*
The Engineer *(9)*
Euphorium Bakery *(7.30, Sun 9)*
Gail's Bread: NW3 *(7, Sat & Sun 8)*

Gallipoli: Upper St N1, Upper St N1 *(10.30)*
Garufa *(10)*
Gilbert Scott *(Mon-Fri 10)*
Ginger & White: *all branches (7.30, Sat & Sun 8.30)*
Giraffe: N1, Rosslyn Hill NW3 *(7.45, Sat & Sun 9)*; Haverstock Hill NW3 *(8, Sat & Sun 9)*
Harry Morgan's *(9)*
Juniper Dining *(Sat 10)*
Kentish Canteen *(10, Sat & Sun 9)*
Kenwood (Brew House) *(9)*
Kipferl *(9, Sun 10)*
Landmark (Winter Gdn) *(7)*
Made In Camden *(Mon-Fri 9.30)*
Ottolenghi: N1 *(8, Sun 9)*
Rugoletta *(10)*
St Pancras Grand *(7, Sun 9)*
Sweet Thursday *(Sat-Sun 9.30 am)*
The Wet Fish Cafe *(10)*
York & Albany *(7)*

South

Abbeville Kitchen *(Sat & Sun 9)*
Annie's: SW13 *(Tue-Sun 10)*
The Bingham *(7, Sat-Sun 8)*
Bistro Union *(Sat & Sun 9.30)*
The Bolingbroke *(Sat & Sun 10)*
Brasserie Toulouse-Lautrec *(11, Sat & Sun 10)*
Browns: SE1 *(11 am)*
Brunswick House Cafe *(8am, Sat & Sun 10am)*
Buenos Aires Café: SE10 *(7.30 am)*
Butcher & Grill *(8.30)*
Caffé Vergnano: SE1 *(8, Sat & Sun 11)*
Canteen: SE1 *(8, Sat & Sun 9)*
Chapters *(8, Sun 9)*
The Depot *(Sat 9.30)*
Dirty Burger: SW8 *(Mon-Thu 7, Sat 9, Sun 10)*
Eco *(Sat & Sun 9)*
Elliot's Cafe *(7)*
Fat Boy's: TW8 *(Mon-Fri 11.30)*
fish! *(Thu-Sat 8, Sun 10)*
Florence *(Sat 11)*
Franklins *(Sat 10)*
Frizzante Cafe *(10)*
Garrison *(8, Sat & Sun 9)*
Gastro *(8)*
Gazette: SW12 *(7)*; SW11 *(8)*
Giraffe: SE1 *(7.45, Sat & Sun 9)*
Harrison's *(Sat & Sun 9)*
Hudsons *(9.30, Sat & Sun 9)*
Joanna's *(10)*
Konditor & Cook: *all south branches (7.30 am)*
The Lido Cafe *(9)*
Lola Rojo *(Sat & Sun 11)*
Monmouth Coffee Company: SE1 *(7.30)*
Orange Pekoe *(8.30)*
Le P'tit Normand *(Sun 9)*
Pantry *(8, Sat 8.30 & Sun 9)*
Petersham Hotel *(Mon-Fri 7, Sat & Sun 8)*
Plane Food *(5.30)*
The Riverfront *(9, Sun 10)*
Rivington Grill: SE10 *(Thurs-Sun 10)*
Roast *(7, Sat 8)*
San Lorenzo Fuoriporta *(10, Sun 10.30)*

Mango Tree: *Grosvenor Pl SW1*
Marcus Wareing
MASH Steakhouse
Massimo
Matsuri
maze Grill
Miyama
Mon Plaisir
Murano
Nobu
The Northall
One-O-One
Orrery
Oscar
Osteria Dell'Angolo
The Palm
The Pantechnicon
Paramount
Pétrus
Pied à Terre
Quilon
Quirinale
Quo Vadis
Refuel
Rib Room
RIBA Café
Roka: *all branches*
Roux at Parliament Square
Roux at the Landau
Rules
Santini
Sartoria
Savoy Grill
Scott's
J Sheekey
Simpsons-in-the-Strand
The Square
Tamarind
Theo Randall
Thirty Six
2 Veneti
Veeraswamy
Il Vicolo
The Wallace
Wild Honey
Wiltons
The Wolseley
Zafferano

West
Bibendum
The Frontline Club
Gaucho: *all branches*
Gordon Ramsay
The Ledbury
Manicomio: *all branches*
Outlaw's Seafood and Grill
Poissonnerie de l'Avenue
Racine
Sam's Brasserie
Tom Aikens
La Trompette
Zuma

North
Frederick's
Gaucho: *all branches*
Landmark (Winter Gdn)
Rotunda Bar & Restaurant
St Pancras Grand

South
Blueprint Café
Butlers Wharf Chop House
Gaucho: *all branches*
The Glasshouse
Hutong
Magdalen
Oblix
Oxo Tower (Brass')
Oxo Tower (Rest')
Le Pont de la Tour
Roast
Skylon
Vivat Bacchus: *all branches*
Zucca

East
Alba
L'Anima
Barbecoa
Bevis Marks
Bleeding Heart
Boisdale of Canary Wharf
Bonds
Café du Marché
Chamberlain's
The Chancery
Chinese Cricket Club
Chiswell Street Dining Rms
Cinnamon Kitchen
City Miyama
Club Gascon
Coq d'Argent
Dockmaster's House
The Don
Eyre Brothers
Fish Market
Forman's
The Fox and Anchor
Galvin La Chapelle
Gaucho: *all branches*
Goodman: *all branches*
Gow's
Hawksmoor: *all branches*
High Timber
The Hoxton Grill
Imperial City
Lutyens
Manicomio: *all branches*
The Mercer
Moro
New Street Grill
1901
One Canada Square
1 Lombard Street
Paternoster Chop House
Plateau
Portal
Refettorio
Roka: *all branches*
The Royal Exchange Grand Café
St John
Sauterelle
Smiths (Top Floor)
Smiths (Dining Rm)
Sweetings
Taberna Etrusca
28-50: *EC4*
Vertigo 42
Vivat Bacchus: *all branches*
The White Swan

BYO

*(Bring your own wine at no
or low – less than £3 – corkage.
Note for £5-£15 per bottle,
you can normally negotiate
to take your own wine to many,
if not most, places.)*

Central

Cyprus Mangal
Food for Thought
Fryer's Delight
Golden Hind
India Club
Patogh
Ragam
Viet

West

Adams Café
Alounak: *all branches*
Bedlington Café
Café 209
Chelsea Bun Diner
Faanoos: *all branches*
Fez Mangal
Fitou's Thai Restaurant
Miran Masala
Mirch Masala: *all branches*
Pappa Ciccia: *Munster Rd SW6*

North

Ali Baba
Chutneys
Diwana Bhel-Poori House
Huong-Viet
Jai Krishna
Rugoletta
Toff's
Vijay

South

Amaranth
Apollo Banana Leaf
Cah-Chi: *all branches*
Faanoos: *all branches*
Hot Stuff
Kaosarn: *SW9*
Lahore Karahi
Lahore Kebab House: *all branches*
Mien Tay: *all branches*
Mirch Masala: *all branches*
The Paddyfield
Sree Krishna
Thai Corner Café

East

Lahore Kebab House: *all branches*
Little Georgia Café: *E2*
Mangal 1
Mien Tay: *all branches*
Mirch Masala: *all branches*
Needoo
Rochelle Canteen
Tayyabs

CHILDREN

*(h – high or special chairs
m – children's menu
p – children's portions
e – weekend entertainments
o – other facilities)*

Central

A Wong *(h)*
Abeno: *WC2 (h); WC1 (hm)*
About Thyme *(hp)*
Al Duca *(hp)*
Al Hamra *(hp)*
Al Sultan *(hp)*
Albannach *(hmp)*
All Star Lanes: *all branches (hm)*
Alloro *(p)*
Alyn Williams *(hp)*
Amaranto *(hm)*
Ametsa with Arzak Instruction *(h)*
Apsleys *(hp)*
aqua nueva *(p)*
Arbutus *(hp)*
Asadal *(h)*
Asia de Cuba *(hp)*
L'Atelier de Joel Robuchon *(hp)*
Athenaeum *(m)*
Aubaine: *all branches (h)*
Automat *(h)*
L'Autre Pied *(hp)*
Axis *(hmp)*
Babbo *(hp)*
Balans: *all central branches (hm)*
The Balcon *(hmp)*
Bank Westminster *(hp)*
Bar Boulud *(hp)*
Bar Italia *(hp)*
Il Baretto *(hp)*
Barrica *(p)*
Bar Shu *(h)*
Beiteddine *(p)*
Belgo Centraal: *Earlham
    St WC2 (hm); Kingsway WC2 (m)*
Bellamy's *(hp)*
Benares *(h)*
Benihana: *W1 (hm)*
Benito's Hat: *Goodge St W1 (hp)*
Bentley's *(h)*
Bincho Yakitori *(hp)*
Bocca Di Lupo *(hp)*
Bodean's: *W1 (ehm)*
La Bodega Negra *(hp)*
Bonnie Gull *(hp)*
The Botanist *(h)*
Boudin Blanc *(hp)*
Boulevard *(hm)*
Brasserie Chavot *(hp)*
Brasserie Max *(hp)*
Brasserie Zédel *(hp)*
Briciole *(hp)*
Browns (Albemarle) *(hmp)*
Browns: *W1, WC2 (hm)*
Byron: *Wellington St WC2 (hm)*
C London *(hp)*
Café Bohème *(h)*
Café des Amis *(h)*
Café in the Crypt *(hp)*
Café Pacifico *(hm)*
Caffè Caldesi *(hp)*
Caffè Vergnano: *WC1 (hm); WC2 (p)*
Cantina Laredo *(hm)*

221

ENTERTAINMENT
(Check times before you go)

LATE
(open till midnight or later as shown; may be earlier Sunday)

Circus *(midnight, Fri & Sat 2 am)*
Côte: *W1 (Thu-Sat midnight)*
Dean Street Townhouse *(Fri & Sat midnight)*
The Delaunay
Le Deuxième
Diner: *W1 (12.30 am, Sun midnight)*
Dishoom: *WC2 (Fri & Sat midnight)*
Downtown Mayfair
Ed's Easy Diner: *Rupert St W1, Moor St W1 (midnight, Fri & Sat 1 am)*
Gaby's
Gelupo *(Thu-Sat 12.30 am)*
Hakkasan: *Hanway Pl W1 (12.30 am, not Sun)*
Harbour City *(Fri & Sat midnight)*
Hard Rock Café
Inamo: *SW1 (Fri & Sat 12.30 am)*
Indali Lounge
Joe Allen *(Fri & Sat 12.45 am)*
Levant *(Fri & Sat midnight)*
Maroush: *W1 (12.30 am)*
MEATLiquor *(Fri & Sat 1 am)*
Carom at Meza *(2 am, Thu-Sat 3 am)*
Mr Kong *(2.45 am, Sun 1.45 am)*
New Mayflower *(4 am)*
ping pong: *Gt Marlborough St W1, Paddington St W1*
La Porchetta Pizzeria: *WC1 (Sat & Sun midnight)*
Princi
Ranoush: *SW1*
Refuel
Rossopomodoro: *WC2*
San Carlo Cicchetti
J Sheekey
J Sheekey Oyster Bar
Shoryu Ramen: *W1*
Sofra: *all branches*
Sophie's Steakhouse: *all branches (12.45 am, not Sun)*
VQ: *all branches (24 hours)*
The Wolseley

West
Anarkali
Balans: *W8 ; SW5 (2 am)*
Basilico: *SW6*
Beirut Express: *SW7 ; W2 (2 am)*
Best Mangal: *SW6 ; North End Rd W14 (midnight, Sat 1 am)*
Buona Sera: *all branches*
El Ieven Park Walk
Gifto's *(Sat & Sun midnight)*
Halepi
Jam Tree: *SW6 (Fri & Sat 2 am)*
Khan's *(Sat & Sun midnight)*
Maroush: *I) 21 Edgware Rd W2 (1.45 am); VI) 68 Edgware Rd W2 (12.30 am); SW3 (3.30 am)*
Mirch Masala: *all branches*
Monty's: *W5*
Il Pagliaccio
ping pong: *W2*
Pizza East Portobello: *W10 (Fri & Sat midnight)*
Ciro's (Pizza Pomodoro) *(1 am)*
Ranoush: *SW3 ; W8 (1.30 am); W2 (2.30 am)*
Rossopomodoro: *all west branches*
The Sands End *(Thu-Sat midnight)*
Shilpa *(Thu-Sat midnight)*

Sophie's Steakhouse: *all branches (12.45 am, not Sun)*
The Thatched House *(Thu-Sat midnight)*
VQ: *all branches (24 hours)*
The Walmer Castle *(Fri & Sat midnight)*

North
Ali Baba
Banners *(Fri & Sat midnight)*
Basilico: *N1, NW3*
Bistro Aix
Chilango: *N1 (Fri & Sat midnight)*
Diner: *N1*
Dirty Burger: *NW5 (Mon-Thu midnight, Fri & Sat 1 am)*
Gallipoli: *all branches (Fri & Sat midnight)*
Gem *(Fri & Sat midnight)*
Mangal II *(1 am)*
Meat Mission
Mem & Laz *(Fri & Sat midnight)*
Le Mercury *(12.30 am, not Sun)*
Pizzeria Pappagone
La Porchetta Pizzeria: *NW1 (Fri & Sat midnight); N4 (Sat & Sun midnight); N1 (weekends midnight)*
Yum Yum *(Fri & Sat midnight)*

South
The Balham Bowls Club *(Fri & Sat midnight)*
Basilico: *all south branches*
Belgo: *SW4 (midnight, Thu 1 am, Fri & Sat 2 am)*
Boqueria *(Fri & Sat midnight)*
Buona Sera: *all branches*
Caffè Vergnano: *SE1*
Cah-Chi: *SW18 (not Sat & Sun)*
Champor-Champor
Dirty Burger: *SW8 (Fri & Sat 2 am)*
Everest Inn
Fish in a Tie
Gastro
Indian Moment *(Fri & Sat midnight)*
Lahore Karahi
Lahore Kebab House: *all branches*
Mirch Masala: *all branches*
Nazmins
Tandoori Nights *(Fri & Sat midnight)*
Tsunami: *SW4 (Fri-Sun midnight)*
Zero Degrees

East
Brick Lane Beigel Bake *(24 hours)*
Cellar Gascon
The Diner: *EC2 (not Sun & Mon)*
Elephant Royale *(Fri & Sat midnight)*
The Jugged Hare *(Thu-Sat midnight)*
Lahore Kebab House: *all branches*
Mangal I *(midnight, Sat-Sun 1 am)*
Mirch Masala: *all branches*
Pizza East: *E1 (Thu midnight, Fri & Sat 1 am)*
La Porchetta Pizzeria: *EC1 (Sat & Sun midnight)*
Rocket: *E14*
Sushisamba *(midnight, Fri & Sat 1 am)*
Wapping Food

The Peasant
E Pellicci
Pilpel: *Brushfield Street, London E1*
Plateau
Portal
Relais de Venise L'Entrecôte: *EC2*
Le Rendezvous du Café
Rochelle Canteen
Royal China: *E14*
Santore
Smiths (Top Floor)
Smiths (Ground Floor)
Spianata & Co: *E1*
Taberna Etrusca
Vinoteca: *EC1*
Wapping Food

PRIVATE ROOMS

**(for the most comprehensive
listing of venues for functions –
from palaces to pubs – visit
www.hardens.com/party, or buy
*Harden's London Party, Event
& Conference Guide*, available
in all good bookshops)
* particularly recommended**

Central
A Wong *(30)*
About Thyme *(40)*
Al Hamra *(24)*
Alain Ducasse *(7,12,30)*
Albannach *(20)*
Alloro *(16)*
Alyn Williams *(18,8)*
Amaranto *(8)*
Amaya *(14)*
Ametsa with Arzak Instruction *(24)*
Antidote *(30)*
Apsleys *(14,14)*
aqua kyoto *(10)*
aqua nueva *(16)*
Archipelago *(65)*
L'Artiste Musclé *(45)*
Asadal *(12,12,12)*
L'Atelier de Joel Robuchon *(60)*
Athenaeum *(8,12,60)*
Aurora *(20)*
L'Autre Pied *(16)*
The Avenue *(20)*
Axis *(20)*
Ba Shan *(10)*
Babbo *(12)*
The Balcon *(18)*
Bam-Bou *(20,30,12,12,8)*
Bank Westminster *(20,20,10)*
Bar Boulud *(20)*
Bar Shu *(14,14,12)*
Bedford & Strand
Belgo Centraal: *Earlham St WC2 (25,30)*
Benares *(16,34,6,10)*
Benihana: *all branches (10)*
Bentley's *(14,60)*
Bibimbap Soho *(25)*
Bincho Yakitori *(20)*
Bo London *(20)*
Bob Bob Ricard *(10)*
Bocca Di Lupo *(32)*
Bodean's: *W1 (10)*
Boisdale *(20,22,45)*
Boudin Blanc *(16)*

Boulevard *(36,70)*
The Bountiful Cow *(45)*
Brasserie Max *(10,12,32)*
Briciole *(20)*
Browns: *WC2 (35,80,50)*
Busaba Eathai: *WC1 (15)*
C London *(40)*
Café des Amis *(24)*
Caffè Caldesi *(70)*
Il Calcio: *W1 (28)*
Cantina Laredo *(20)*
Cecconi's *(12)*
Le Cercle *(12,26)*
Chabrot Bistrot d'Amis *(20)*
China Tang *(18,16,16)*
Chisou: *W1 (14)*
Chor Bizarre *(30)*
Christopher's *(40)*
Chuen Cheng Ku *(50)*
Cigala *(24)*
Le Cigalon *(8)*
The Cinnamon Club *(60,30)*
Cinnamon Soho *(150)*
Clos Maggiore *(23)*
Como Lario *(28)*
Il Convivio *(14)*
Coopers Restaurant & Bar *(60,40)*
Corrigan's Mayfair *(12,30,26)*
Côte: *W1 (40)*
Cotidie *(30,40,70)*
Cut *(70)*
Defune *(10)*
Dehesa *(13)*
The Delaunay *(24)*
Delfino *(40)*
Les Deux Salons *(10,24)*
dim T: *W1 (20)*
Dinner *(10)*
Donostia *(16)*
Downtown Mayfair *(40)*
Elena's L'Etoile *(10,14,16,34)*
Empress of Sichuan *(18)*
L'Escargot *(24,60,20)*
Fairuz *(22)*
Fire & Stone: *WC2 (23)*
Franco's *(16,55)*
La Fromagerie Café *(12)*
Galvin at Windows *(30)*
Galvin Bistrot de Luxe *(22)*
Gauthier Soho *(40,4,12,18,24)*
Gay Hussar *(12,25)*
The Giaconda Dining Rooms *(30)*
Golden Dragon *(14,14)*
Golden Hind *(30)*
Gopal's of Soho *(18)*
Gordon's Wine Bar *(8)*
The Goring Hotel *(18,14,50,6)*
Goya *(90)*
Gran Paradiso *(30,12)*
The Grand Imperial *(30)*
Grazing Goat *(50)*
Green's *(36)*
The Greenhouse *(12)*
Grumbles *(10)*
The Guinea Grill *(28)*
Gustoso Ristorante & Enoteca *(16)*
Haozhan *(40)*
Harbour City *(40)*
Hard Rock Café *(200)*
Hardy's Brasserie *(28,16,12,48)*
Hawksmoor: *WC2 (16)*
Hazuki *(25)*

235

ROMANTIC

The Swan at the Globe
Trinity
Upstairs
The Wharf

East
Beach Blanket Babylon: *all branches*
Bleeding Heart
Café du Marché
Club Gascon
Comptoir Gascon
Galvin La Chapelle
The Little Bay: *all branches*
LMNT
Moro
Pizza East: *E1*
Les Trois Garçons
Vertigo 42
Wapping Food

ROOMS WITH A VIEW

Central
Dinner
Galvin at Windows
Inn the Park
Kaspar's Seafood and Grill
The National Dining Rooms
Orrery
Paramount
The Portrait

West
Babylon
Belvedere
Cheyne Walk Brasserie
Min Jiang
Pissarro
The Summerhouse
The Waterway

North
Rotunda Bar & Restaurant

South
Alquimia
The Bingham
Blueprint Café
Butlers Wharf Chop House
The Depot
dim T: *SE1*
Gourmet Pizza Company
Hutong
Joanna's
China Boulevard
Oblix
Oxo Tower (Brass')
Oxo Tower (Rest')
Petersham Hotel
Le Pont de la Tour
Roast
The Ship
Skylon
Skylon Grill
The Swan at the Globe
Tate Modern (Level 7)
Thai Square: *SW15*
Upstairs
The Wharf

East
Barbecoa
Boisdale of Canary Wharf
Coq d'Argent
Duck & Waffle
Elephant Royale
Forman's
The Grapes
The Gun
High Timber
Lotus Chinese Floating Restaurant
The Narrow
Northbank
The Oyster Shed
Plateau
Smiths (Top Floor)
Sushisamba
Vertigo 42
Yi-Ban

NOTABLE WINE LISTS

Central
Alyn Williams
Andrew Edmunds
Antidote
Apsleys
Arbutus
Barrica
Bedford & Strand
Boisdale
Café des Amis
Le Cercle
Cigala
Clos Maggiore
Copita
Cork & Bottle
Dehesa
Ebury Rest' & Wine Bar
L'Escargot
The Fifth Floor Restaurant
Fino
The Fountain (Fortnum's)
1707
La Fromagerie Café
Galvin Bistrot de Luxe
Le Gavroche
Gordon's Wine Bar
Green Man & French Horn
The Greenhouse
Hardy's Brasserie
Hibiscus
The Ivy
Kai Mayfair
Latium
Locanda Locatelli
Marcus Wareing
Olivo
Olivomare
Opera Tavern
Orrery
Otto's
Pétrus
Pied à Terre
The Providores
Providores (Tapa Room)
Quo Vadis
The Ritz Restaurant
St Moritz
Salt Yard
Sardo
Savoy Grill

CUISINES

An asterisk (*) after an entry indicates exceptional or very good cooking

AMERICAN
Central
All Star Lanes (WC1)
Automat (W1)
Big Easy (WC2)
Bodean's (W1)
Bubbledogs (W1)
Christopher's (WC2)
Hard Rock Café (W1)
Jackson & Whyte (W1)
Joe Allen (WC2)
The Lockhart (W1)
Mishkin's (WC2)
The Palm (SW1)
Pitt Cue Co (W1)*
Soho Diner (W1)
Spuntino (W1)*

West
All Star Lanes (W2)
Big Easy (SW3)
Bodean's (SW6)
Lucky Seven (W2)
Sticky Fingers (W8)

North
Chicken Shop (NW5)
John Salt (N1)
Karpo (NW1)
Red Dog Saloon (N1)
Shrimpy's (N1)

South
Bodean's (SW4)
Oblix (SE1)
Wishbone (SW9)

East
All Star Lanes (E1, E20)
Beard to Tail (EC2)
Bodean's (EC3)
The Hoxton Grill (EC2)

AUSTRALIAN
Central
Lantana Cafe (W1)

West
Granger & Co (W11)

BELGIAN
Central
Belgo (WC2)

North
Belgo Noord (NW1)

South
Belgo (SW4)

BRITISH, MODERN
Central
Alyn Williams (W1)*
Andrew Edmunds (W1)
The Angel & Crown (WC2)
Arbutus (W1)
Athenaeum (W1)*
Aurora (W1)
The Avenue (SW1)

Axis (WC2)
Balthazar (WC2)
Bank Westminster (SW1)
Bellamy's (W1)
The Berners Tavern (W1)
Bob Bob Ricard (W1)
The Botanist (SW1)
Brasserie Max (WC2)
Le Caprice (SW1)
Coopers Restaurant & Bar (WC2)
Criterion (W1)
Daylesford Organic (SW1)
Dean Street Townhouse (W1)
Le Deuxième (WC2)
Dorchester Grill (W1)
Ducksoup (W1)
Ebury Rest' & Wine Bar (SW1)
The Fifth Floor Restaurant (SW1)
Gordon's Wine Bar (WC2)
The Goring Hotel (SW1)
Grazing Goat (W1)
Hardy's Brasserie (W1)
Hix (W1)
Homage (WC2)
Hush (W1, WC1)
Indigo (WC2)
Inn the Park (SW1)
The Ivy (WC2)
Kettners (W1)
Langan's Brasserie (W1)
Little Social (W1)*
Mews of Mayfair (W1)
Newman Street Tavern (W1)
No 11 Pimlico Road (SW1)
The Norfolk Arms (WC1)
The Northall (WC2)
The Only Running Footman (W1)
The Orange (SW1)
Oscar (W1)
Ozer (W1)
The Pantechnicon (SW1)
Paramount (WC1)
Picture (W1)*
Pollen Street Social (W1)*
The Portrait (WC2)
Quaglino's (SW1)
The Queens Arms (SW1)
Quo Vadis (W1)
Randall & Aubin (W1)*
Refuel (W1)
RIBA Café (W1)
Roux at Parliament Square (SW1)
Roux at the Landau (W1)
Seven Park Place (SW1)
Seven Stars (WC2)
1707 (W1)
Shampers (W1)
Social Eating House (W1)
Sotheby's Café (W1)
Tate Britain (Rex Whistler) (SW1)
10 Greek Street (W1)*
Thirty Six (SW1)
The Thomas Cubitt (SW1)
Tom's Kitchen (WC2)
The Union Café (W1)
Union Jacks (WC2)
Villandry (W1)
The Vincent Rooms (SW1)
Vinoteca (W1)
VQ (WC1)
Whyte & Brown (W1)
Wild Honey (W1)
The Wolseley (W1)

West

The Abingdon (W8)
The Anglesea Arms (W6)*
The Anglesea Arms (SW7)
Babylon (W8)
Beach Blanket Babylon (W11)
Belvedere (W8)
Bluebird (SW3)
Brinkley's (SW10)
Brompton Bar & Grill (SW3)
The Builders Arms (SW3)
Bush Dining Hall (W12)
Butcher's Hook (SW6)
The Cadogan Arms (SW3)
The Carpenter's Arms (W6)
Carvosso's (W4)
The Chelsea Ram (SW10)
Clarke's (W8)
The Cow (W2)
The Dartmouth Castle (W6)
Daylesford Organic (W11)
The Dock Kitchen (W10)
Duke of Sussex (W4)
The Enterprise (SW3)
First Floor (W11)
The Five Fields (SW3)*
Formosa Dining Room (W9)
The Frontline Club (W2)
Harwood Arms (SW6)*
The Havelock Tavern (W14)*
Hedone (W4)*
The Henry Root (SW10)
High Road Brasserie (W4)
Hole in the Wall (W4)
Jam Tree (SW6)
Joe's Brasserie (SW6)
Julie's (W11)
Kensington Place (W8)
Kensington Square Kitchen (W8)
Kitchen W8 (W8)*
The Ladbroke Arms (W11)*
Launceston Place (W8)*
The Ledbury (W11)*
The Magazine Restaurant (W2)
The Mall Tavern (W8)
Marianne (W2)
Medlar (SW10)*
Megan's Delicatessen (SW6)
Paradise by Way of Kensal
    Green (W10)
Pissarro (W4)
Princess Victoria (W12)
Queen's Head (W6)
The Roebuck (W4)
Sam's Brasserie (W4)
The Sands End (SW6)
The Shed (W8)
The Thatched House (W6)
Tom Aikens (SW3)*
Tom's Deli (W11)
Tom's Kitchen (SW3)
Union Jacks (W4)
VQ (SW10)
Vinoteca (W4)
The Waterway (W9)
White Horse (SW6)
Whits (W8)*

North

The Albion (N1)
Bald Faced Stag (N2)
Bradley's (NW3)
Caravan King's Cross (N1)
Charles Lamb (N1)
The Clissold Arms (N2)

Le Coq (N1)
The Drapers Arms (N1)
The Duke of Cambridge (N1)
The Engineer (NW1)
The Fellow (N1)
Frederick's (N1)
Freemasons Arms (NW3)
Grain Store (N1)*
The Haven (N20)
The Horseshoe (NW3)
The Junction Tavern (NW5)
Juniper Dining (N5)*
Landmark (Winter Gdn) (NW1)
Made In Camden (NW1)
Mango Room (NW1)
Market (NW1)
Mosaica (N22)
The North London Tavern (NW6)
The Northgate (N1)*
Odette's (NW1)
The Old Bull & Bush (NW3)
Pig & Butcher (N1)*
Plum + Spilt Milk (N1)
Rising Sun (NW7)
Rotunda Bar & Restaurant (N1)
St Pancras Grand (NW1)
Season Kitchen (N4)*
Somerstown Coffee House (NW1)
The Wells (NW3)
The Wet Fish Cafe (NW6)

South

The Abbeville (SW4)
Abbeville Kitchen (SW4)*
Albion (SE1)
Antelope (SW17)
Avalon (SW12)
The Balham Bowls Club (SW12)
Ben's Canteen (SW11)
The Bingham (TW10)*
Bistro Union (SW4)
Blueprint Café (SE1)
The Bolingbroke (SW11)
The Brown Dog (SW13)
Brunswick House Cafe (SW8)
Cannizaro House (SW19)
Cantina Vinopolis (SE1)
Chapters (SE3)
Chez Bruce (SW17)*
The Crooked Well (SE5)*
The Dairy (SW4)
The Dartmouth Arms (SE23)
The Depot (SW14)
Earl Spencer (SW18)
Elliot's Cafe (SE1)
Emile's (SW15)
Entrée (SW11)
The Fentiman Arms (SW8)
Florence (SE24)
40 Maltby Street (SE1)*
Franklins (SE22)
Garrison (SE1)
The Glasshouse (TW9)*
Harrison's (SW12)
Inside (SE10)*
Jam Tree (SW4)
Lamberts (SW12)*
The Lido Cafe (SE24)
Magdalen (SE1)*
Menier Chocolate Factory (SE1)
Mezzanine (SE1)
The Old Brewery (SE10)
Oxo Tower (Rest') (SE1)
The Palmerston (SE22)
Petersham Hotel (TW10)

Petersham Nurseries *(TW10)*
Plane Food *(TW6)*
Le Pont de la Tour *(SE1)*
Rivington Grill *(SE10)*
Rock & Rose *(TW9)*
RSJ *(SE1)*
Skylon *(SE1)*
Skylon Grill *(SE1)*
Sonny's Kitchen *(SW13)*
Story *(SE1)**
The Swan at the Globe *(SE1)*
The Table *(SE1)*
Tate Modern (Level 7) *(SE1)*
Trinity *(SW4)**
Union Street Café *(SE1)*
The Victoria *(SW14)*
Waterloo Bar & Kitchen *(SE1)*
The Wharf *(TW11)*

East
The Anthologist *(EC2)*
Balans *(E20)*
Beach Blanket Babylon *(E1)*
Bevis Marks *(E1)*
Bird of Smithfield *(EC1)*
Bistrotheque *(E2)*
The Boundary *(E2)**
Brasserie on St John Street *(EC1)*
Bread Street Kitchen *(EC4)*
Café Below *(EC2)*
Caravan *(EC1)*
The Chancery *(EC4)*
Chiswell Street Dining Rms *(EC1)*
The Clove Club *(EC1)**
The Don *(EC4)*
Duck & Waffle *(EC2)*
The Empress *(E9)**
Foxlow *(EC1)*
Gin Joint *(EC2)*
Gow's *(EC2)*
The Gun *(E14)*
The Gunmakers *(EC1)**
High Timber *(EC4)*
Hilliard *(EC4)**
Hoi Polloi *(E1)*
The Jugged Hare *(EC1Y)*
The Mercer *(EC2)*
The Modern Pantry *(EC1)*
The Morgan Arms *(E3)*
The Narrow *(E14)*
1901 *(EC2)*
Northbank *(EC4)*
One Canada Square *(E14)*
1 Lombard Street *(EC3)*
The Peasant *(EC1)*
Princess of Shoreditch *(EC2)*
The Punch Tavern *(EC4)*
Rivington Grill *(EC2)*
Rochelle Canteen *(E2)**
Sager & Wilde *(E2)*
The Sign of the Don *(EC4)*
Smiths Brasserie *(E1)**
Smiths (Ground Floor) *(EC1)*
Street Kitchen *(EC2)**
3 South Place *(EC2)*
Tom's Kitchen *(E14)*
Vertigo 42 *(EC2)*
Vinoteca *(EC1)*
Wapping Food *(E1)*
The White Swan *(EC4)*
Whitechapel Gallery *(E1)*
Young Turks at the Ten Bells *(E1)*

BRITISH, TRADITIONAL
Central
Boisdale *(SW1)*
Browns (Albemarle) *(W1)*
Canteen *(W1)*
Corrigan's Mayfair *(W1)*
Dinner *(SW1)*
The Fountain (Fortnum's) *(W1)*
Fuzzy's Grub *(SW1)*
Great Queen Street *(WC2)**
Green's *(SW1)*
The Guinea Grill *(W1)*
Hardy's Brasserie *(W1)*
The Keeper's House *(W1)*
The Lady Ottoline *(WC1)*
The National Dining Rooms *(WC2)*
Porters English Restaurant *(WC2)*
Rib Room *(SW1)*
Rules *(WC2)*
Savoy Grill *(WC2)*
Scott's *(W1)**
Simpsons-in-the-Strand *(WC2)*
Wiltons *(SW1)*
The Windmill *(W1)*

West
The Brown Cow *(SW6)*
Bumpkin *(SW3, SW7, W11)*
Ffiona's *(W8)*
The Hampshire Hog *(W6)*
Hereford Road *(W2)**
Maggie Jones's *(W8)*
The Malt House *(SW6)**
The Surprise *(SW3)*

North
Bull & Last *(NW5)**
Gilbert Scott *(NW1)*
Greenberry Cafe *(NW1)*
Kentish Canteen *(NW5)*
The Old White Bear *(NW3)*
St Johns *(N19)*

South
The Anchor & Hope *(SE1)**
Butlers Wharf Chop House *(SE1)*
Canteen *(SE1)*
Canton Arms *(SW8)**
Fox & Grapes *(SW19)*
The Lord Northbrook *(SE12)*
The Manor Arms *(SW16)**
The Riverfront *(SE1)*
Roast *(SE1)*

East
Albion *(E2)*
Bumpkin *(E20)*
Canteen *(E1, E14)*
The Fox and Anchor *(EC1)**
Fuzzy's Grub *(SW1)*
George & Vulture *(EC3)*
Hix Oyster & Chop House *(EC1)*
The Oyster Shed *(EC4)*
Paternoster Chop House *(EC4)*
E Pellicci *(E2)*
The Quality Chop House *(EC1)**
St John *(EC1)**
St John Bread & Wine *(E1)**
Simpson's Tavern *(EC3)*
Sweetings *(EC4)*

EAST & CENT. EUROPEAN
Central
The Delaunay *(WC2)*
Gay Hussar *(W1)*

The Wolseley *(W1)*

FISH & SEAFOOD
Central

West

North

South

East

FRENCH
Central

West

Le Café Anglais (W2)
Charlotte's Bistro (W4)*
Charlotte's Place (W5)
Cheyne Walk Brasserie (SW3)
Chez Patrick (W8)
Le Colombier (SW3)
Côte (SW6,W2,W4,W8)
L'Etranger (SW7)
Garnier (SW5)
Goode & Wright (W11)
Gordon Ramsay (SW3)
The Pig's Ear (SW3)
Poissonnerie de l'Avenue (SW3)*
Quantus (W4)*
Racine (SW3)
La Sophia (W10)*
La Trompette (W4)*
Le Vacherin (W4)
Whits (W8)*

North
L'Absinthe (NW1)
The Almeida (N1)
Assiette Anglaise (N7)*
Les Associés (N8)
L'Aventure (NW8)*
Bistro Aix (N8)*
Blue Legume (N1, N16, N8)
Bradley's (NW3)
La Cage Imaginaire (NW3)
Charles Lamb (N1)
Le Mercury (N1)
Michael Nadra (NW1)*
Mill Lane Bistro (NW6)
One Blenheim Terrace (NW8)
Oslo Court (NW8)*
Le Sacré-Coeur (N1)
The Wells (NW3)

South
Bellevue Rendez-Vous (SW17)
Brasserie Blanc (SE1)
Brasserie Toulouse-Lautrec (SE11)
Brula (TW1)*
La Buvette (TW9)
Casse-Croute (SE1)
Côte (SE1, SW19)
Gastro (SW4)
Gazette (SW11, SW12)
The Lawn Bistro (SW19)
Lobster Pot (SE11)*
Ma Cuisine (TW9)
Le P'tit Normand (SW18)
Soif (SW11)
Toasted (SE22)
Upstairs (SW2)*

East
Bistrot Bruno Loubet (EC1)
Bleeding Heart (EC1)
Bouchon Fourchette (E8)*
Brasserie Blanc (EC2, EC3, EC4)
Brawn (E2)*
Café du Marché (EC1)*
Cellar Gascon (EC1)*
Chabrot Bistrot des Halles (EC1)*
Club Gascon (EC1)*
Comptoir Gascon (EC1)
Coq d'Argent (EC2)
Côte (EC4)
The Don (EC4)
Galvin La Chapelle (E1)*
Lutyens (EC4)
Morgan M (EC1)*
Plateau (E14)

Relais de Venise L'Entrecôte (E14, EC2)
Le Rendezvous du Café (EC1)
The Royal Exchange Grand Café (EC3)
Sauterelle (EC3)
Les Trois Garçons (E1)
28-50 (EC4)

FUSION
Central
Archipelago (W1)
Asia de Cuba (WC2)
Bubbledogs (Kitchen Table @) (W1)*
Kopapa (WC2)
Providores (Tapa Room) (W1)*

West
E&O (W11)*
Eight Over Eight (SW3)
L'Etranger (SW7)
Sushinho (SW3)*

North
XO (NW3)

South
Champor-Champor (SE1)*
Tsunami (SW4)*
Village East (SE1)

East
Caravan (EC1)
Sushinho (EC2)*
Viajante (E2)*

GAME
Central
Boisdale (SW1)
Rules (WC2)
Wiltons (SW1)

West
Harwood Arms (SW6)*

North
San Daniele del Friuli (N5)

GREEK
Central
Hellenic (W1)
Real Greek (W1,WC2)

West
Halepi (W2)
Mazi (W8)
The Real Greek (W12)

North
Carob Tree (NW5)
Lemonia (NW1)
Retsina (NW3)
Vrisaki (N22)

South
Real Greek (SE1)

East
Kolossi Grill (EC1)
Real Greek (E1)

HUNGARIAN
Central
Gay Hussar *(W1)*

INTERNATIONAL
Central
Balans *(W1)*
Bedford & Strand *(WC2)*
Boulevard *(WC2)*
Browns *(SW1,W1,WC2)*
Café in the Crypt *(WC2)*
Cork & Bottle *(WC2)*
Giraffe *(SW1,W1,WC1)*
Gordon's Wine Bar *(WC2)*
Grumbles *(SW1)*
Carom at Meza *(W1)**
Motcombs *(SW1)*
National Gallery Café *(WC2)*
The Providores *(W1)**
Sarastro *(WC2)*
Stock Pot *(SW1)*
The 10 Cases *(WC2)*
Terroirs *(WC2)*

West
Annie's *(W4)*
Balans West *(SW5,W12,W4,W8)*
Chelsea Bun Diner *(SW10)*
The Chelsea Kitchen *(SW10)*
Foxtrot Oscar *(SW3)*
Gallery Mess *(SW3)*
Giraffe *(W11,W4,W8)*
The Kensington Wine Rooms *(W8)*
Michael Nadra *(W4)**
Mona Lisa *(SW10)*
The Scarsdale *(W8)*
Stock Pot *(SW3)*
Troubadour *(SW5)*
The Windsor Castle *(W8)*
Wine Gallery *(SW10)*

North
Banners *(N8)*
Browns *(N1)*
The Flask *(N6)*
Giraffe *(N1, NW3)*
The Haven *(N20)*
The Old Bull & Bush *(NW3)*
The Orange Tree *(N20)*
Petek *(N4)*
Swan & Edgar *(NW1)*

South
Annie's *(SW13)*
Brinkley's Kitchen *(SW17)*
Browns *(SE1)*
Giraffe *(SE1)*
Hudsons *(SW15)*
Joanna's *(SE19)*
The Light House *(SW19)*
The Riverfront *(SE1)*
The Ship *(SW18)*
Telegraph *(SW15)*
Vivat Bacchus *(SE1)*
The Wharf *(TW11)*
The Yellow House *(SE16)**

East
Browns *(E14, EC2)*
Dans le Noir *(EC1)*
Giraffe *(E1)*
LMNT *(E8)*
Les Trois Garçons *(E1)*
Vivat Bacchus *(EC4)*
The Wine Library *(EC3)*

IRISH
East
Lutyens *(EC4)*

ITALIAN
Central
Al Duca *(SW1)*
Alloro *(W1)*
Amaranto *(W1)*
Amico Bio *(WC1)*
Apsleys *(SW1)*
Babbo *(W1)*
Il Baretto *(W1)*
Bocca Di Lupo *(W1)**
La Bottega *(SW1)*
Briciole *(W1)*
C London *(W1)*
Caffè Caldesi *(W1)*
Caffé Vergnano *(WC2)*
Il Calcio *(W1)*
Caraffini *(SW1)*
Cecconi's *(W1)*
Ciao Bella *(WC1)*
Como Lario *(SW1)*
Il Convivio *(SW1)**
Cotidie *(W1)*
Da Mario *(WC2)*
Polpo *(WC2)*
Dehesa *(W1)**
Delfino *(W1)**
Downtown Mayfair *(W1)*
Franco's *(SW1)*
La Genova *(W1)*
Gran Paradiso *(SW1)*
Gustoso Ristorante &
    Enoteca *(SW1)*
Jamie's Italian *(WC2)*
Latium *(W1)**
Locanda Locatelli *(W1)*
Made in Italy *(W1)*
Mele e Pere *(W1)*
Murano *(W1)*
Novikov (Italian restaurant) *(W1)*
Obika *(W1)*
Oliveto *(SW1)**
Olivo *(SW1)**
Olivocarne *(SW1)*
Olivomare *(SW1)**
Opera Tavern *(WC2)**
Orso *(WC2)*
Osteria Dell'Angolo *(SW1)*
Ottolenghi *(SW1)**
Pescatori *(W1)*
Piccolino *(W1)*
Polpo *(W1)*
La Porchetta Pizzeria *(WC1)*
Princi *(W1)*
Quirinale *(SW1)**
Rossopomodoro *(WC2)*
Sale e Pepe *(SW1)*
Salt Yard *(W1)**
San Carlo Cicchetti *(W1)*
Santini *(SW1)*
Sardo *(W1)**
Sartoria *(W1)*
Signor Sassi *(SW1)*
Theo Randall *(W1)**
Tinello *(SW1)**
Tozi *(SW1)**
2 Amici *(SW1)*
2 Veneti *(W1)*
Vapiano *(W1)*
Vasco & Piero's Pavilion *(W1)**
Il Vicolo *(SW1)*
Zafferano *(SW1)*

West

Oak *(W12)**
Aglio e Olio *(SW10)*
Assaggi *(W2)**
Bird in Hand *(W14)*
La Bottega *(SW7)*
Buona Sera *(SW3)*
Calcio *(SW5)*
Canta Napoli *(W4)*
Cibo *(W14)**
Da Mario *(SW7)*
Daphne's *(SW3)*
La Delizia Limbara *(SW3)*
E l l even Park Walk *(SW10)*
Edera *(W11)**
Essenza *(W11)*
La Famiglia *(SW10)*
Frantoio *(SW10)*
Jamie's Italian *(W12)*
Locanda Ottomezzo *(W8)*
Lucio *(SW3)*
Made in Italy *(SW3)*
Manicomio *(SW3)*
Mediterraneo *(W11)*
Mona Lisa *(SW10)*
Napulé *(SW6)*
Nuovi Sapori *(SW6)*
The Oak *(W2)**
Obika *(SW3)*
Osteria Basilico *(W11)*
Osteria dell'Arancio *(SW10)*
Ottolenghi *(W11,W8)**
Il Pagliaccio *(SW6)*
Pappa Ciccia *(SW6)*
Pellicano *(SW3)*
Pentolina *(W14)**
Il Portico *(W8)*
Portobello Ristorante *(W11)**
The Red Pepper *(W9)**
Riccardo's *(SW3)*
Il Ristorante *(SW7)*
The River Café *(W6)*
Rocco *(SW5)*
Rossopomodoro *(SW10,W11)*
San Lorenzo *(SW3)*
Santa Lucia *(SW10)**
Scalini *(SW3)*
Tartufo *(SW3)**
Ziani's *(SW3)*

North

Artigiano *(NW3)*
L'Artista *(NW11)*
Il Bacio *(N16, N5)*
La Collina *(NW1)*
Fabrizio *(N19)*
Fifteen *(N1)*
500 *(N19)*
Marine Ices *(NW3)*
Mimmo la Bufala *(NW3)*
Ostuni *(NW6)*
Ottolenghi *(N1)**
Pizzeria Oregano *(N1)**
Pizzeria Pappagone *(N4)*
La Porchetta Pizzeria *(N1, N4, NW1)*
Rugoletta *(N2)*
The Salusbury *(NW6)*
San Daniele del Friuli *(N5)*
Sarracino *(NW6)**
Trullo *(N1)**
Villa Bianca *(NW3)*
York & Albany *(NW1)*

South

A Cena *(TW1)*

Al Forno *(SW15, SW19)*
Antico *(SE1)*
Antipasto & Pasta *(SW11)*
La Barca *(SE1)*
Al Boccon di'vino *(TW9)**
Buona Sera *(SW11)*
Canta Napoli *(TW11)*
Donna Margherita *(SW11)**
Enoteca Turi *(SW15)**
Frizzante Cafe *(SE16)*
Isola del Sole *(SW15)*
Lorenzo *(SE19)*
Numero Uno *(SW11)*
Osteria Antica Bologna *(SW11)*
Pizza Metro *(SW11)**
Le Querce *(SE23)**
Riva *(SW13)**
San Lorenzo Fuoriporta *(SW19)*
Sapori Sardi *(SW6)**
The Table *(SE1)*
Tentazioni *(SE1)*
Zucca *(SE1)**

East

Alba *(EC1)*
Amico Bio *(EC1)*
L'Anima *(EC2)**
Il Bordello *(E1)**
Fabrizio *(EC1)**
La Figa *(E14)*
Frizzante at City Farm *(E2)**
Jamie's Italian *(E14)*
Lardo *(E8)*
Manicomio *(EC2)*
Obika *(E14)*
E Pellicci *(E2)*
Piccolino *(EC2)*
Polpo *(EC1)*
La Porchetta Pizzeria *(EC1)*
Refettorio *(EC4)*
Santore *(EC1)**
Taberna Etrusca *(EC4)*

MEDITERRANEAN

Central

About Thyme *(SW1)**
Bistro 1 *(W1,WC2)*
Dabbous *(W1)**
Hummus Bros *(W1,WC1)*
Massimo *(SW1)*
Nopi *(W1)**
The Norfolk Arms *(WC1)*
Riding House Café *(W1)*

West

The Atlas *(SW6)**
Cumberland Arms *(W14)**
Locanda Ottomezzo *(W8)*
Made in Italy *(SW3)*
Mediterraneo *(W11)*
Raoul's Cafe *(W9)*
Raoul's Café & Deli *(W11,W6)*
La Sophia *(W10)**
The Swan *(W4)**
Tom's Deli *(W11)*
Troubadour *(SW5)*

North

Blue Legume *(N16)*
The Little Bay *(NW6)*
Mem & Laz *(N1)*
Petek *(N4)*

South

Cantina Vinopolis *(SE1)*

WESTERN | **CUISINES**

Fish in a Tie *(SW11)*
The Fox & Hounds *(SW11)**
Oxo Tower (Brass') *(SE1)*
The Wharf *(TW11)*

East
Bonds *(EC2)*
The Eagle *(EC1)*
Hummus Bros *(EC1, EC2)*
The Little Bay *(EC1)*
Morito *(EC1)**
Portal *(EC1)*
Rocket *(E14, EC2)*
Vinoteca *(EC1)*

ORGANIC
Central
Daylesford Organic *(SW1)*

West
Daylesford Organic *(W11)*

North
The Duke of Cambridge *(N1)*

East
Smiths (Dining Rm) *(EC1)*

POLISH
West
Daquise *(SW7)*
Polish Club *(SW7)*
Patio *(W12)*

South
Baltic *(SE1)*

PORTUGUESE
West
Lisboa Pâtisserie *(W10)*

East
Corner Room *(E2)**
Eyre Brothers *(EC2)*
The Gun *(E14)*
Portal *(EC1)*

RUSSIAN
Central
Bob Bob Ricard *(W1)*
Mari Vanna *(SW1)*

SCANDINAVIAN
Central
Nordic Bakery *(W1)*
Scandinavian Kitchen *(W1)**
Texture *(W1)**
Verru *(W1)**

West
Madsen *(SW7)*

SCOTTISH
Central
Albannach *(WC2)*
Boisdale *(SW1)*

East
Boisdale of Canary Wharf *(E14)*

SPANISH
Central
Ametsa with Arzak

Instruction *(SW1)*
aqua nueva *(W1)*
Barrafina *(W1, WC2)**
Barrica *(W1)**
Cigala *(WC1)*
Copita *(W1)*
Dehesa *(W1)**
Donostia *(W1)*
Fino *(W1)*
Goya *(SW1)*
Ibérica *(W1)*
Navarro's *(W1)*
Opera Tavern *(WC2)**
El Pirata *(W1)*
Salt Yard *(W1)**
Tapas Brindisa Soho *(W1)**

West
Cambio de Tercio *(SW5)**
Capote Y Toros *(SW5)**
Casa Brindisa *(SW7)*
Duke of Sussex *(W4)*
Galicia *(W10)*
Notting Hill Kitchen *(W11)**
El Pirata de Tapas *(W2)*
Tendido Cero *(SW5)**
Tendido Cuatro *(SW6)**

North
La Bota *(N8)*
Café del Parc *(N19)**
Camino *(N1)*
El Parador *(NW1)**

South
Alquimia *(SW15)**
Angels & Gypsies *(SE5)**
Boqueria *(SW2)**
don Fernando's *(TW9)*
José *(SE1)**
Lola Rojo *(SW11)*
Mar I Terra *(SE1)*
Meson don Felipe *(SE1)*
Pizarro *(SE1)**
Tapas Brindisa *(SE1)**

East
Eyre Brothers *(EC2)*
Ibérica *(E14)*
Morito *(EC1)**
Moro *(EC1)**
Tramontana Brindisa *(EC2)*

STEAKS & GRILLS
Central
Black & Blue *(W1)*
Bodean's *(W1)*
The Bountiful Cow *(WC1)*
Chop Shop *(SW1)*
Christopher's *(WC2)*
Cut *(W1)*
Flat Iron *(W1)*
Garufin *(WC1)*
Gaucho *(W1, WC2)*
Goodman *(W1)**
Grillshack *(W1)*
The Guinea Grill *(W1)*
Hawksmoor *(W1, WC2)**
JW Steakhouse *(W1)*
MASH Steakhouse *(W1)*
maze Grill *(W1)*
Carom at Meza *(W1)**
The Palm *(SW1)*
Le Relais de Venise L'Entrecôte *(W1)*
Rib Room *(SW1)*

Rowley's *(SW1)*
Sophie's Steakhouse *(WC2)*
STK Steakhouse *(WC2)*
34 *(W1)*
Wolfe's *(WC2)*

West
Admiral Codrington *(SW3)*
Black & Blue *(W8)*
Bodean's *(SW6)*
The Cabin *(W4)*
Casa Malevo *(W2)*
Gaucho *(SW3)*
Haché *(SW10)*
Kings Road Steakhouse *(SW3)*
Lola & Simón *(W6)*
Maxela *(SW7)*
The Meat & Wine Co *(W12)*
PJ's Bar and Grill *(SW3)*
Popeseye *(W14)*
Sophie's Steakhouse *(SW10)*

North
Garufa *(N5)*
Gaucho *(NW3)*
Haché *(NW1)*
The Smokehouse Islington *(N1)*

South
Archduke Wine Bar *(SE1)*
Black & Blue *(SE1)*
Bodean's *(SW4)*
Buenos Aires Café *(SE10, SE3)*
Butcher & Grill *(SW11)*
Cattle Grid *(SW11, SW12)*
Constancia *(SE1)*
Gaucho *(SE1, SE10, TW10)*
Kew Grill *(TW9)*
Popeseye *(SW15)*
Santa Maria del Sur *(SW8)*

East
Barbecoa *(EC4)*
Buen Ayre *(E8)*
Gaucho *(E14, EC1, EC2, EC3)*
Goodman *(E14)*
Goodman City *(EC2)*
Hawksmoor *(E1, EC2)*
Hix Oyster & Chop House *(EC1)*
New Street Grill *(EC2)*
Relais de Venise L'Entrecôte *(E14, EC2)*
Simpson's Tavern *(EC3)*
Smiths (Top Floor) *(EC1)*
Smiths (Dining Rm) *(EC1)*
Smiths (Ground Floor) *(EC1)*
The Tramshed *(EC2)*

SWISS
Central
St Moritz *(W1)*

VEGETARIAN
Central
Amico Bio *(WC1)*
Chettinad *(W1)*
Food for Thought *(WC2)*
Hummus Bros *(W1, WC1)*
Malabar Junction *(WC1)*
Masala Zone *(W1)*
Mildreds *(W1)*
Orchard *(WC1)*
Ragam *(W1)*
Rasa Maricham *(WC1)*

Sagar *(W1)*
tibits *(W1)*
Woodlands *(SW1, W1)*

West
The Gate *(W6)*
Masala Zone *(SW5, SW6, W2)*
Sagar *(W6)*

North
Chutneys *(NW1)*
Diwana Bhel-Poori House *(NW1)*
Jai Krishna *(N4)*
Manna *(NW3)*
Masala Zone *(N1)*
Rani *(N3)*
Rasa Travancore *(N16)*
Sakonis *(HA0)*
Vijay *(NW6)*
Woodlands *(NW3)*

South
Blue Elephant *(SW6)*
Cocum *(SW20)*
Ganapati *(SE15)*
Le Pont de la Tour *(SE1)*
Sree Krishna *(SW17)*

East
Amico Bio *(EC1)*
The Gate *(EC1)*
Hummus Bros *(EC2)*
Vanilla Black *(EC4)*

AFTERNOON TEA
Central
Athenaeum *(W1)*
The Diamond Jub' Salon (Fortnum's) *(W1)*
The Fountain (Fortnum's) *(W1)*
La Fromagerie Café *(W1)*
Ladurée *(SW1, W1, WC2)*
Maison Bertaux *(W1)*
Notes *(WC2)*
Oscar *(W1)*
Ritz (Palm Court) *(W1)*
Royal Academy *(W1)*
The Sketch (Parlour) *(W1)*
Villandry *(W1)*
The Wallace *(W1)*
William Curley *(SW1)*
The Wolseley *(W1)*
Yauatcha *(W1)*

North
Kenwood (Brew House) *(NW3)*
Landmark (Winter Gdn) *(NW1)*

South
Cannizaro House *(SW19)*
San Lorenzo Fuoriporta *(SW19)*
William Curley *(TW9)*

East
Ladurée *(EC3)*

BURGERS, ETC
Central
Automat *(W1)*
Bar Boulud *(SW1)*
Black & Blue *(W1)*
The Bountiful Cow *(WC1)*
Burger & Lobster *(SW1, W1)*
Byron *(SW1, W1, WC2)*

Diner *(W1,WC2)*
Ed's Easy Diner *(W1)*
Five Guys *(WC2)*
Goodman *(W1)**
Hard Rock Café *(W1)*
Hawksmoor *(W1,WC2)**
Honest Burgers *(W1)**
Joe Allen *(WC2)*
Kettners *(W1)*
MEATLiquor *(W1)**
MEATmarket *(WC2)*
Opera Tavern *(WC2)**
Patty and Bun *(W1)**
Shake Shack *(WC2)*
Tommi's Burger Joint *(W1)**
Wolfe's *(WC2)*

West
Admiral Codrington *(SW3)*
Big Easy *(SW3)*
Black & Blue *(W8)*
Byron *(SW3, SW5, SW7,W12,W8)*
The Chelsea Ram *(SW10)*
Diner *(SW7)*
Haché *(SW10)*
Honest Burgers *(W11)**
Lucky Seven *(W2)*
Sticky Fingers *(W8)*
Troubadour *(SW5)*

North
Byron *(N1)*
Diner *(N1, NW1, NW10)*
Dirty Burger *(NW5)**
Duke's Brew & Que *(N1)**
Haché *(NW1)*
Harry Morgan's *(NW8)*
Honest Burgers *(NW1)**
Meat Mission *(N1)**
Red Dog Saloon *(N1)*
The Rib Man *(N1)**

South
Ben's Canteen *(SW11)*
Black & Blue *(SE1)*
Byron *(SW15)*
Cattle Grid *(SW11, SW12)*
Dirty Burger *(SW8)**
Haché *(SW4)*
Honest Burgers *(SW9)**
The Old Brewery *(SE10)*
Village East *(SE1)*

East
Big Apple Hot Dogs *(EC1)**
Burger & Lobster *(EC1, EC4)**
Byron *(E14, EC2)*
Comptoir Gascon *(EC1)*
The Diner *(EC2)*
Goodman *(E14)**
Goodman City *(EC2)**
Haché *(EC2)*
Hawksmoor *(E1, EC2)**
Smiths (Dining Rm) *(EC1)*

FISH & CHIPS
Central
Fryer's Delight *(WC1)*
Golden Hind *(W1)*
North Sea Fish *(WC1)*
Seafresh *(SW1)*

West
Geales *(W8)*
Geales Chelsea Green *(SW3)*

Kerbisher & Malt *(W5,W6)*

North
The Fish & Chip Shop *(N1)**
Nautilus *(NW6)**
The Sea Shell *(NW1)**
Skipjacks *(HA3)**
Toff's *(N10)**
Two Brothers *(N3)*

South
Brady's *(SW18)*
Fish Club *(SW11, SW4)**
Masters Super Fish *(SE1)**
Moxon's Fish Bar *(SW12)**
Olley's *(SE24)**
The Sea Cow *(SE22)**

East
Ark Fish *(E18)**
Faulkner's *(E8)**

ICE CREAM
Central
Gelupo *(W1)**

North
Marine Ices *(NW3)*

PIZZA
Central
Il Baretto *(W1)*
Delfino *(W1)**
Fire & Stone *(WC2)*
Kettners *(W1)*
Made in Italy *(W1)*
Oliveto *(SW1)**
The Orange *(SW1)*
Piccolino *(W1)*
Pizza Pilgrims *(W1)*
La Porchetta Pizzeria *(WC1)*
Princi *(W1)*
Rossopomodoro *(WC2)*
Union Jacks *(WC2)*

West
Oak *(W12)**
Basilico *(SW6)*
Bird in Hand *(W14)*
Buona Sera *(SW3)*
Canta Napoli *(W4)*
Da Mario *(SW7)*
La Delizia Limbara *(SW3)*
Fire & Stone *(W12)*
Franco Manca *(W4)**
Made in Italy *(SW3)*
The Oak *(W2)**
Osteria Basilico *(W11)*
Otto Pizza *(W2)**
Il Pagliaccio *(SW6)*
Pappa Ciccia *(SW6)*
Pizza East Portobello *(W10)**
Ciro's (Pizza Pomodoro) *(SW3)*
Portobello Ristorante *(W11)**
The Red Pepper *(W9)**
Rocca Di Papa *(SW7)*
Rossopomodoro *(SW10,W11)*
Santa Lucia *(SW10)**
Santa Maria *(W5)**
Union Jacks *(W4)*

North
Il Bacio *(N16, N5)*
Basilico *(N1, N8, NW3)*

Fabrizio (N19)
Marine Ices (NW3)
Mimmo la Bufala (NW3)
Pizza East (NW5)*
Pizzeria Oregano (N1)*
Pizzeria Pappagone (N4)
La Porchetta Pizzeria (N1, N4, NW1)
Rossopomodoro (N1, NW1)
Sacro Cuore (NW10)*
The Salusbury (NW6)
Sweet Thursday (N1)*
White Rabbit (N16)*

South
Al Forno (SW15, SW19)
Basilico (SW11, SW14)
Bianco43 (SE10)
Buona Sera (SW11)
Donna Margherita (SW11)*
Eco (SW4)*
Franco Manca (SW11, SW9)*
Gourmet Pizza Company (SE1)
The Gowlett (SE15)*
Lorenzo (SE19)
Pizza Metro (SW11)*
Pizzeria Rustica (TW9)
Rocca Di Papa (SE21)
Rossopomodoro (SW18)
San Lorenzo Fuoriporta (SW19)
The Yellow House (SE16)*
Zero Degrees (SE3)

East
Il Bordello (E1)*
La Figa (E14)
Fire & Stone (E1)
Franco Manca (E20)*
Piccolino (EC2)
Pizza East (E1)*
La Porchetta Pizzeria (EC1)
Rocket (E14, EC2)
Story Deli (E2)*

SANDWICHES, CAKES, ETC
Central
Abokado (W1)
Baker & Spice (SW1)
Bar Italia (W1)
Benugo (W1)
Caffè Vergnano (WC1)
The Courtauld Gallery Café (WC2)
Fernandez & Wells (W1, WC2)
Flat White (W1)*
Fleet River Bakery (WC2)*
La Fromagerie Café (W1)*
Fuzzy's Grub (SW1)
Kaffeine (W1)
Konditor & Cook (W1, WC1)
Ladurée (SW1, W1)*
Leon (W1, WC2)
Maison Bertaux (W1)*
Monmouth Coffee Company (WC2)*
Natural Kitchen (W1)
Nordic Bakery (W1)
Notes (WC2)
Paul (W1, WC2)
Pod (WC1)
Royal Academy (W1)
Scandinavian Kitchen (W1)*
The Sketch (Parlour) (W1)
Spianata & Co (W1)
Taylor St Baristas (W1)*
William Curley (SW1)*

West
Baker & Spice (SW3, W9)
Benugo (SW7, W12)
Bluebird Café (SW3)
Gail's Bakery (W4)
Gail's Bread (W11)
Lisboa Pâtisserie (W10)
Tom's Deli (W11)

North
Benugo (NW1)
Euphorium Bakery (N1)
Gail's Bread (NW3, NW8)
Ginger & White (NW3)
Kenwood (Brew House) (NW3)
Notes (N7)

South
Benugo (SE1)
Caffè Vergnano (SE1)
Fulham Wine Rooms (SW6)
Gail's Bread (SW11)
Konditor & Cook (SE1)
Leon (SE1)
Monmouth Coffee Company (SE1, SE1)*
Orange Pekoe (SW13)*
Pantry (SW18)
Pod (SE1)
Spianata & Co (SE1)
Taylor St Baristas (TW9)*
William Curley (TW9)*

East
Abokado (EC1, EC4)
Benugo (E2, EC1)
Brick Lane Beigel Bake (E1)*
Caffè Vergnano (EC4)
Department of Coffee (EC1)
Dose (EC1)*
Fuzzy's Grub (EC4)
Gail's Bakery (EC1)
Konditor & Cook (EC3)
Leon (E1, E14, EC4)
Look Mum No Hands! (EC1)
Natural Kitchen (EC4)
Nusa Kitchen (EC1, EC2)*
Pod (EC1, EC2, EC3, EC4)
Prufrock Coffee (EC1)*
Spianata & Co (E1, EC1, EC2, EC4)
Taylor St Baristas (E14, EC2, EC3)*
Workshop Coffee (EC1)

SALADS
Central
Kaffeine (W1)
Natural Kitchen (W1)

West
Beirut Express (SW7, W2)*

East
Natural Kitchen (EC3, EC4)

ARGENTINIAN
Central
Gaucho (W1, WC2)
Zoilo (W1)*

West
Casa Malevo (W2)
Gaucho (SW3)
Lola & Simón (W6)
Quantus (W4)*

North
Garufa (N5)*
Gaucho (NW3)

South
Buenos Aires Café (SE10, SE3)
Constancia (SE1)
Gaucho (SE1, SE10, TW10)
Santa Maria del Sur (SW8)

East
Buen Ayre (E8)*
Gaucho (E14, EC1, EC2, EC3)

BRAZILIAN
West
Sushinho (SW3)*

East
Sushisamba (EC2)

MEXICAN/TEXMEX
Central
Benito's Hat (W1, WC2)
La Bodega Negra (W1)
Café Pacifico (WC2)
Cantina Laredo (WC2)
Chilango (WC2)*
Chipotle (W1, WC2)
Lupita (WC2)
Tortilla (W1, WC2)
Wahaca (W1, WC2)

West
Taqueria (W11)
Tortilla (W6)
Wahaca (W12)

North
Benito's Hat (N1)
Chilango (N1)*
Chipotle (N1)
Mestizo (NW1)
Tortilla (N1)
Wahaca (N1)

South
Chipotle (SW19)
Tortilla (SE1, SW19)
Wahaca (SE1)

East
Chilango (E1, EC2, EC4)*
Daddy Donkey (EC1)*
Tortilla (E14, E20, EC3)
Wahaca (E14, E20)

PERUVIAN
Central
Ceviche (W1)
Coya (W1)*
Lima (W1)

North
Tierra Peru (N1)

East
Sushisamba (EC2)

SOUTH AMERICAN
West
Quantus (W4)*

South
El Vergel (SE1)*

AFRO-CARIBBEAN
North
Mango Room (NW1)

MOROCCAN
West
Adams Café (W12)

East
Kenza (EC2)

NORTH AFRICAN
Central
Momo (W1)

West
Azou (W6)

East
Kenza (EC2)

TUNISIAN
West
Adams Café (W12)

EGYPTIAN
North
Ali Baba (NW1)

ISRAELI
Central
Gaby's (WC2)

North
Solly's (NW11)

KOSHER
Central
Reubens (W1)

North
Kaifeng (NW4)*
Solly's (NW11)

East
Bevis Marks (E1)
Brick Lane Beigel Bake (E1)*

LEBANESE
Central
Al Hamra (W1)
Al Sultan (W1)
Beiteddine (SW1)
Comptoir Libanais (W1)
Fairuz (W1)
Ishbilia (SW1)
Levant (W1)
Maroush (W1)*
Noura (SW1, W1)
Ranoush (SW1)
Yalla Yalla (W1)

West
Al-Waha (W2)*
Beirut Express (SW7, W2)*
Chez Marcelle (W14)*
Comptoir Libanais (SW7, W12)
Maroush (W2)*
Maroush (SW3)*
Ranoush (SW3, W2, W8)

South
Meza *(SW17)**
Palmyra *(TW9)**

East
Comptoir Libanais *(E20)*
Kenza *(EC2)*
Yalla Yalla *(E1)*

MIDDLE EASTERN
Central
Honey & Co *(W1)**
Patogh *(W1)**

North
Solly's *(NW11)*

East
Morito *(EC1)**
Pilpel *(E1, EC4)**

PERSIAN
West
Alounak *(W14, W2)*
Colbeh *(W2)**
Faanoos *(W4)*
Kateh *(W9)**
Sufi *(W12)*

North
Gilak *(N19)*

South
Faanoos *(SW14)*

SYRIAN
West
Abu Zaad *(W12)*

TURKISH
Central
Cyprus Mangal *(SW1)**
Ishtar *(W1)*
Kazan *(SW1)*
Sofra *(W1, WC2)*
Tas *(WC1)*

West
Best Mangal *(SW6, W14)**
Fez Mangal *(W11)**

North
Antepliler *(N1, N4)*
Beyoglu *(NW3)*
Gallipoli *(N1)*
Gem *(N1)*
Izgara *(N3)*
Mangal II *(N16)*
Petek *(N4)*

South
Tas (Cafe) *(SE1)*
Tas Pide *(SE1)*

East
Haz *(E1, EC2, EC3)*
Hazev *(E14)*
Mangal I *(E8)**
Tas *(EC1)*

AFGHANI
North
Afghan Kitchen *(N1)**

BURMESE
West
Mandalay *(W2)*

CHINESE
Central
A Wong *(SW1)*
Ba Shan *(W1)**
Baozi Inn *(WC2)*
Bar Shu *(W1)**
Bo London *(W1)*
The Bright Courtyard *(W1)*
Chilli Cool *(WC1)*
China Tang *(W1)*
Chuen Cheng Ku *(W1)*
Empress of Sichuan *(WC2)**
The Four Seasons *(W1)**
Golden Dragon *(W1)*
The Grand Imperial *(SW1)*
Hakkasan *(W1)*
Haozhan *(W1)**
Harbour City *(W1)*
Hunan *(SW1)**
Imperial China *(WC2)*
Jenny Lo's Tea House *(SW1)*
Joy King Lau *(WC2)*
Kai Mayfair *(W1)*
Ken Lo's Memories *(SW1)*
Mr Chow *(SW1)*
Mr Kong *(WC2)*
New Mayflower *(W1)**
New World *(W1)*
Plum Valley *(W1)**
Princess Garden *(W1)**
Royal China *(W1)**
Royal China Club *(W1)**
Shanghai Blues *(WC1)*
Wong Kei *(W1)*
Yauatcha *(W1)**
Yming *(W1)**

West
Choys *(SW3)*
Fortune Cookie *(W2)**
The Four Seasons *(W2)**
Gold Mine *(W2)*
Good Earth *(SW3)**
Ken Lo's Memories of China *(W8)*
Mandarin Kitchen *(W2)**
Maxim *(W13)*
Min Jiang *(W8)**
Mr Wing *(SW5)*
North China *(W3)**
Pearl Liang *(W2)**
Royal China *(SW6, W2)**
Seventeen *(W11)*
Stick & Bowl *(W8)**
Taiwan Village *(SW6)**
Tian Fu *(W12)*

North
Good Earth *(NW7)**
Green Cottage *(NW3)*
Gung-Ho *(NW6)*
Kaifeng *(NW4)**
Phoenix Palace *(NW1)*
Sakonis *(HA0)**
Singapore Garden *(NW6)**
Yipin China *(N1)**

South
Bayee Village *(SW19)*
Dalchini *(SW19)*
Dragon Castle *(SE17)**
Four Regions *(TW9)*

Hutong *(SE1)*
China Boulevard *(SW18)*

East
Chinese Cricket Club *(EC4)*
Gourmet San *(E2)*
HKK *(EC2)*
Imperial City *(EC3)*
Lotus Chinese Floating
    Restaurant *(E14)*
My Old Place *(E1)*
Royal China *(E14)*
Sedap *(EC1)*
Shanghai *(E8)*
Sichuan Folk *(E1)*
Yi-Ban *(E16)*

CHINESE, DIM SUM
Central
The Bright Courtyard *(W1)*
Chuen Cheng Ku *(W1)*
dim T *(W1)*
Golden Dragon *(W1)*
The Grand Imperial *(SW1)*
Hakkasan *(W1)*
Harbour City *(W1)*
Imperial China *(WC2)*
Joy King Lau *(WC2)*
Leong's Legends *(W1)*
New World *(W1)*
ping pong *(W1)*
Princess Garden *(W1)*
Royal China *(W1)*
Royal China Club *(W1)*
Shanghai Blues *(WC1)*
Yauatcha *(W1)*

West
Min Jiang *(W8)*
Pearl Liang *(W2)*
ping pong *(W2)*
Royal China *(SW6,W2)*

North
dim T *(N6, NW3)*
Phoenix Palace *(NW1)*

South
dim T *(SE1)*
Dragon Castle *(SE17)*
China Boulevard *(SW18)*
ping pong *(SE1)*

East
Lotus Chinese Floating
    Restaurant *(E14)*
ping pong *(E1, EC4)*
Royal China *(E14)*
Shanghai *(E8)*
Yi-Ban *(E16)*

GEORGIAN
West
Colchis *(W2)*

North
Little Georgia Café *(N1)*

East
Little Georgia Café *(E2)*

INDIAN
Central
Amaya *(SW1)*

Benares *(W1)*
Chettinad *(W1)*
Chor Bizarre *(W1)*
The Cinnamon Club *(SW1)*
Cinnamon Soho *(W1)*
Dishoom *(WC2)*
Gaylord *(W1)*
Gopal's of Soho *(W1)*
Gymkhana *(W1)*
Imli Street *(W1)*
Indali Lounge *(W1)*
India Club *(WC2)*
Malabar Junction *(WC1)*
Masala Zone *(W1,WC2)*
Mela *(WC2)*
Mint Leaf *(SW1)*
Moti Mahal *(WC2)*
La Porte des Indes *(W1)*
Punjab *(WC2)*
Ragam *(W1)*
Red Fort *(W1)*
Roti Chai *(W1)*
Sagar *(W1,WC2)*
Salaam Namaste *(WC1)*
Salloos *(SW1)*
Tamarind *(W1)*
Trishna *(W1)*
Veeraswamy *(W1)*
Woodlands *(SW1,W1)*
Zayna *(W1)*

West
Anarkali *(W6)*
Bombay Brasserie *(SW7)*
Bombay Palace *(W2)*
Brilliant *(UB2)*
Chakra *(W11)*
Chutney Mary *(SW10)*
Durbar *(W2)*
Gifto's *(UB1)*
The Greedy Buddha *(SW6)*
Indian Zing *(W6)*
Karma *(W14)*
Khan's *(W2)*
Khan's of Kensington *(SW7)*
Madhu's *(UB1)*
Malabar *(W8)*
Masala Zone *(SW5, SW6,W2)*
Miran Masala *(W14)*
Mirch Masala *(UB1)*
Monty's *(SW6,W13,W5)*
Noor Jahan *(SW5,W2)*
The Painted Heron *(SW10)*
Potli *(W6)*
Rasoi *(SW3)*
Sagar *(W6)*
Star of India *(SW5)*
Thali *(SW5)*
Zaika *(W8)*

North
Anglo Asian Tandoori *(N16)*
Chutneys *(NW1)*
Delhi Grill *(N1)*
Diwana Bhel-Poori House *(NW1)*
Eriki *(NW3)*
Great Nepalese *(NW1)*
Guglee *(NW3, NW6)*
Indian Rasoi *(N2)*
Jai Krishna *(N4)*
Masala Zone *(N1, NW1)*
Paradise Hampstead *(NW3)*
Rani *(N3)*
Roots at N1 *(N1)*
Sakonis *(HA0)*

Vijay *(NW6)*
Woodlands *(NW3)*
Zaffrani *(N1)*

South
Apollo Banana Leaf *(SW17)*
Babur *(SE23)*
Bangalore Express *(SE1)*
Bengal Clipper *(SE1)*
Chutney *(SW18)*
Cocum *(SW20)*
Dalchini *(SW19)*
Everest Inn *(SE3)*
Ganapati *(SE15)*
Gandhi's *(SE11)*
Holy Cow *(SW11)*
Hot Stuff *(SW8)*
Indian Moment *(SW11)*
Indian Ocean *(SW17)*
Indian Zilla *(SW13)*
Kennington Tandoori *(SE11)*
Lahore Karahi *(SW17)*
Lahore Kebab House *(SW16)*
Ma Goa *(SW15)*
Mango & Silk *(SW14)*
Mango Food of India *(SE1)*
Mirch Masala *(SW16, SW17)*
Nazmins *(SW18)*
Sree Krishna *(SW17)*
Tandoori Nights *(SE22)*

East
Bangalore Express *(EC3)*
Café Spice Namaste *(E1)*
Cinnamon Kitchen *(EC2)*
Dishoom *(E2)*
Dockmaster's House *(E14)*
Lahore Kebab House *(E1)*
Mint Leaf *(EC2)*
Mirch Masala *(E1)*
Needoo *(E1)*
Tayyabs *(E1)*

INDIAN, SOUTHERN
Central
India Club *(WC2)*
Malabar Junction *(WC1)*
Quilon *(SW1)*
Ragam *(W1)*
Rasa Maricham *(WC1)*
Rasa Samudra *(W1)*
Sagar *(W1, WC2)*
Woodlands *(SW1, W1)*

West
Sagar *(W6)*
Shilpa *(W6)*

North
Chutneys *(NW1)*
Rani *(N3)*
Rasa Travancore *(N16)*
Vijay *(NW6)*
Woodlands *(NW3)*

South
Cocum *(SW20)*
Ganapati *(SE15)*
Sree Krishna *(SW17)*

JAPANESE
Central
Abeno *(WC1, WC2)*
Abokado *(W1, WC2)*

aqua kyoto *(W1)*
Atari-Ya *(W1)*
Benihana *(W1)*
Bincho Yakitori *(W1)*
Bone Daddies *(W1)*
Chisou *(W1)*
Chotto Matte *(W1)*
Defune *(W1)*
Dinings *(W1)*
Eat Tokyo *(WC1, WC2)*
Flesh and Buns *(WC2)*
Hazuki *(WC2)*
Ikeda *(W1)*
Kiku *(W1)*
Kikuchi *(W1)*
Kirazu *(W1)*
Koya *(W1)*
Koya-Ko *(W1)*
Kulu Kulu *(W1, WC2)*
Matsuri *(SW1)*
Miyama *(W1)*
Nizuni *(W1)*
Nobu *(W1)*
Nobu Berkeley *(W1)*
Roka *(W1)*
Sakana-tei *(W1)*
Sake No Hana *(SW1)*
Sakura *(W1)*
Shoryu Ramen *(SW1, W1)*
Sticks'n'Sushi *(WC2)*
Sumosan *(W1)*
Taro *(W1)*
Toku *(SW1)*
Tokyo Diner *(WC2)*
Tonkotsu *(W1)*
Tsunami *(W1)*
Umu *(W1)*
Wagamama *(SW1, W1, WC1, WC2)*
Yoisho *(W1)*
Yoshino *(W1)*

West
Atari-Ya *(W3, W5)*
Benihana *(SW3)*
Chisou *(SW3, W4)*
Eat Tokyo *(W6, W8)*
Inaho *(W2)*
Itsu *(SW3, W11)*
Kiraku *(W5)*
Kulu Kulu *(SW7)*
Maguro *(W9)*
Nozomi *(SW3)*
Okawari *(W5)*
The Shiori *(W2)*
Sushinho *(SW3)*
Tosa *(W6)*
Wagamama *(W8)*
Yashin *(SW7, W8)*
Zuma *(SW7)*

North
Akari *(N1)*
Asakusa *(NW1)*
Atari-Ya *(N12, NW4, NW6)*
Bento Cafe *(NW1)*
Café Japan *(NW11)*
Dotori *(N4)*
Eat Tokyo *(NW11)*
Jin Kichi *(NW3)*
Soho Japan *(NW1)*
Sushi-Say *(NW2)*
Wagamama *(N1, NW1)*

South
Cho-San *(SW15)*

Fujiyama *(SW9)*
Hashi *(SW20)**
Matsuba *(TW9)**
Sticks'n'Sushi *(SW19)*
Tsunami *(SW4)**
Wagamama *(SE1, SW15, SW19)*

East
Abokado *(EC1, EC4)*
City Miyama *(EC4)*
Itsu *(E14)*
K10 *(EC2)**
Kurumaya *(EC4)*
Mugen *(EC4)*
Pham Sushi *(EC1)**
Roka *(E14)**
Sushisamba *(EC2)*
Sushi Tetsu *(EC1)**
Tajima Tei *(EC1)**
Taro *(EC4)*
Wagamama *(E14, EC2, EC3, EC4)*

KOREAN
Central
Asadal *(WC1)*
Bibimbap Soho *(W1)*
Kimchee *(WC1)*
Koba *(W1)*

North
Dotori *(N4)**

South
Cah-Chi *(SW18, SW20)**

East
Jubo *(EC2)*

MALAYSIAN
Central
C&R Cafe *(W1)*
Spice Market *(W1)*

West
Satay House *(W2)*

North
Singapore Garden *(NW6)**

South
Champor-Champor *(SE1)**

East
Sedap *(EC1)*

PAKISTANI
Central
Salloos *(SW1)**

West
Miran Masala *(W14)**
Mirch Masala *(UB1)**

South
Lahore Karahi *(SW17)**
Lahore Kebab House *(SW16)**
Mirch Masala *(SW16, SW17)**

East
Lahore Kebab House *(E1)**
Mirch Masala *(E1)**
Needoo *(E1)**
Tayyabs *(E1)**

PAN-ASIAN
Central
Banana Tree Canteen *(W1)*
Circus *(WC2)*
dim T *(SW1, W1)*
Haozhan *(W1)**
Hare & Tortoise *(WC1)*
Inamo *(SW1, W1)*
Novikov (Asian restaurant) *(W1)*
Spice Market *(W1)*

West
Banana Tree Canteen *(W2, W9)*
E&O *(W11)**
Eight Over Eight *(SW3)*
Hare & Tortoise *(W14, W5)*
Mao Tai *(SW6)**

North
The Banana Tree Canteen *(NW6)*
dim T *(N6, NW3)*
Gilgamesh *(NW1)*
XO *(NW3)*

South
The Banana Tree Canteen *(SW11)*
dim T *(SE1)*
Hare & Tortoise *(SW15)*

East
Banana Tree Canteen *(EC1)*
Hare & Tortoise *(EC4)*

THAI
Central
Busaba Eathai *(SW1, W1, WC1, WC2)*
C&R Cafe *(W1)*
Crazy Bear *(W1)*
Mango Tree *(SW1)*
Patara *(W1)**
Rosa's Soho *(W1)*
Siam Central *(W1)*
Spice Market *(W1)*
Suda *(WC2)*
Thai Square *(SW1, W1, WC2)*

West
Addie's Thai Café *(SW5)**
Bangkok *(SW7)**
Bedlington Café *(W4)**
Busaba Eathai *(SW3, W12)*
C&R Cafe *(W2)*
Café 209 *(SW6)*
Churchill Arms *(W8)*
Esarn Kheaw *(W12)**
Fat Boy's *(W4, W5)*
Fitou's Thai Restaurant *(W10)**
Old Parr's Head *(W14)*
101 Thai Kitchen *(W6)**
Patara *(SW3)**
Sukho Fine Thai Cuisine *(SW6)**
Thai Square *(SW7)*
The Walmer Castle *(W11)*

North
Isarn *(N1)**
Thai Square *(N1)*
Yum Yum *(N16)**

South
Amaranth *(SW18)**
The Begging Bowl *(SE15)**
Blue Elephant *(SW6)*
Fat Boy's *(SW14, TW1, TW8)*

Kaosarn *(SW11, SW9)**
The Paddyfield *(SW12)**
The Pepper Tree *(SW4)*
Suk Saran *(SW19)*
Talad Thai *(SW15)*
Thai Corner Café *(SE22)*
Thai Garden *(SW11)*
Thai Square *(SW15)*
Thai Square City *(SW6)*

East
Busaba Eathai *(E20, EC1)*
Elephant Royale *(E14)*
Naamyaa Café *(EC1)*
Rosa's *(E1)*
Thai Square *(EC4)*
Thai Square City *(EC3)*

VIETNAMESE
Central
Bam-Bou *(W1)*
Cây Tre *(W1)*
Pho *(W1)**
Viet *(W1)*

West
Pho *(W12)**
Saigon Saigon *(W6)*

North
Huong-Viet *(N1)*
Ladudu *(NW6)*

South
Cafe East *(SE16)**
Mien Tay *(SW11)**
The Paddyfield *(SW12)**

East
Cây Tre *(EC1)*
City Càphê *(EC2)**
Green Papaya *(E8)**
Mien Tay *(E2)**
Pho *(E1, EC1)**
Sông Quê *(E2)*
Viet Grill *(E2)**
Viet Hoa *(E2)**

AREA OVERVIEWS

CENTRAL

Soho, Covent Garden & Bloomsbury
(Parts of W1, all WC2 and WC1)

£80+	L'Atelier de Joel Robuchon	*French*	②②②
	Asia de Cuba	*Fusion*	④⑤④
£70+	Christopher's	*American*	⑤③②
	Brasserie Max	*British, Modern*	④④③
	Homage	*"*	④④③
	The Ivy	*"*	④③②
	Refuel	*"*	④④②
	Rules	*British, Traditional*	③②①
	Savoy Grill	*"*	④③③
	Simpsons-in-the-Strand	*"*	④④③
	Kaspar's Seafood and Grill	*Fish & seafood*	③②③
	J Sheekey	*"*	②①①
	Gaucho	*Steaks & grills*	③④④
	MASH Steakhouse		③③③
	aqua kyoto	*Japanese*	④④③
	Spice Market	*Pan-Asian*	④④④
£60+	Axis	*British, Modern*	④④④
	Balthazar	*"*	⑤④③
	Bob Bob Ricard	*"*	③②①
	Hix	*"*	④④⑤
	Indigo	*"*	④③④
	Paramount	*"*	④④②
	Tom's Kitchen	*"*	④③③
	The Delaunay	*East & Cent. European*	③②①
	J Sheekey Oyster Bar	*Fish & seafood*	②①①
	Gauthier Soho	*French*	①①②
	aqua nueva	*Spanish*	⑤⑤④
	Hawksmoor	*Steaks & grills*	②②③
	STK Steakhouse	*"*	④④③
	Ladurée	*Afternoon tea*	②④③
	Shanghai Blues	*Chinese*	④⑤⑤
	Yauatcha	*"*	①④②
	Red Fort	*Indian*	③④④
	Circus	*Pan-Asian*	④④②
£50+	Big Easy	*American*	③③②
	Joe Allen	*"*	⑤④②
	Dean Street Townhouse	*British, Modern*	④④②
	Le Deuxième	*"*	④④⑤
	Ducksoup	*"*	④④④
	Hush	*"*	④⑤④
	Kettners	*"*	④③③
	The Northall	*"*	③②②
	The Portrait	*"*	④④①
	Quo Vadis	*"*	③③②
	Social Eating House	*"*	③③③
	The National Dining Rms	*British, Traditional*	⑤⑤④
	Wright Brothers	*Fish & seafood*	②③②
	Antidote	*French*	③④③
	Brasserie Blanc	*"*	④③④
	Café des Amis	*"*	④④④

	Restaurant	Cuisine	Ratings
	Clos Maggiore	"	②⑪⑪
	Les Deux Salons	"	④④❸
	L'Escargot	"	❸②②
	The Giaconda	"	❸②④
	Mon Plaisir	"	④❸❸
	Otto's	"	②②❸
	Randall & Aubin	"	②②⑪
	Kopapa	Fusion	❸④④
	Sarastro	International	⑤⑤❸
	The 10 Cases	"	④⑪②
	Bocca Di Lupo	Italian	⑪②②
	Orso	"	④❸④
	Vasco & Piero's Pavilion	"	②②❸
	Nopi	Mediterranean	②②❸
	Albannach	Scottish	④④❸
	The Bountiful Cow	Steaks & grills	④④④
	Sophie's Steakhouse	"	④④④
	St Moritz	Swiss	❸④❸
	Cantina Laredo	Mexican/TexMex	❸②⑤
	Bar Shu	Chinese	②⑤④
	Moti Mahal	Indian	②②④
	Chotto Matte	Japanese	– – –
	Flesh and Buns	"	– – –
	Haozhan	Pan-Asian	②④⑤
	Patara	Thai	②❸❸
£40+	All Star Lanes	American	④❸❸
	Bodean's	"	❸④❸
	Mishkin's	"	⑤④❸
	Spuntino	"	②❸②
	Belgo	Belgian	④④④
	Andrew Edmunds	British, Modern	❸②⑪
	The Angel & Crown	"	❸④④
	Arbutus	"	❸❸④
	Aurora	"	❸②⑪
	Coopers	"	❸❸④
	The Norfolk Arms	"	❸④④
	Shampers	"	❸②②
	10 Greek Street	"	②⑪❸
	Union Jacks	"	⑤④④
	Vinoteca	"	④❸②
	VQ	"	④❸④
	Great Queen Street	British, Traditional	②❸❸
	The Lady Ottoline	"	④④❸
	Porters	"	④❸❸
	Cape Town Fish Market	Fish & seafood	④④❸
	Loch Fyne	"	④❸④
	Café Bohème	French	❸❸②
	Le Cigalon	"	❸②②
	Côte	"	④❸④
	Le Garrick	"	④④❸
	Green Man & French Horn	"	❸②❸
	Terroirs	"	❸❸❸
	Gay Hussar	Hungarian	④❸②
	Balans	International	⑤④④
	Bedford & Strand	"	④④❸
	Boulevard	"	④④❸
	Browns	"	⑤④④

			Ratings
	Cork & Bottle	"	4 4 2
	Giraffe	"	5 5 5
	National Gallery Café	"	3 4 3
	Ciao Bella	Italian	4 2 2
	Da Mario	"	3 2 3
	Dehesa	"	1 2 2
	Jamie's Italian	"	5 5 4
	Made in Italy	"	3 4 3
	Mele e Pere	"	3 3 4
	San Carlo Cicchetti	"	3 4 4
	Barrafina	Spanish	1 1 2
	Cigala	"	3 3 4
	Copita	"	3 4 3
	Opera Tavern	"	2 3 3
	Tapas Brindisa Soho	"	2 3 3
	Garufin	Steaks & grills	3 2 3
	Mildreds	Vegetarian	2 4 3
	Orchard	"	3 3 3
	Burger & Lobster	Burgers, etc	2 3 3
	Wolfe's	"	3 4 4
	Fire & Stone	Pizza	4 4 4
	La Bodega Negra	Mexican/TexMex	4 3 2
	Café Pacifico	"	4 4 2
	Ceviche	Peruvian	3 3 2
	Ba Shan	Chinese	2 4 4
	Imperial China	"	4 4 4
	Plum Valley	"	2 3 2
	Yming	"	2 2 4
	Cinnamon Soho	Indian	4 4 4
	Dishoom	"	3 3 1
	Malabar Junction	"	3 4 3
	Mela	"	3 4 4
	Abeno	Japanese	3 3 3
	Hazuki	"	3 4 4
	Sticks'n'Sushi	"	3 3 2
	Inamo	Pan-Asian	4 4 4
	Suda	Thai	3 3 3
	Thai Square	"	4 4 4
£35+	Soho Diner	American	3 2 2
	Whyte & Brown	British, Modern	– – –
	Brasserie Zédel	French	5 3 1
	Prix Fixe	"	3 2 3
	Savoir Faire	"	3 3 4
	Real Greek	Greek	5 4 4
	Polpo	Italian	4 3 1
	Amico Bio	Vegetarian	3 4 3
	Byron	Burgers, etc	3 3 3
	Honest Burgers	"	1 2 3
	North Sea Fish	Fish & chips	3 3 4
	Rossopomodoro	Pizza	3 3 3
	Lupita	Mexican/TexMex	4 4 3
	Sofra	Turkish	4 3 4
	Tas	"	4 3 3
	Chuen Cheng Ku	Chinese	3 4 4
	Empress of Sichuan	"	2 3 2
	Harbour City	"	3 4 5
	New Mayflower	"	2 2 4

New World	"	④④❸
Leong's Legends	Chinese, Dim sum	❸④❸
Imli Street	Indian	❸❷❷
Sagar	"	❸❸④
Rasa Maricham	Indian, Southern	❷❷❸
Bincho Yakitori	Japanese	❸❸❸
Kirazu	"	– – –
Wagamama	"	④❸④
Asadal	Korean	❸④④
Kimchee	"	④④❸
Busaba Eathai	Thai	❸❸❷
Rosa's Soho	"	❸❷❸
Cây Tre	Vietnamese	❸④❸
Pho	"	❷❷❷

£30+			
	Café in the Crypt	International	④④④
	Gordon's Wine Bar	"	⑤④❶
	Carom at Meza	"	❷❷❸
	Caffé Vergnano	Italian	④❸❷
	La Porchetta Pizzeria	"	❸❸❸
	Princi	"	❸④❷
	Diner	Burgers, etc	④❸❷
	Ed's Easy Diner	"	④④❸
	MEATmarket	"	❸④④
	Caffé Vergnano	Sandwiches, cakes, etc	④❸❷
	The Courtauld (Café)	"	④❸❸
	Fernandez & Wells	"	❸❸❷
	Wahaca	Mexican/TexMex	❸❸❷
	Gaby's	Israeli	❸❸④
	Yalla Yalla	Lebanese	❸④❸
	Chilli Cool	Chinese	❸⑤⑤
	The Four Seasons	"	❷⑤⑤
	Golden Dragon	"	❸④❸
	Joy King Lau	"	❸④④
	Mr Kong	"	④❸④
	ping pong	Chinese, Dim sum	④❷❸
	Gopal's of Soho	Indian	❸❸④
	Masala Zone	"	❸❷❷
	Salaam Namaste	"	❷④④
	Koya	Japanese	❷❸❸
	Koya-Ko	"	– – –
	Kulu Kulu	"	④⑤④
	Taro	"	❸❸❸
	Tonkotsu	"	❸❸❸
	Banana Tree Canteen	Pan-Asian	④④❸

£25+			
	Pitt Cue Co	American	❶❸❸
	Seven Stars	British, Modern	❸④❷
	Bar Italia	Sandwiches, cakes, etc	④❷❶
	Konditor & Cook	"	❸④④
	Leon	"	④❸❸
	Paul	"	④⑤④
	Benito's Hat	Mexican/TexMex	❸❸④
	Comptoir Libanais	Lebanese	④④❸
	Wong Kei	Chinese	④⑤⑤
	India Club	Indian	❸❸⑤
	Punjab	"	❷❷④
	Shoryu Ramen	Japanese	❷❸❸

	Tokyo Diner	"	❸②❸
	Bibimbap Soho	Korean	❸❸④
	Hare & Tortoise	Pan-Asian	❸❸❸
	C&R Cafe	Thai	❸④④
£20+	Bistro 1	Mediterranean	④❷❸
	Flat Iron	Steaks & grills	❸❷❷
	Grillshack	"	❸❷④
	Food for Thought	Vegetarian	❸❸④
	Shake Shack	Burgers, etc	– – –
	Pizza Pilgrims	Pizza	– – –
	Fleet River Bakery	Sandwiches, cakes, etc	❷④❸
	Bone Daddies	Japanese	❷④❸
	Eat Tokyo	"	❸❸④
	Viet	Vietnamese	❸④④
£15+	Hummus Bros	Mediterranean	❸❸④
	Nordic Bakery	Scandinavian	❸④❸
	Maison Bertaux	Afternoon tea	❷❸❶
	Notes	Sandwiches, cakes, etc	④❷❷
	Chilango	Mexican/TexMex	❷❷❸
	Chipotle	"	❸❸④
	Tortilla	"	❸❸❸
	Baozi Inn	Chinese	❸④④
	Abokado	Japanese	④④④
£10+	Five Guys	Burgers, etc	– – –
	Fryer's Delight	Fish & chips	❸④⑤
	Gelupo	Ice cream	❶❷❸
	Flat White	Sandwiches, cakes, etc	❷❷❷
	Monmouth Coffee Co	"	❶❶❷
	Pod	"	❸❸④

Mayfair & St James's (Parts of W1 and SW1)

£130+	Le Gavroche	French	❶❶❷
£120+	Alain Ducasse	French	④❸④
	Hélène Darroze	"	❸❸❷
	Hibiscus	"	④④④
£110+	The Ritz Restaurant	French	④❸❶
	Sketch (Lecture Rm)	"	④❸❶
£100+	The Greenhouse	French	❷❶❷
	The Square	"	❷❶❸
	Umu	Japanese	❸④❸
£90+	Dorchester Grill	British, Modern	❸❷④
	Seven Park Place	"	❸❸❸
	Wiltons	British, Traditional	❸④❷
	Galvin at Windows	French	④❸❶
	C London	Italian	⑤⑤④
	Downtown Mayfair	"	④④④
	Murano	"	❸❷❸
	Cut	Steaks & grills	⑤⑤⑤
	Kai Mayfair	Chinese	④④④

£80+			
Pollen Street Social	British, Modern		2 2 3
Thirty Six	"		3 5 4
Corrigan's Mayfair	British, Traditional		4 4 4
maze	French		4 4 4
La Petite Maison	"		2 3 2
Amaranto	Italian		4 4 5
Theo Randall	"		2 3 4
Bo London	Chinese		3 2 4
Hakkasan	"		3 5 2
Benares	Indian		2 2 3
Matsuri	Japanese		3 2 5
Nobu, Park Ln	"		2 4 4
Nobu, Berkeley St	"		3 4 4

£70+			
Alyn Williams	British, Modern		2 0 4
Athenaeum	"		2 0 3
Le Caprice	"		3 2 2
Browns (Albemarle)	British, Traditional		4 3 3
Bentley's	Fish & seafood		2 3 2
Scott's	"		2 2 2
Brasserie Chavot	French		2 2 3
Sketch (Gallery)	"		4 4 4
Babbo	Italian		5 4 4
Cecconi's	"		4 4 2
Franco's	"		3 3 3
Novikov (Italian restaurant)	"		5 5 4
Gaucho	Steaks & grills		3 4 4
JW Steakhouse	"		4 4 3
maze Grill	"		4 4 4
34	"		4 3 3
Coya	Peruvian		2 2 0
China Tang	Chinese		4 4 3
Tamarind	Indian		2 3 4
Veeraswamy	"		2 2 2
Sumosan	Japanese		2 4 4
Novikov (Asian restaurant)	Pan-Asian		3 4 3

£60+			
Automat	American		4 4 4
Bellamy's	British, Modern		3 2 2
The Berners Tavern	"		– – –
Criterion	"		4 4 0
Langan's Brasserie	"		4 2 2
Little Social	"		2 2 2
Mews of Mayfair	"		4 3 2
Quaglino's	"		5 4 4
Wild Honey	"		3 4 4
The Fountain (Fortnum's)	British, Traditional		4 3 3
Green's	"		3 3 4
The Keeper's House	"		– – –
Boudin Blanc	French		4 4 2
Boulestin	"		3 0 3
Goodman	Steaks & grills		2 2 3
The Guinea Grill	"		3 2 2
Hawksmoor	"		2 2 3
Rowley's	"		4 4 4
Ladurée	Afternoon tea		2 4 3
The Sketch (Parlour)	Sandwiches, cakes, etc		4 4 2
Momo	North African		4 4 0

	Name	Cuisine	Rating
	Gymkhana	Indian	– – –
	Benihana	Japanese	4 4 4
	Ikeda	"	2 2 5
	Sake No Hana	"	4 3 4
£50+	The Avenue	British, Modern	3 3 3
	Hush	"	4 5 4
	Sotheby's Café	"	4 2 2
	The Wolseley	"	3 2 1
	Fishworks	Fish & seafood	3 4 4
	Pescatori	"	3 3 4
	Aubaine	French	5 5 4
	Brasserie Blanc	"	4 3 4
	28-50	"	3 2 3
	Alloro	Italian	3 3 4
	Il Calcio	"	– – –
	La Genova	"	4 4 4
	Piccolino	"	4 3 4
	Sartoria	"	3 3 3
	Diamond Jub' (Fortnum's)	Afternoon tea	3 0 0
	Delfino	Pizza	2 3 4
	Royal Academy	Sandwiches, cakes, etc	5 4 4
	Al Hamra	Lebanese	4 4 4
	Noura	"	3 4 3
	Princess Garden	Chinese	1 2 3
	Chor Bizarre	Indian	2 2 2
	Mint Leaf	"	2 3 3
	Chisou	Japanese	2 3 4
	Kiku	"	2 2 5
	Miyama	"	2 2 5
	Patara	Thai	2 3 3
£40+	Hard Rock Café	American	3 3 2
	Inn the Park	British, Modern	4 3 2
	The Only Running Footman	"	3 4 2
	1707	"	3 2 3
	L'Artiste Musclé	French	4 4 3
	Browns	International	5 4 4
	Al Duca	Italian	4 4 5
	Il Vicolo	"	3 2 4
	Chop Shop	Steaks & grills	3 3 4
	Ritz (Palm Court)	Afternoon tea	3 2 1
	Burger & Lobster	Burgers, etc	2 3 3
	Al Sultan	Lebanese	3 2 4
	Woodlands	Indian	3 4 4
	Toku	Japanese	– – –
	Yoshino	"	3 0 5
	Inamo	Pan-Asian	4 4 4
	Thai Square	Thai	4 4 4
£35+	The Windmill	British, Traditional	3 4 3
	El Pirata	Spanish	4 2 1
	Byron	Burgers, etc	3 3 3
	Benugo	Sandwiches, cakes, etc	4 4 2
	Sofra	Turkish	4 3 4
	Rasa Samudra	Indian, Southern	2 2 3
	Wagamama	Japanese	4 3 4
	Busaba Eathai	Thai	3 3 2

£30+	tibits	Vegetarian	③③③
	Ed's Easy Diner	Burgers, etc	④④③
	Sakana-tei	Japanese	②②⑤
	Sakura	"	③③④
£25+	Stock Pot	International	④③③
	Shoryu Ramen	Japanese	②③③
£15+	La Bottega	Italian	③③②
	Taylor St Baristas	Sandwiches, cakes, etc	②③③
£10+	Fuzzy's Grub	Sandwiches, cakes, etc	③④④
	Spianata & Co	"	③②③

Fitzrovia & Marylebone (Part of W1)

£100+	Pied à Terre	French	⓪⓪③
£90+	Roux at the Landau	British, Modern	③③②
	Bubbledogs (Kitchen Table@)	Fusion	⓪②②
	Texture	Scandinavian	②②③
£80+	Hakkasan	Chinese	③⑤②
£70+	L'Autre Pied	French	②②④
	Orrery	"	③②②
	The Providores	International	②④⑤
	Cotidie	Italian	– – –
	Locanda Locatelli	"	③③④
	Gaucho	Steaks & grills	③④④
	Roka	Japanese	⓪③③
£60+	Oscar	British, Modern	④④②
	Galvin Bistrot de Luxe	French	②②②
	Il Baretto	Italian	– – –
	Dabbous	Mediterranean	⓪⓪③
	Royal China Club	Chinese	②③④
	La Porte des Indes	Indian	③②②
	Defune	Japanese	②③⑤
	Crazy Bear	Thai	③④②
£50+	The Lockhart	American	– – –
	Grazing Goat	British, Modern	③④③
	The Union Café	"	④④④
	Fishworks	Fish & seafood	③④④
	Pescatori	"	③③④
	Elena's L'Etoile	French	④④④
	28-50	"	③②③
	Villandry	"	④④④
	The Wallace	"	④⑤①
	Archipelago	Fusion	④④③
	Providores (Tapa Room)	"	②④③
	Caffè Caldesi	Italian	③②③
	Sardo	"	②③④
	Riding House Café	Mediterranean	④④①
	Verru	Scandinavian	②②③
	Black & Blue	Steaks & grills	③③④

	Zoilo	*Argentinian*	② ② ④
	Lima	*Peruvian*	③ ④ ④
	Reubens	*Kosher*	③ ④ ④
	Levant	*Lebanese*	④ ③ ②
	The Bright Courtyard	*Chinese*	④ ④ ④
	Gaylord	*Indian*	③ ③ ④
	Trishna	"	② ③ ③
	Zayna	"	② ② ④
	Dinings	*Japanese*	① ② ⑤
	Bam-Bou	*Vietnamese*	③ ③ ②
£40+	Hardy's Brasserie	*British, Modern*	③ ④ ③
	Newman Street Tavern	"	④ ④ ③
	Ozer	"	④ ② ④
	RIBA Café	"	④ ④ ②
	Vinoteca Seymour Place	"	④ ③ ②
	Canteen	*British, Traditional*	⑤ ⑤ ⑤
	Bonnie Gull	*Fish & seafood*	② ③ ②
	Hellenic	*Greek*	– – –
	Giraffe	*International*	⑤ ⑤ ⑤
	Latium	*Italian*	② ⓪ ③
	Made in Italy	"	③ ④ ③
	Obika	"	③ ③ ③
	2 Veneti	"	④ ② ④
	Donostia	*Spanish*	③ ② ②
	Fino	"	③ ③ ③
	Ibérica	"	③ ③ ③
	Navarro's	"	③ ④ ③
	Salt Yard	"	② ③ ③
	Le Relais de Venise	*Steaks & grills*	③ ④ ③
	Fairuz	*Lebanese*	③ ② ③
	Maroush	"	② ③ ④
	Ishtar	*Turkish*	③ ② ③
	Royal China	*Chinese*	② ④ ④
	Indali Lounge	*Indian*	② ② ④
	Roti Chai	"	② ③ ③
	Woodlands	"	③ ④ ④
	Kikuchi	*Japanese*	① ④ ⑤
	Nizuni	"	② ② ④
	Tsunami	"	② ④ ④
	Yoisho	"	② ④ ⑤
	Koba	*Korean*	③ ③ ④
£35+	Real Greek	*Greek*	⑤ ④ ④
	Briciole	*Italian*	③ ③ ③
	Barrica	*Spanish*	② ② ①
	MEATLiquor	*Burgers, etc*	② ④ ③
	Benugo	*Sandwiches, cakes, etc*	④ ④ ②
	La Fromagerie Café	"	② ④ ②
	Natural Kitchen	*Salads*	③ ④ ③
	Sofra	*Turkish*	④ ③ ④
	Sagar	*Indian*	③ ③ ④
	Wagamama	*Japanese*	④ ③ ④
	Pho	*Vietnamese*	② ② ②
£30+	Bubbledogs	*American*	④ ③ ②
	Lantana Cafe	*Australian*	③ ③ ②
	Picture	*British, Modern*	② ② ④

	Wahaca	Mexican/TexMex	❸❸❷
	Yalla Yalla	Lebanese	❸❹❸
	Honey & Co	Middle Eastern	❷❷❹
	ping pong	Chinese, Dim sum	❹❷❸
	Chettinad	Indian	❸❸❹
	Atari-Ya	Japanese	❶❹❺
	dim T	Pan-Asian	❹❹❹
	Siam Central	Thai	❹❸❸
£25+	Vapiano	Italian	❸❸❸
	Golden Hind	Fish & chips	❸❶❸
	Leon	Sandwiches, cakes, etc	❹❸❸
	Paul	"	❹❺❹
	Benito's Hat	Mexican/TexMex	❸❸❹
	Comptoir Libanais	Lebanese	❹❹❸
	Ragam	Indian	❶❸❺
£20+	Patty and Bun	Burgers, etc	❶❸❸
	Patogh	Middle Eastern	❷❷❹
£15+	Nordic Bakery	Scandinavian	❸❹❸
	Scandinavian Kitchen	"	❷❷❸
	Tommi's Burger Joint	Burgers, etc	❷❹❹
	Nordic Bakery	Sandwiches, cakes, etc	❸❹❸
	Chipotle	Mexican/TexMex	❸❸❹
	Tortilla	"	❸❸❸
	Abokado	Japanese	❹❹❹
£10+	Kaffeine	Sandwiches, cakes, etc	❸❷❶

Belgravia, Pimlico, Victoria & Westminster (SW1, except St James's)

£110+	Marcus Wareing	French	❸❷❷
£100+	Apsleys	Italian	❹❹❸
	Rib Room	Steaks & grills	❸❷❹
£90+	Dinner	British, Traditional	❸❸❸
	One-O-One	Fish & seafood	❶❸❺
	Pétrus	French	❷❶❸
£80+	Koffmann's	French	❷❶❸
	Massimo	Mediterranean	❺❺❹
	Ametsa	Spanish	❺❹❺
	The Palm	Steaks & grills	❹❺❹
	Mr Chow	Chinese	❹❹❹
£70+	The Goring Hotel	British, Modern	❸❶❶
	Roux at Parliament Square	"	❸❷❹
	Zafferano	Italian	❸❸❹
	Amaya	Indian	❶❸❷
£60+	Bank Westminster	British, Modern	❹❹❹
	The Botanist	"	❺❺❺
	The Thomas Cubitt	"	❸❸❷
	Olivomare	Fish & seafood	❶❸❸

	The Balcon	*French*	❸❸❸
	Bar Boulud	"	❸❷❸
	Colbert	"	④④❸
	Motcombs	*International*	④❸❷
	Quirinale	*Italian*	❶❷④
	Sale e Pepe	"	④④❸
	Santini	"	④④④
	Signor Sassi	"	④❸❸
	Mari Vanna	*Russian*	④⑤❷
	Ladurée	*Afternoon tea*	❷④❸
	Hunan	*Chinese*	❶❸④
	Ken Lo's Memories	"	❸❸④
	The Cinnamon Club	*Indian*	❷❸❷
	Quilon	*Indian, Southern*	❶❷④
£50+	Ebury Rest' & Wine Bar	*British, Modern*	④④④
	The Fifth Floor Restaurant	"	❸❸❸
	The Orange	"	❸❸❷
	The Pantechnicon	"	❸❸❷
	Tate Britain (Rex Whistler)	"	– – –
	Le Cercle	*French*	❸❷❸
	Chabrot Bistrot d'Amis	"	❸❷❸
	La Poule au Pot	"	❸❸❶
	Caraffini	*Italian*	❸❶❷
	Il Convivio	"	❷❷❸
	Olivo	"	❷❷④
	Olivocarne	"	❸❷④
	Osteria Dell'Angolo	"	❸❷④
	About Thyme	*Mediterranean*	❷❶❸
	Boisdale	*Scottish*	❸❸❷
	Oliveto	*Pizza*	❷④④
	Beiteddine	*Lebanese*	❸❷④
	Ishbilia	"	❸❷⑤
	Noura	"	❸④❸
	The Grand Imperial	*Chinese*	❸❷❷
	Salloos	*Pakistani*	❷❷④
	Mango Tree	*Thai*	❸④④
£40+	Daylesford Organic	*British, Modern*	④⑤④
	No 11 Pimlico Road	"	④⑤④
	The Queens Arms	"	❸❸❷
	Browns	*International*	⑤④④
	Giraffe	"	⑤⑤⑤
	Grumbles	"	④❸❸
	Como Lario	*Italian*	④④❸
	Gran Paradiso	"	④❸④
	Gustoso	"	❸❶❸
	Ottolenghi	"	❶❷❸
	Tinello	"	❷❷❸
	Tozi	"	❷❷❷
	2 Amici	"	④❸④
	Goya	*Spanish*	④❸④
	Burger & Lobster	*Burgers, etc*	❷❸❸
	Baker & Spice	*Sandwiches, cakes, etc*	④④④
	Ranoush	*Lebanese*	❸❸④
	Kazan (Cafe)	*Turkish*	❸❸④
£35+	Seafresh	*Fish & chips*	❸④⑤

	Wagamama	*Japanese*	④❸④
£30+	The Vincent Rooms	*British, Modern*	❸❸❸
	Cyprus Mangal	*Turkish*	❷❸④
	A Wong	*Chinese*	❸❸❸
	Jenny Lo's	*"*	❸❷④
	dim T	*Pan-Asian*	④④④
£15+	La Bottega	*Italian*	❸❸❷
	William Curley	*Afternoon tea*	❷❸❸

WEST

Chelsea, South Kensington, Kensington, Earl's Court & Fulham (SW3, SW5, SW6, SW7, SW10 & W8)

£120+	Gordon Ramsay	*French*	④④④
£100+	Rasoi	*Indian*	❷❸❸
£90+	Tom Aikens	*British, Modern*	❷❸❸
£80+	Outlaw's Seafood and Grill	*Fish & seafood*	❷❶❸
	Il Ristorante	*Italian*	④❷④
	Nozomi	*Japanese*	④④⑤
	Yashin	"	❶❸❸
	Zuma	"	❶❸❷
£70+	Babylon	*British, Modern*	④④❷
	The Five Fields	"	❷❶❷
	Launceston Place	"	❷❷❷
	Bibendum	*French*	❸❷❶
	Scalini	*Italian*	❸❷❷
	Gaucho	*Steaks & grills*	❸④④
	Min Jiang	*Chinese*	❷❷❶
£60+	Bluebird	*British, Modern*	⑤④④
	Clarke's	"	❸❷ –
	Kitchen W8	"	❶❷❸
	Medlar	"	❷❷④
	Tom's Kitchen	"	④❸❸
	Poissonnerie de l'Av.	*Fish & seafood*	❷❷④
	Belvedere	*French*	④④❷
	Cheyne Walk Bras'	"	④④❸
	L'Etranger	"	❸④❸
	Racine	"	❸❸❸
	Daphne's	*Italian*	④❷❷
	La Famiglia	"	④④❸
	Lucio	"	❸④④
	San Lorenzo	"	– – –
	Locanda Ottomezzo	*Mediterranean*	④④④
	Cambio de Tercio	*Spanish*	❷❷❷
	Zaika	*Indian*	❷❸❸
	Benihana	*Japanese*	④④④
	Mao Tai	*Pan-Asian*	❷❷❷
£50+	Big Easy	*American*	❸❸❷
	The Abingdon	*British, Modern*	❸❸❷
	Brinkley's	"	⑤④❸
	Brompton Bar & Grill	"	❸❷❸
	The Enterprise	"	④❸❷
	Harwood Arms	"	❶❷❸
	The Henry Root	"	④④❸
	Kensington Place	"	❸❸④
	The Sands End	"	❸④❷
	White Horse	"	④④❸
	Bumpkin	*British, Traditional*	⑤⑤④
	Ffiona's	"	④❸❸

Maggie Jones's	"		④④❶
The Malt House	"		❷❸❸
Bibendum Oyster Bar	Fish & seafood		❷❸❸
Aubaine	French		⑤⑤④
La Brasserie	"		❸④❷
Le Colombier	"		❸❷❷
Garnier	"		❸❷④
The Pig's Ear	"		④④❸
Sushinho	Fusion		❷❸❸
Mazi	Greek		❸④④
Foxtrot Oscar	International		④④⑤
Gallery Mess	"		④④④
The Kensington Wine Rms	"		④❸❸
Calcio	Italian		– – –
El l even Park Walk	"		❸❸④
Frantoio	"		④❷❷
Manicomio	"		❸④❸
Osteria dell'Arancio	"		❸❸❸
Pellicano	"		④❶④
Rocco	"		④❷④
Tartufo	"		❶❶❸
Ziani's	"		❸❷❷
Polish Club	Polish		④④❷
Admiral Codrington	Steaks & grills		❸④④
Black & Blue	"		❸❸④
Kings Road Steakhouse	"		④④⑤
PJ's Bar and Grill	"		④❷❷
Sophie's Steakhouse	"		④④④
Good Earth	Chinese		❷❸❸
Ken Lo's Memories	"		❸④④
Bombay Brasserie	Indian		❸④④
Chutney Mary	"		❷❶❷
The Painted Heron	"		❶❷❸
Star of India	"		❷④④
Chisou	Japanese		❷❸④
Eight Over Eight	Pan-Asian		❸❷❸
Patara	Thai		❷❸❸
Sukho Fine Thai Cuisine	"		❶❶④
£40+			
Bodean's	American		❸④❸
Sticky Fingers	"		❸❸❸
The Anglesea Arms	British, Modern		④④❷
The Builders Arms	"		④❸❸
Butcher's Hook	"		❸❷❸
The Cadogan Arms	"		❸④❸
The Chelsea Ram	"		④❸❷
Jam Tree	"		❸❸❷
Joe's Brasserie	"		❸❷❸
The Mall Tavern	"		❸❸❸
Megan's Delicatessen	"		❸❸❷
VQ	"		④❸④
Whits	"		❷❶❷
The Brown Cow	British, Traditional		❸❸❷
The Surprise	"		④❸❷
L'Art du Fromage	French		❷❸❸
La Bouchée	"		④④❸
Chez Patrick	"		❸❶❸
Côte	"		④❸④

	Balans West	*International*	⑤	④	④
	Giraffe	"	⑤	⑤	⑤
	Troubadour	"	④	④	❶
	The Windsor Castle	"	④	④	❷
	Wine Gallery	"	④	❸	❸
	Aglio e Olio	*Italian*	❸	❸	④
	Da Mario	"	❸	❸	❸
	Made in Italy	"	❸	④	❸
	Nuovi Sapori	"	❸	❶	❸
	Obika	"	❸	❸	❸
	Ottolenghi	"	❶	❷	❸
	Il Portico	"	④	❸	❸
	Riccardo's	"	⑤	⑤	④
	The Atlas	*Mediterranean*	❷	❷	❷
	Daquise	*Polish*	④	❸	④
	Madsen	*Scandinavian*	❸	④	⑤
	Capote Y Toros	*Spanish*	❷	❸	❸
	Casa Brindisa	"	④	④	④
	Tendido Cero	"	❷	❷	❷
	Tendido Cuatro	"	❷	❷	❸
	Maxela	*Steaks & grills*	❶	❸	④
	Geales Chelsea Green	*Fish & chips*	④	④	④
	Ciro's (Pizza Pomodoro)	*Pizza*	❸	④	❷
	Rocca Di Papa	"	④	④	❸
	Santa Lucia	"	❷	❸	❸
	Baker & Spice	*Sandwiches, cakes, etc*	④	④	④
	Bluebird Café	"	⑤	⑤	④
	Beirut Express	*Lebanese*	❷	④	④
	Maroush	"	❷	❸	④
	Ranoush	"	❸	❸	④
	Choys	*Chinese*	④	❸	④
	Mr Wing	"	④	④	❷
	Royal China	"	❷	④	④
	Khan's of Kensington	*Indian*	❸	❸	④
	Malabar	"	❷	❷	❸
	Thali	"	❷	❸	④
	Thai Square	*Thai*	④	④	④
£35+	The Shed	*British, Modern*	❸	❷	❶
	The Scarsdale	*International*	④	❸	❶
	Buona Sera	*Italian*	④	❸	❸
	Napulé	"	❸	❸	❸
	Il Pagliaccio	"	❸	❷	❸
	Pappa Ciccia	"	❸	❸	❸
	Haché	*Steaks & grills*	❸	❸	❷
	Byron	*Burgers, etc*	❸	❸	❸
	Basilico	*Pizza*	❸	❷	④
	La Delizia Limbara	"	❸	④	④
	Rossopomodoro	"	❸	❸	❸
	Benugo	*Sandwiches, cakes, etc*	④	④	❷
	Best Mangal	*Turkish*	❷	❸	❸
	Noor Jahan	*Indian*	❷	❷	❸
	Wagamama	*Japanese*	④	❸	④
	Bangkok	*Thai*	❷	❷	❸
	Busaba Eathai	"	❸	❸	❷
£30+	Kensington Square Kitchen	*British, Modern*	❸	❶	❷
	Diner	*Burgers, etc*	④	❸	❷

	Taiwan Village	*Chinese*	❸❸❸
	The Greedy Buddha	*Indian*	❸④④
	Masala Zone	"	❸❷❷
	Monty's	"	❸❸❸
	Itsu	*Japanese*	④❸④
	Kulu Kulu	"	④⑤④
	Addie's Thai Café	*Thai*	❷❸❸
	Churchill Arms	"	❸❷❶
£25+	Chelsea Bun Diner	*International*	❸④④
	The Chelsea Kitchen	"	④④❸
	Mona Lisa	"	❸❷❷
	Stock Pot	"	④❸❸
	Comptoir Libanais	*Lebanese*	④④❸
£20+	Stick & Bowl	*Chinese*	❷❷❸
	Eat Tokyo	*Japanese*	❸❸④
	Café 209	*Thai*	④❸❶
£15+	La Bottega	*Italian*	❸❸❷

Notting Hill, Holland Park, Bayswater, North Kensington & Maida Vale (W2, W9, W10, W11)

£110+	The Ledbury	*British, Modern*	❶❶❷
£80+	Marianne	*British, Modern*	– – –
	The Shiori	*Japanese*	❶❷④
£70+	Angelus	*French*	❸❷❸
	Assaggi	*Italian*	❶❶❸
£60+	Beach Blanket Babylon	*British, Modern*	⑤④❸
	Julie's	"	④④❶
	Edera	*Italian*	❷❶④
	Chakra	*Indian*	❸④④
£50+	The Cow	*British, Modern*	❸❸❶
	The Dock Kitchen	"	❸❸❶
	The Frontline Club	"	❸④❸
	The Waterway	"	④⑤❸
	Bumpkin	*British, Traditional*	⑤⑤④
	The Summerhouse	*Fish & seafood*	④❸❷
	Le Café Anglais	*French*	❸④❷
	Goode & Wright	"	❸④④
	Essenza	*Italian*	❸❸④
	Mediterraneo	"	❸❸❸
	The Oak	"	❷❸❶
	Osteria Basilico	"	❸❸❷
	Casa Malevo	*Argentinian*	❸❸❸
	Colchis	*Georgian*	❷❸❸
	Bombay Palace	*Indian*	❶❶❸
	E&O	*Pan-Asian*	❷❸❶
£40+	All Star Lanes	*American*	④❸❸
	Granger & Co	*Australian*	④⑤❸
	Daylesford Organic	*British, Modern*	④⑤④

			Rating		
	First Floor	"	3	4	1
	Formosa Dining Room	"	4	4	3
	The Ladbroke Arms	"	2	3	2
	Paradise, Kensal Green	"	3	3	2
	Hereford Road	British, Traditional	2	3	3
	Côte	French	4	3	4
	La Sophia	"	2	3	4
	Halepi	Greek	3	1	3
	Giraffe	International	5	5	5
	Ottolenghi	Italian	1	2	3
	Portobello Ristorante	"	2	2	2
	Raoul's Cafe	Mediterranean	4	3	3
	El Pirata de Tapas	Spanish	3	3	2
	Pizza East Portobello	Pizza	2	3	1
	The Red Pepper	"	2	3	4
	Baker & Spice	Sandwiches, cakes, etc	4	4	4
	Al-Waha	Lebanese	2	4	4
	Beirut Express	"	2	4	4
	Maroush	"	2	3	4
	Ranoush	"	3	3	4
	Kateh	Persian	2	2	2
	Mandarin Kitchen	Chinese	2	4	5
	Pearl Liang	"	2	3	3
	Royal China	"	2	4	4
	Seventeen	"	3	3	3
£35+	Lucky Seven	American	3	3	2
	Galicia	Spanish	3	3	2
	Honest Burgers	Burgers, etc	1	2	3
	Rossopomodoro	Pizza	3	3	3
	Tom's Deli	Sandwiches, cakes, etc	3	3	3
	Noor Jahan	Indian	2	2	3
	Inaho	Japanese	1	5	5
	Maguro	"	1	2	3
	The Walmer Castle	Thai	3	3	2
£30+	Notting Hill Kitchen	Spanish	2	3	2
	Taqueria	Mexican/TexMex	3	3	4
	The Four Seasons	Chinese	2	5	5
	Gold Mine	"	3	4	5
	ping pong	Chinese, Dim sum	4	2	3
	Durbar	Indian	2	2	2
	Masala Zone	"	3	2	2
	Itsu	Japanese	4	3	4
	Satay House	Malaysian	3	4	4
	Banana Tree Canteen	Pan-Asian	4	4	3
£25+	Otto Pizza	Pizza	2	2	2
	Gail's Bread	Sandwiches, cakes, etc	4	4	3
	Alounak	Persian	3	4	3
	Colbeh	"	2	4	4
	Mandalay	Burmese	3	2	5
	Fortune Cookie	Chinese	2	4	5
	C&R Cafe	Thai	3	4	4
	Fitou's Thai Restaurant	"	2	3	4
£20+	Fez Mangal	Turkish	1	2	3
	Khan's	Indian	3	4	3

| £5+ | Lisboa Pâtisserie | Sandwiches, cakes, etc | ③③④ |

Hammersmith, Shepherd's Bush, Olympia, Chiswick, Brentford & Ealing (W4, W5, W6, W12, W13, W14, TW8)

£90+	The River Café	Italian	③④②
£70+	Hedone	British, Modern	②③③
£60+	La Trompette	French	②②③
£50+	The Anglesea Arms	British, Modern	②③②
	Le Vacherin	French	③③③
	Michael Nadra	International	①③④
	Oak	Italian	②③①
	Cibo	"	②①③
	The Meat & Wine Co	Steaks & grills	④③④
	Popeseye	"	④④⑤
	Chisou	Japanese	②③④
£40+	Bush Dining Hall	British, Modern	③④③
	The Carpenter's Arms	"	③③③
	Carvosso's	"	④③②
	The Dartmouth Castle	"	④③③
	Duke of Sussex	"	③④②
	The Havelock Tavern	"	②④②
	High Road Brasserie	"	④④③
	Hole in the Wall	"	④③③
	Pissarro	"	④④①
	Princess Victoria	"	④②②
	The Roebuck	"	④③③
	Sam's Brasserie	"	④③②
	The Thatched House	"	③④③
	Union Jacks	"	⑤④④
	Vinoteca	"	④③②
	The Hampshire Hog	British, Traditional	④③③
	Charlotte's Bistro	French	②②②
	Charlotte's Place	"	③②③
	Côte	"	④③④
	Annie's	International	④②②
	Balans	"	⑤④④
	Giraffe	"	⑤⑤⑤
	Jamie's Italian	Italian	⑤⑤④
	Pentolina	"	②②③
	Cumberland Arms	Mediterranean	②②③
	Raoul's Café & Deli	"	④③③
	The Swan	"	②②①
	The Cabin	Steaks & grills	④④④
	The Gate	Vegetarian	③④④
	Bird in Hand	Pizza	③③③
	Fire & Stone	"	④④④
	Lola & Simón	Argentinian	③②③
	Azou	North African	③②②
	North China	Chinese	②②②
	Indian Zing	Indian	①②③
	Tosa	Japanese	②④④

Saigon Saigon	*Vietnamese*	❸④❸
£35+		
Queen's Head	*British, Modern*	④❸❷
The Real Greek	*Greek*	⑤④④
Canta Napoli	*Italian*	❸❸④
Patio	*Polish*	④❷⓪
Byron	*Burgers, etc*	❸❸❸
Benugo	*Sandwiches, cakes, etc*	④④❷
Quantus	*South American*	❷⓪❷
Best Mangal	*Turkish*	❷❸❸
Maxim	*Chinese*	❸④❸
Brilliant	*Indian*	❷⓪④
Karma	*"*	❷④④
Potli	*"*	❸❸④
Sagar	*"*	❸④❸
Okawari	*Japanese*	❸❸❷
Busaba Eathai	*Thai*	❷❷❷
Pho	*Vietnamese*	❷❷❷
£30+		
Albertine	*French*	④❷❷
Santa Maria	*Pizza*	⓪❸❸
Wahaca	*Mexican/TexMex*	❸❸❷
Adams Café	*Moroccan*	⓪❺④
Chez Marcelle	*Lebanese*	❸❷❸
Sufi	*Persian*	❸⑤⑤
Tian Fu	*Chinese*	❸❸④
Anarkali	*Indian*	❸❸❸
Madhu's	*"*	❸❸❸
Monty's	*"*	❷❸⑤
Shilpa	*Indian, Southern*	⓪④⑤
Atari-Ya	*Japanese*	⓪❷❸
Kiraku	*"*	❷❸④
Bedlington Café	*Thai*	❷❸⑤
Esarn Kheaw	*"*	④④❸
Fat Boy's	*"*	❷❸⑤
101 Thai Kitchen	*"*	
£25+		
Gail's Bakery	*Sandwiches, cakes, etc*	④④❸
Comptoir Libanais	*Lebanese*	④④❸
Alounak	*Persian*	❸④❸
Faanoos	*"*	❸④❸
Hare & Tortoise	*Pan-Asian*	❸❸❸
£20+		
Franco Manca	*Pizza*	❷❸❸
Abu Zaad	*Syrian*	❸❸④
Eat Tokyo	*Japanese*	❸❸④
Miran Masala	*Pakistani*	⓪❷❸
Mirch Masala	*"*	❷④⑤
Old Parr's Head	*Thai*	❸❸④
£15+		
Kerbisher & Malt	*Fish & chips*	❸❸④
Tortilla	*Mexican/TexMex*	❸❸❸
Gifto's	*Indian*	❷❸④

NORTH

Hampstead, West Hampstead, St John's Wood, Regent's Park, Kilburn & Camden Town (NW postcodes)

£80+	Landmark (Winter Gdn)	British, Modern	❸❷❶
£70+	Gaucho	Steaks & grills	❸④④
	Gilgamesh	Pan-Asian	❸❸❷
£60+	Bull & Last	British, Traditional	❷❸❸
	Gilbert Scott	"	④④❷
	One Blenheim Terrace	French	⑤④④
	Oslo Court	"	❷❶❶
	Villa Bianca	Italian	⑤④④
£50+	Bradley's	British, Modern	④❸④
	The Engineer	"	④④❸
	Odette's	"	❸④❸
	St Pancras Grand	"	⑤⑤④
	L'Aventure	French	❷❶❶
	Michael Nadra	"	❶❸④
	La Collina	Italian	❸❸❷
	Mimmo la Bufala	"	④❸④
	York & Albany	"	④④④
	Manna	Vegetarian	④④④
	Good Earth	Chinese	❷❸❸
	Kaifeng	"	❷❷❸
	Phoenix Palace	"	❸④④
£40+	Karpo	American	❸④④
	Belgo Noord	Belgian	④④④
	Freemasons Arms	British, Modern	⑤⑤④
	The Horseshoe	"	❸❸❸
	The Junction Tavern	"	❸❶❷
	Market	"	❸④④
	The North London Tavern	"	④④❸
	The Old Bull & Bush	"	④④④
	Rising Sun	"	❸❷❸
	The Wells	"	❸❸❷
	The Wet Fish Cafe	"	❸❷❷
	Greenberry Cafe	British, Traditional	❸❸④
	Kentish Canteen	"	④❸❸
	The Old White Bear	"	❸❷❸
	L'Absinthe	French	④❷❸
	La Cage Imaginaire	"	④④❸
	Mill Lane Bistro	"	❸❷❷
	Lemonia	Greek	④❷❶
	Retsina	"	④④❸
	Giraffe	International	⑤⑤⑤
	Artigiano	Italian	❸④❸
	Ostuni	"	– – –
	The Salusbury	"	④④❸
	Sarracino	"	❷❸④
	Nautilus	Fish & chips	❶❷⑤
	The Sea Shell	"	❷❸④
	Pizza East	Pizza	❷❸❶

	Mestizo	Mexican/TexMex	④④❸
	Mango Room	Afro-Caribbean	❸❸❸
	Solly's	Israeli	❸④④
	Green Cottage	Chinese	❸④⑤
	Woodlands	Indian	❸④④
	Café Japan	Japanese	❷④④
	Jin Kichi	"	❶❷④
	Soho Japan	"	❷❷④
	Sushi-Say	"	❶❷④
	Singapore Garden	Malaysian	❷❸④
	XO	Pan-Asian	④④④
£35+	Made In Camden	British, Modern	❸❸❸
	Somerstown Coffee House	"	❸❷❸
	Swan & Edgar	International	④❸❷
	Marine Ices	Italian	– – –
	El Parador	Spanish	❷❷❷
	Haché	Steaks & grills	❸❸❷
	Harry Morgan's	Burgers, etc	❸❸④
	Honest Burgers	"	❶❷❸
	Skipjacks	Fish & chips	❶❷④
	Basilico	Pizza	❸❷④
	Rossopomodoro	"	❸❸❸
	Benugo	Sandwiches, cakes, etc	④④❷
	Beyoglu	Turkish	❸❸④
	Gung-Ho	Chinese	❸❷❸
	Eriki	Indian	❷❸④
	Asakusa	Japanese	❶④④
	Bento Cafe	"	❷❷④
	Wagamama	"	④❸④
	Ladudu	Vietnamese	❸❸④
£30+	Chicken Shop	American	❸❷❷
	Carob Tree	Greek	❸❷❷
	L'Artista	Italian	④❸❸
	La Porchetta Pizzeria	"	❸❸❸
	The Little Bay	Mediterranean	④❷❶
	Diner	Burgers, etc	④❸❷
	Sacro Cuore	Pizza	❷❷❸
	Kenwood (Brew House)	Sandwiches, cakes, etc	④❸❶
	Chutneys	Indian	④❸④
	Diwana B-P House	"	④④⑤
	Great Nepalese	"	❸❷⑤
	Guglee	"	❸❸④
	Masala Zone	"	❸❷❷
	Paradise Hampstead	"	❶❷❸
	Vijay	"	❸❷④
	Atari-Ya	Japanese	❶④⑤
	The Banana Tree Canteen	Pan-Asian	④④❸
	dim T	"	④④④
£25+	Sea Pebbles	Fish & seafood	❸④❸
	Gail's Bread	Sandwiches, cakes, etc	④④❸
£20+	Ali Baba	Egyptian	❸❷④
	Sakonis	Indian	❷④⑤
	Eat Tokyo	Japanese	❸❸④

£15+	Ginger & White	Sandwiches, cakes, etc	❸❷❷
£10+	Dirty Burger	Burgers, etc	❷❸❸

Hoxton, Islington, Highgate, Crouch End, Stoke Newington, Finsbury Park, Muswell Hill & Finchley (N postcodes)

£60+	Frederick's	British, Modern	❸❷❷
	Fifteen Restaurant	Italian	– – –
£50+	The Duke of Cambridge	British, Modern	❸❸❷
	Grain Store	"	❷❷❶
	Rotunda Bar & Restaurant	"	④④❸
	The Almeida	French	❸④④
	Bistro Aix	"	❷❶❷
	Trullo	Italian	❷❷❷
	Isarn	Thai	❷❷④
£40+	Red Dog Saloon	American	❸❷❷
	Shrimpy's	"	④④❸
	The Albion	British, Modern	❸❸❶
	Bald Faced Stag	"	❸④❸
	Caravan King's Cross	"	❸❸❷
	Charles Lamb	"	❸❸❶
	The Clissold Arms	"	④❸❸
	The Drapers Arms	"	❸❸❸
	The Fellow	"	❸④④
	The Haven	"	④④⑤
	Juniper Dining	"	❷❸❸
	Mosaica	"	④④❸
	The Northgate	"	❷❷❸
	Pig & Butcher	"	❷❷❷
	Plum + Spilt Milk	"	❸❸❷
	St Johns	British, Traditional	❸❷❶
	Kipferl	East & Cent. European	❸④❸
	Assiette Anglaise	French	❷❸❸
	Les Associés	"	❸❷④
	Blue Legume	"	④❷❷
	Banners	International	❸❸❶
	Browns	"	⑤④④
	The Flask	"	④④❷
	Giraffe	"	⑤⑤⑤
	The Orange Tree	"	④⑤❸
	500	Italian	❸❸④
	Ottolenghi	"	❶❷❸
	Pizzeria Oregano	"	❷❷❸
	San Daniele	"	❸❷❸
	Camino	Spanish	❸❷❷
	Garufa	Steaks & grills	❷④❸
	The Smokehouse Islington	"	– – –
	Duke's Brew & Que	Burgers, etc	❷❸④
	The Fish & Chip Shop	Fish & chips	❶❷❷
	Two Brothers	"	❸④④
	Il Bacio	Pizza	❸❸❸
	Tierra Peru	Peruvian	④❸④
	Yipin China	Chinese	❶❷⑤

	Name	Cuisine	Ratings
	Roots at N1	Indian	②②③
	Zaffrani	"	②②②
	Thai Square	Thai	④④④
£35+	John Salt	American	④④③
	Le Coq	British, Modern	– – –
	Season Kitchen	"	②②③
	Le Sacré-Coeur	French	④③③
	Vrisaki	Greek	④③③
	Pizzeria Pappagone	Italian	③②②
	Rugoletta	"	③③④
	Café del Parc	Spanish	②⓪②
	Byron	Burgers, etc	③③③
	Toff's	Fish & chips	②②④
	Basilico	Pizza	③②④
	Rossopomodoro	"	③③③
	Gilak	Persian	③②④
	Gallipoli	Turkish	④②③
	Mangal II	"	③③④
	Little Georgia Café	Georgian	③④③
	Anglo Asian Tandoori	Indian	③②③
	Indian Rasoi	"	②②③
	Rasa	Indian, Southern	②②③
	Akari	Japanese	②③③
	Wagamama	"	④③④
	Yum Yum	Thai	②③②
£30+	Olympus Fish	Fish & seafood	②③④
	La Porchetta Pizzeria	Italian	③③③
	La Bota	Spanish	③④④
	Diner	Burgers, etc	④③②
	Meat Mission	"	②④③
	Fabrizio	Pizza	③②④
	Sweet Thursday	"	②③②
	Wahaca	Mexican/TexMex	③③②
	Antepliler	Turkish	③④③
	Gem	"	③②③
	Izgara	"	③④⑤
	Petek	"	③②②
	Delhi Grill	Indian	②②③
	Masala Zone	"	③②②
	Atari-Ya	Japanese	①④⑤
	dim T	Pan-Asian	④④④
	Huong-Viet	Vietnamese	③④④
£25+	Prawn On The Lawn	Fish & seafood	– – –
	Le Mercury	French	④④③
	Mem & Laz	Mediterranean	④③③
	White Rabbit	Pizza	⓪⓪②
	Benito's Hat	Mexican/TexMex	③③④
	Afghan Kitchen	Afghani	②④④
	Rani	Indian	③④④
	Dotori	Korean	②④④
£15+	Notes	Sandwiches, cakes, etc	④②②
	Chilango	Mexican/TexMex	②②③
	Chipotle	"	③③④
	Tortilla	"	③③③

	Jai Krishna	*Indian*	❷④④
£10+	The Rib Man	*Burgers, etc*	❶❸ –
	Euphorium Bakery	*Sandwiches, cakes, etc*	❸④❸

SOUTH

South Bank (SE1)

£80+	Oxo Tower (Rest')	*British, Modern*	⑤⑤④
£70+	Le Pont de la Tour	*British, Modern*	④④❷
	Roast	*British, Traditional*	④④❸
	Oxo Tower (Brass')	*Mediterranean*	⑤⑤④
	Gaucho	*Steaks & grills*	❸④④
	Hutong	*Chinese*	❸④❶
£60+	Story	*British, Modern*	❶❶❸
	Butlers W'f Chop-house	*British, Traditional*	④④④
£50+	Oblix	*American*	④❸❶
	Cantina Vinopolis	*British, Modern*	④④❸
	Elliot's Cafe	"	❸④④
	Magdalen	"	❷❸❸
	Mezzanine	"	④④④
	Skylon	"	④④❷
	Skylon Grill	"	❸❸❷
	The Swan at the Globe	"	④④❷
	fish!	*Fish & seafood*	④④❸
	Wright Brothers	"	❷❸❷
	Brasserie Blanc	*French*	④❸④
	Village East	*Fusion*	– – –
	Vivat Bacchus	*International*	④④④
	La Barca	*Italian*	④❷❷
	Tentazioni	"	❸❸❸
	Baltic	*Polish*	❸❸❷
	Archduke Wine Bar	*Steaks & grills*	⑤⑤④
	Black & Blue	"	❸❸④
	Mango Food of India	*Indian*	❸❸④
£40+	Albion	*British, Modern*	④④❸
	Blueprint Café	"	④④❶
	40 Maltby Street	"	❷❸❸
	Garrison	"	❸❸❷
	Menier Chocolate Factory	"	⑤④❸
	RSJ	"	❸❸④
	The Table	"	❸④④
	Tate Modern (Level 7)	"	⑤④❸
	Union Street Café	"	– – –
	Waterloo Bar & Kitchen	"	④❸④
	The Anchor & Hope	*British, Traditional*	❶❶❸
	Canteen	"	⑤⑤⑤
	The Riverfront	"	④④❸
	Applebee's Cafe	*Fish & seafood*	❸❸④
	Côte	*French*	④❸④
	Champor-Champor	*Fusion*	❷❸❶
	Browns	*International*	⑤④④
	Giraffe	"	⑤⑤⑤
	Antico	*Italian*	❸❸④
	Zucca	"	❶❷❷
	José	*Spanish*	❶❷❶
	Pizarro	"	❷❷❶
	Tapas Brindisa	"	❷❸❸

			Rating
	Constancia	*Argentinian*	❸❸❸
	Bengal Clipper	*Indian*	❸❸❷
£35+	Casse-Croute	*French*	– – –
	Real Greek	*Greek*	❺❹❹
	Meson don Felipe	*Spanish*	❹❹❸
	Benugo	*Sandwiches, cakes, etc*	❹❹❷
	Tas (Cafe)	*Turkish*	❹❸❸
	Bangalore Express	*Indian*	❹❹❸
	Wagamama	*Japanese*	❹❸❹
£30+	Mar I Terra	*Spanish*	❸❸❷
	Gourmet Pizza Co.	*Pizza*	❹❹❸
	Caffé Vergnano	*Sandwiches, cakes, etc*	❹❸❷
	Wahaca	*Mexican/TexMex*	❸❸❷
	El Vergel	*South American*	❷❸❷
	Tas Pide	*Turkish*	❹❸❸
	ping pong	*Chinese, Dim sum*	❹❷❸
	dim T	*Pan-Asian*	❹❹❹
£25+	Masters Super Fish	*Fish & chips*	❷❹❺
	Konditor & Cook	*Sandwiches, cakes, etc*	❸❹❹
	Leon	"	❹❸❸
£15+	Tortilla	*Mexican/TexMex*	❸❸❸
£10+	Monmouth Coffee Co	*Sandwiches, cakes, etc*	❶❶❷
	Pod	"	❸❸❹
	Spianata & Co	"	❸❷❸

Greenwich, Lewisham, Dulwich & Blackheath
(All SE postcodes, except SE1)

			Rating
£70+	Gaucho	*Steaks & grills*	❸❹❹
£60+	Lobster Pot	*Fish & seafood*	❷❸❹
£50+	The Palmerston	*British, Modern*	❸❹❹
	Buenos Aires Café	*Argentinian*	❸❹❸
	Babur	*Indian*	❶❶❷
£40+	Chapters	*British, Modern*	❹❸❹
	The Crooked Well	"	❷❷❷
	Florence	"	❹❹❷
	Franklins	"	❸❹❸
	Inside	"	❷❷❺
	The Lido Cafe	"	❸❸❷
	The Old Brewery	"	❹❹❷
	Rivington Grill	"	❹❸❹
	Toasted	*French*	– – –
	Joanna's	*International*	❸❷❷
	The Yellow House	"	❷❷❹
	Lorenzo	*Italian*	❹❷❸
	Angels & Gypsies	*Spanish*	❷❸❷
	Bianco43	*Pizza*	❸❸❹
	Rocca Di Papa	"	❹❹❸
	Zero Degrees	"	❸❹❹

	Ganapati	Indian	①①②
	Kennington Tandoori	"	②②②
£35+	The Dartmouth Arms	British, Modern	④③③
	The Lord Northbrook	British, Traditional	③②②
	Brasserie Toulouse-Lautrec	French	③②②
	Le Querce	Italian	①②③
	Olley's	Fish & chips	②③③
	Dragon Castle	Chinese	②③④
	Tandoori Nights	Indian	③②③
	The Begging Bowl	Thai	①②③
£30+	Frizzante Cafe	Italian	③②③
	The Sea Cow	Fish & chips	②③③
	The Gowlett	Pizza	②③②
	Everest Inn	Indian	②②③
£25+	Gandhi's	Indian	③④③
£20+	Thai Corner Café	Thai	③③③
	Cafe East	Vietnamese	②④④
£10+	Monmouth Coffee Company	Sandwiches, cakes, etc	①①②

Battersea, Brixton, Clapham, Wandsworth Barnes, Putney & Wimbledon
(All SW postcodes south of the river)

£60+	Cannizaro House	British, Modern	④④②
	Chez Bruce	"	①①②
	Trinity	"	①①②
	San Lorenzo Fuoriporta	Italian	⑤⑤④
£50+	Entrée	British, Modern	③②②
	Sonny's Kitchen	"	④④④
	Fox & Grapes	British, Traditional	④④③
	The Lawn Bistro	French	④②④
	Upstairs	"	②②②
	Brinkley's Kitchen	International	④④③
	Enoteca Turi	Italian	②①③
	Numero Uno	"	③②②
	Riva	"	②②④
	Alquimia	Spanish	②②②
	Popeseye	Steaks & grills	④④⑤
	Fulham Wine Rooms	Sandwiches, cakes, etc	③③③
	Santa Maria del Sur	Argentinian	③④③
	Suk Saran	Thai	③④⑤
£40+	Bodean's	American	③④③
	Belgo	Belgian	④④④
	The Abbeville	British, Modern	④③②
	Abbeville Kitchen	"	②②③
	Antelope	"	③②②
	Avalon	"	④④③
	The Balham Bowls Club	"	③③②
	Ben's Canteen	"	④④④
	Bistro Union	"	③②③

	The Bolingbroke	"	④❸❸
	The Brown Dog	"	❸❸❷
	Brunswick House Cafe	"	❸④❷
	The Depot	"	❸❷❷
	Earl Spencer	"	❸④❸
	Emile's	"	❸❷④
	The Fentiman Arms	"	❸❸❷
	Harrison's	"	④④❸
	Jam Tree	"	❸❸❷
	Lamberts	"	❶❶❷
	The Victoria	"	❸❷❸
	Canton Arms	British, Traditional	❷❷❷
	Bellevue Rendez-Vous	French	❸❷❷
	Côte	"	④❸④
	Gastro	"	④④❷
	Le P'tit Normand	"	❸❷❸
	Soif	"	④④④
	Annie's	International	④❷❷
	Hudsons	"	④④❸
	The Light House	"	④❸❸
	The Ship	"	④④❸
	Antipasto & Pasta	Italian	❸❷④
	Donna Margherita	"	❷❸④
	Isola del Sole	"	④④④
	Ost. Antica Bologna	"	❸❸❸
	Pizza Metro	"	❷④④
	Sapori Sardi	"	❷❸④
	The Fox & Hounds	Mediterranean	❷❷❷
	Lola Rojo	Spanish	❸④④
	Butcher & Grill	Steaks & grills	④❸❸
	Cattle Grid	"	❸④④
	Bayee Village	Chinese	❸④④
	China Boulevard	"	❸④❸
	Indian Zilla	Indian	❶❶❸
	Cho-San	Japanese	❷❷❸
	Sticks'n'Sushi	"	❸❸❷
	Tsunami	"	❷④④
	Blue Elephant	Thai	❸❸❷
	Thai Square	"	④④④
£35+	The Dairy	British, Modern	– – –
	The Manor Arms	British, Traditional	❷❸④
	Gazette	French	④④❷
	Telegraph	International	④④❸
	Buona Sera	Italian	④❸❸
	Fish in a Tie	Mediterranean	④❷❷
	Byron	Burgers, etc	❸❸❸
	Haché	"	❸❸❷
	Honest Burgers	"	❶❷❸
	Fish Club	Fish & chips	❷❷④
	Al Forno	Pizza	④❸❷
	Basilico	"	❸❷④
	Rossopomodoro	"	❸❸❸
	Dalchini	Chinese	④❸④
	Ma Goa	Indian	❷❶❷
	Nazmins	"	❸❸❸
	Hashi	Japanese	❷❷❸
	Wagamama	"	④❸④

	Cah-Chi	*Korean*	②②③
£30+	Boqueria	*Spanish*	②②②
	Brady's	*Fish & chips*	②②②
	Eco	*Pizza*	②③②
	Pantry	*Sandwiches, cakes, etc*	③②③
	Chutney	*Indian*	②③③
	Cocum	"	②②③
	Indian Moment	"	③④④
	Mango & Silk	"	②②③
	The Banana Tree Canteen	*Pan-Asian*	④④③
	Amaranth	*Thai*	②③②
	Fat Boy's	"	④④③
	Talad Thai	"	③④⑤
	Thai Garden	"	③③④
	Mien Tay	*Vietnamese*	②④④
£25+	Moxon's Fish Bar	*Fish & chips*	①③⑤
	Gail's Bread	*Sandwiches, cakes, etc*	④④③
	Orange Pekoe	"	②②②
	Faanoos	*Persian*	③④③
	Holy Cow	*Indian*	②④③
	Indian Ocean	"	②②③
	Sree Krishna	"	②③④
	Fujiyama	*Japanese*	③④④
	Lahore Kebab House	*Pakistani*	①④④
	Hare & Tortoise	*Pan-Asian*	③③③
	Kaosarn	*Thai*	②②②
	The Pepper Tree	"	③②④
	The Paddyfield	*Vietnamese*	②②③
£20+	Franco Manca	*Pizza*	②③③
	Apollo Banana Leaf	*Indian*	①②⑤
	Hot Stuff	"	②②③
	Lahore Karahi	*Pakistani*	②④④
	Mirch Masala SW17	"	②④⑤
£15+	Wishbone	*American*	⑤④④
	Chipotle	*Mexican/TexMex*	③③④
	Tortilla	"	③③③
	Meza	*Lebanese*	②③③
£10+	Dirty Burger	*Burgers, etc*	②③③

Outer western suburbs
Kew, Richmond, Twickenham, Teddington

£70+	The Bingham	*British, Modern*	②②①
	Petersham Nurseries	"	③⑤③
	Gaucho	*Steaks & grills*	③④④
£60+	The Glasshouse	*British, Modern*	②②③
	Petersham Hotel	"	④③②
	Al Boccon di'vino	*Italian*	①②②
£50+	Plane Food	*British, Modern*	④④④
	Rock & Rose	"	⑤⑤③

	Brula	*French*	❷❶❷
	A Cena	*Italian*	❸❷❸
	Kew Grill	*Steaks & grills*	❸❷❸
£40+	The Wharf	*British, Modern*	④❸❷
	La Buvette	*French*	❸❷❷
	Ma Cuisine	*"*	❸❸❸
	don Fernando's	*Spanish*	④❷④
	Palmyra	*Lebanese*	❷❷④
	Four Regions	*Chinese*	❸❷④
	Matsuba	*Japanese*	❷④④
£35+	Canta Napoli	*Italian*	❸❸④
	Pizzeria Rustica	*Pizza*	❸❸④
£30+	Fat Boy's	*Thai*	④④❸
£15+	William Curley	*Afternoon tea*	❷❸❸
	Taylor St Baristas	*Sandwiches, cakes, etc*	❷❸❸

EAST

Smithfield & Farringdon (EC1)

£70+			
	Club Gascon	*French*	② ③ ③
	Dans le Noir	*International*	④ ④ ④
	Gaucho	*Steaks & grills*	③ ④ ④
	Smiths (Top Floor)	"	⑤ ④ ④

£60+			
	Chiswell Street Dining Rms	*British, Modern*	④ ③ ④
	The Clove Club	"	② ⓪ ②
	Bleeding Heart	*French*	③ ② ⓪
	Morgan M	"	② ③ ⑤

£50+			
	Bird of Smithfield	*British, Modern*	④ ④ ③
	The Modern Pantry	"	④ ④ ④
	St John	*British, Traditional*	② ② ②
	Bistrot Bruno Loubet	*French*	③ ③ ③
	Café du Marché	"	② ② ⓪
	Fabrizio	*Italian*	② ⓪ ⑤
	Portal	*Portuguese*	④ ④ ③
	Moro	*Spanish*	⓪ ② ②
	Hix	*Steaks & grills*	④ ③ ③
	Smiths (Dining Rm)	"	④ ④ ④
	Sushi Tetsu	*Japanese*	⓪ ⓪ ③

£40+			
	Brasserie on St John Street	*British, Modern*	③ ④ ④
	Caravan	"	③ ③ ②
	Foxlow	"	– – –
	The Gunmakers	"	② ② ③
	The Peasant	"	③ ② ③
	Vinoteca	"	④ ③ ②
	The Fox and Anchor	*British, Traditional*	② ② ⓪
	The Quality Chop House	"	② ② ②
	Chabrot Bistrot des Halles	*French*	② ② ③
	Comptoir Gascon	"	③ ④ ③
	Le Rendezvous du Café	"	③ ③ ③
	Alba	*Italian*	③ ② ④
	Santore	"	② ② ④
	The Gate	*Vegetarian*	③ ④ ④
	Burger & Lobster	*Burgers, etc*	② ③ ③
	Workshop Coffee	*Sandwiches, cakes, etc*	③ ③ ②

£35+			
	Cellar Gascon	*French*	② ③ ②
	Polpo	*Italian*	④ ③ ⓪
	Morito	*Spanish*	② ② ③
	Amico Bio	*Vegetarian*	③ ④ ③
	Benugo	*Sandwiches, cakes, etc*	④ ④ ②
	Tas	*Turkish*	④ ③ ③
	Pham Sushi	*Japanese*	⓪ ④ ⑤
	Tajima Tei	"	② ③ ③
	Busaba Eathai	*Thai*	③ ③ ②
	Naamyaa Café	"	④ ④ ③
	Cây Tre	*Vietnamese*	③ ④ ③
	Pho	"	② ② ②

£30+			
	Smiths (Ground Floor)	*British, Modern*	④ ④ ③
	Kolossi Grill	*Greek*	④ ② ②

	La Porchetta Pizzeria	*Italian*	③③③
	The Eagle	*Mediterranean*	③④❷
	The Little Bay	*"*	④❷❶
	Banana Tree Canteen	*Pan-Asian*	④④③
£25+	Fish Central	*Fish & seafood*	③❷④
	Gail's Bakery	*Sandwiches, cakes, etc*	④④③
	Look Mum No Hands!	*"*	③③❷
	Sedap	*Malaysian*	④④④
£15+	Hummus Bros	*Mediterranean*	③③④
	Department of Coffee	*Sandwiches, cakes, etc*	③❷❷
	Daddy Donkey	*Mexican/TexMex*	❷③ –
	Abokado	*Japanese*	④④④
£10+	Big Apple Hot Dogs	*Burgers, etc*	❷❷ –
	Dose	*Sandwiches, cakes, etc*	❷③④
	Nusa Kitchen	*"*	❷③④
	Pod	*"*	③③④
	Prufrock Coffee	*"*	❷❷③
	Spianata & Co	*"*	③❷③

The City (EC2, EC3, EC4)

£120+	HKK	*Chinese*	❷❷④
£70+	Chamberlain's	*Fish & seafood*	③④④
	Lutyens	*French*	④④④
	Sauterelle	*"*	③③③
	L'Anima	*Italian*	❷❷③
	Gaucho	*Steaks & grills*	③④④
	Sushisamba	*Japanese*	③④❷
£60+	Bread Street Kitchen	*British, Modern*	④④④
	The Don	*"*	③❷③
	Duck & Waffle	*"*	④④❶
	1901	*"*	④④③
	1 Lombard Street	*"*	④④③
	3 South Place	*"*	④③④
	Vertigo 42	*"*	⑤④❷
	Angler	*Fish & seafood*	③❷❷
	Coq d'Argent	*French*	④④③
	Bonds	*Mediterranean*	④④③
	Barbecoa	*Steaks & grills*	④④④
	Goodman City	*"*	❷❷③
	Hawksmoor	*"*	❷❷③
	New Street Grill	*"*	④❷❷
	Ladurée	*Afternoon tea*	❷④③
£50+	The Hoxton Grill	*American*	④④❷
	The Chancery	*British, Modern*	③③④
	Gin Joint	*"*	– – –
	High Timber	*"*	④③③
	The Jugged Hare	*"*	④④③
	The Mercer	*"*	③③③
	Northbank	*"*	③④③
	The White Swan	*"*	③③③

	Restaurant	Cuisine			
	Paternoster Chop House	British, Traditional	⑤	⑤	⑤
	Fish Market	Fish & seafood	❸	❷	❸
	Gow's	"	❸	❸	❹
	Sweetings	"	❸	❸	❷
	Brasserie Blanc	French	④	❸	④
	The Royal Exchange	"	④	❸	❷
	28-50	"	❸	❷	❸
	Sushinho	Fusion	❷	❸	❸
	Vivat Bacchus	International	④	④	④
	Manicomio	Italian	❸	④	❸
	Piccolino	"	④	❸	④
	Refettorio	"	❸	❸	④
	Taberna Etrusca	"	❸	❷	❸
	Eyre Brothers	Spanish	❸	❸	❸
	The Tramshed	Steaks & grills	④	④	❸
	Vanilla Black	Vegetarian	❸	⓿	❸
	Kenza	Lebanese	④	④	❸
	Chinese Cricket Club	Chinese	④	④	⑤
	Cinnamon Kitchen	Indian	❷	❷	❸
	Mint Leaf	"	❷	❸	❸
	City Miyama	Japanese	❸	④	⑤
£40+	Beard to Tail	American	④	❸	④
	Bodean's	"	❸	④	❸
	The Anthologist	British, Modern	❸	❸	❷
	Princess of Shoreditch	"	❸	④	❸
	Rivington Grill	"	④	❸	④
	George & Vulture	British, Traditional	④	❸	❷
	The Oyster Shed	"	④	④	❸
	Loch Fyne	Fish & seafood	④	❸	④
	Orpheus	"	❷	❷	④
	Côte	French	④	❸	④
	Browns	International	⑤	④	④
	Rocket	Mediterranean	❸	❸	❸
	Relais de Venise L'Entrecôte	Steaks & grills	❸	④	❸
	Burger & Lobster	Burgers, etc	❷	❸	❸
	Imperial City	Chinese	④	④	④
	Kurumaya	Japanese	❸	❸	④
	Mugen	"	❸	❸	④
	Thai Square	Thai	④	④	④
£35+	The Punch Tavern	British, Modern	④	❸	❷
	Simpson's Tavern	British, Traditional	④	❸	⓿
	Tramontana Brindisa	Spanish	❸	④	❸
	Byron	Burgers, etc	❸	❸	❸
	Haché	"	❸	❸	❷
	Natural Kitchen	Salads	❸	④	❸
	Haz	Turkish	④	④	❸
	Bangalore Express	Indian	④	④	❸
	K10	Japanese	❷	❷	④
	Wagamama	"	④	❸	④
£30+	Café Below	British, Modern	④	④	❸
	The Diner	Burgers, etc	④	❸	❷
	Caffè Vergnano	Sandwiches, cakes, etc	④	❸	❷
	ping pong	Chinese, Dim sum	④	❷	❸
	Taro	Japanese	❸	❸	❸

£25+	Hilliard	British, Modern	② ② ❸
	The Wine Library	International	⑤ ② ❶
	Konditor & Cook	Sandwiches, cakes, etc	❸ ④ ④
	Leon	"	④ ❸ ❸
	Hare & Tortoise	Pan-Asian	❸ ❸ ❸

£15+	Street Kitchen	British, Modern	② ❸ –
	Hummus Bros	Mediterranean	❸ ❸ ④
	Taylor St Baristas	Sandwiches, cakes, etc	② ❸ ❸
	Chilango	Mexican/TexMex	② ② ❸
	Tortilla	"	❸ ❸ ❸
	Abokado	Japanese	④ ④ ④
	Jubo	Korean	– – –

£10+	Fuzzy's Grub	Sandwiches, cakes, etc	❸ ④ ④
	Nusa Kitchen	"	② ❸ ④
	Pod	"	❸ ❸ ④
	Spianata & Co	"	❸ ② ❸
	City Càphê	Vietnamese	❶ ❸ ⑤

| £5+ | Pilpel | Middle Eastern | ② ② ④ |

East End & Docklands (All E postcodes)

| £100+ | Viajante | Fusion | ② ❸ ❸ |

£70+	Galvin La Chapelle	French	② ② ❶
	Les Trois Garçons	"	❸ ❶ ❶
	Gaucho	Steaks & grills	❸ ④ ④
	Roka	Japanese	❶ ❸ ❸

£60+	Beach Blanket Babylon	British, Modern	⑤ ④ ❸
	The Boundary	"	② ② ②
	Tom's Kitchen	"	④ ❸ ❸
	Boisdale of Canary Wharf	Scottish	④ ④ ❸
	Goodman	Steaks & grills	② ② ❸
	Hawksmoor	"	② ② ❸
	Bevis Marks	Kosher	④ ④ ④

£50+	Bistrotheque	British, Modern	❸ ❸ ②
	The Gun	"	❸ ❸ ②
	Hoi Polloi	"	– – –
	One Canada Square	"	– – –
	Smiths Brasserie	"	② ❸ ②
	Wapping Food	"	④ ④ ❶
	Young Turk at the Ten Bells	"	❸ ❶ ❸
	Bumpkin	British, Traditional	⑤ ⑤ ④
	St John Bread & Wine	"	❶ ❸ ❸
	Forman's	Fish & seafood	② ❸ ④
	Wright Brothers	"	② ❸ ②
	Plateau	French	⑤ ④ ⑤
	Buen Ayre	Argentinian	❶ ④ ④
	Café Spice Namaste	Indian	② ② ❸
	Dockmaster's House	"	② ❸ ④

| £40+ | All Star Lanes | American | ④ ❸ ❸ |
| | Balans | British, Modern | ⑤ ④ ④ |

Name	Cuisine			
The Empress	"	②	③	②
The Morgan Arms	"	③	③	②
The Narrow	"	⑤	④	④
Rochelle Canteen	"	②	②	②
Whitechapel Gallery	"	③	③	③
Albion	British, Traditional	④	④	③
Canteen	"	⑤	⑤	⑤
The Grapes	Fish & seafood	④	④	②
Brawn	French	②	②	③
Browns	International	⑤	④	④
Giraffe	"	⑤	⑤	⑤
Il Bordello	Italian	②	⓪	②
La Figa	"	③	②	④
Jamie's Italian	"	⑤	⑤	④
Obika	"	③	③	③
Rocket	Mediterranean	③	③	③
Corner Room	Portuguese	⓪	②	③
Ibérica	Spanish	③	③	③
Relais de Venise L'Entrecôte	Steaks & grills	③	④	③
Ark Fish	Fish & chips	⓪	②	④
Fire & Stone	Pizza	④	④	④
Pizza East	"	②	③	⓪
Story Deli	"	②	④	②
Lotus	Chinese	④	④	③
Royal China	"	②	④	④
Sichuan Folk	"	②	③	⑤
Yi-Ban	"	③	③	④
Dishoom	Indian	③	③	⓪
Elephant Royale	Thai	③	④	③
£35+ Bouchon Fourchette	French	②	②	③
Real Greek	Greek	⑤	④	④
LMNT	International	④	③	⓪
Lardo	Italian	③	④	③
Byron	Burgers, etc	③	③	③
Benugo	Sandwiches, cakes, etc	④	④	②
Haz	Turkish	④	④	③
My Old Place	Chinese	②	⑤	④
Shanghai	"	③	④	③
Little Georgia Café	Georgian	③	④	③
Wagamama	Japanese	④	③	④
Busaba Eathai	Thai	③	③	②
Rosa's	"	③	②	③
Pho	Vietnamese	②	②	②
Viet Grill	"	②	④	③
£30+ Frizzante at City Farm	Italian	②	④	④
Wahaca	Mexican/TexMex	③	③	②
Yalla Yalla	Lebanese	③	④	③
Hazev	Turkish	④	③	③
Mangal 1	"	⓪	④	④
ping pong	Chinese, Dim sum	④	②	③
Itsu	Japanese	④	③	④
Green Papaya	Vietnamese	②	③	④
Mien Tay	"	②	④	④
Sông Quê	"	③	⑤	④
Viet Hoa	"	②	⑤	④

£25+	Faulkner's	Fish & chips	❷④④
	Leon	Sandwiches, cakes, etc	④❸❸
	Comptoir Libanais	Lebanese	④④❸
	Gourmet San	Chinese	❷⑤⑤
	Lahore Kebab House	Pakistani	❶④④
	Needoo	"	❷④④
	Tayyabs	"	❶⑤❸
£20+	Sager & Wilde	British, Modern	– – –
	E Pellicci	Italian	④❷❶
	Franco Manca	Pizza	❷❸❸
	Mirch Masala	Pakistani	❷④⑤
£15+	Taylor St Baristas	Sandwiches, cakes, etc	❷❸❸
	Chilango	Mexican/TexMex	❷❷❸
	Tortilla	"	❸❸❸
£10+	Spianata & Co	Sandwiches, cakes, etc	❸❷❸
£5+	Brick Lane Beigel Bake	Sandwiches, cakes, etc	❶❷④
	Pilpel	Middle Eastern	❷❷④